MAKING CONNECTIONS: Foundations for Algebra
Course 2, Version 3.0

Managing Editors / Authors

Leslie Dietiker (Both Texts)
Michigan State University
East Lansing, MI

Evra Baldinger (Course 1)
Phillip and Sala Burton Academic High School
San Francisco, CA

Barbara Shreve (Course 2)
San Lorenzo High School
San Lorenzo, CA

Contributing Authors

Elizabeth Baker
Zane Middle School
Eureka, CA

Tara Bianchi
American Canyon Middle School
American Canyon, CA

Bev Brockhoff
Glen Edwards Middle School
Lincoln, CA

Mark Coté
Beaver Lake Middle School
Issaquah, WA

Suzanne Cisco Cox
Turner Middle School
Berthoud, CO

Kathleen Davies
Rincon Valley Middle School
Santa Rosa, CA

Josea Eggink
Bloomington Public Schools
Bloomington, MN

William Funkhouser
Zane Middle School
Eureka, CA

Brian Hoey
CPM Educational Program
Sacramento, CA

Janet Hollister
La Cumbre Jr. High School
Santa Barbara, CA

Carol Jancsi
CPM Mentor Teacher
Cardiff by the Sea, CA

Rakesh Khanna
Hotmath, Inc.
Berkeley, CA

Judy Kysh, Ph.D.
San Francisco State University
San Francisco, CA

Bruce Melhorn
Whatcom Middle School
Bellingham, WA

Chris Mikles
Post Falls Middle School
Post Falls, ID

Misty Nikula
Whatcom Day Academy
Bellingham, WA

Bob Petersen
CPM Educational Program
Sacramento, CA

Tom Sallee, Ph.D.
Department of Mathematics
University of California, Davis

Lorna Thomas Vázquez
Math Consultant
Neillsville, WI

Stephanie Whitney
Illinois Institute of Technology
Chicago, IL

Program Directors

Leslie Dietiker
Michigan State University
East Lansing, MI

Brian Hoey
CPM Educational Program
Sacramento, CA

Judy Kysh, Ph.D.
Departments of Education and Mathematics
San Francisco State University, CA

Tom Sallee, Ph.D.
Department of Mathematics
University of California, Davis

Puzzle Investigator Problems

Ethan Baldinger
Sonoma State University
Rohnert Park, CA

Susan Baskin
Math Consultant
Oakland, CA

Leslie Dietiker
Michigan State University
East Lansing, MI

Parent Guide

Brian Hoey
Sacramento, CA

Bob Petersen
Sacramento, CA

Extra Practice Materials

Bob Petersen
Sacramento, CA

Based on the Skill Builder materials created for Foundations for Algebra (2003), created by:

Heidi Ackley
Bev Brockhoff
Scott Coyner
Brian Hoey
Robert Petersen
Kristie Sallee

Steve Ackley
Ellen Cafferata
Sara Effenbeck
Judy Kysh
Edwin Reed
Tom Sallee

Elizabeth Baker
Elizabeth Coyner
William Funkhouser
Kris Petersen
Stacy Rocklein
Howard Webb

Assessment Manager

Karen Wootten
Director of Assessment
Odenton, MD

Assessment Assistants

Elizabeth Baker
Zane Middle School
Eureka, CA

William Funkhouser
Zane Middle School
Eureka, CA

Illustration

Jonathan Weast
Sacramento, CA

Cover Art

Kevin Coffey
San Francisco, CA

Technical Managers

Sarah Maile
Sacramento, CA

Aubrie Maze
Sebastopol, CA

Technical Assistants

Robert Ainsworth
Jason Cho
Matthew Donahue
Jerry Luo
Atlanta Parrott
Rachel Smith

Bethany Armstrong
Hannah Coyner
Bethany Firch
Eli Marable
Anna Poehlmann
Alex Yu

Rebecca Bobell
Carmen de la Cruz
Michael Li
James McCardle
John Ramos

3 4 5 6   16 15 14 13   Version 3.0

Printed in the United States of America   ISBN-13: 978-1-60328-039-6

A Note to Students:

Welcome to a new year of math! In this course, you will learn to use new models and methods to think about problems as well as solve them. You will be developing powerful mathematical tools and learning new ways of thinking about and investigating situations. You will be making connections, discovering relationships, figuring out what strategies can be used to solve problems, and explaining your thinking. Learning to think in these ways and communicate about your thinking is useful in mathematical contexts, other subjects in school, and situations outside the classroom. The mathematics you have learned in the past will be valuable for learning in this course, and will prepare you for future courses.

In meeting the challenges of this course, you will not be learning alone. You will cooperate with other students as a member of a study team. Being a part of a team means speaking up and interacting with other people. You will explain your ideas, listen to what others have to say, and ask questions if there is something you do not understand. In this course, a single problem can often be solved several ways. You will see problems in different ways than your teammates do. Each of you has something to contribute while you work on the lessons in this course.

Together, your team will complete problems and activities that will help you discover mathematical ideas and develop solution methods. Your teacher will support you as you work, but will not take away your opportunity to think and investigate for yourself. Each topic will be revisited many times and will connect to other topics. If something is not clear to you the first time you work on it, you will have more chances to build your understanding as the course continues.

Learning math this way has an advantage: as long as you actively participate, make sure everyone in your study team is involved, and ask good questions, you will find yourself understanding mathematics at a deeper level than ever before. By the end of this course, you will have a powerful set of mathematical tools to use to solve new problems. With your teammates you will meet mathematical challenges you would not have known how to approach before.

In addition to the support provided by your teacher and your study team, CPM has also created online resources to help you, including help with homework, a parent guide, and extra practice. You will find these resources and more at www.cpm.org.

We wish you well and are confident that you will enjoy this next year of learning!

Sincerely,

The CPM Team

Making Connections: Foundations for Algebra
Course 2
Student Edition
Version 3.0

Chapter 8 Percents and More Solving Equations   455

Chapter 9 Proportions and Pythagorean Theorem   501

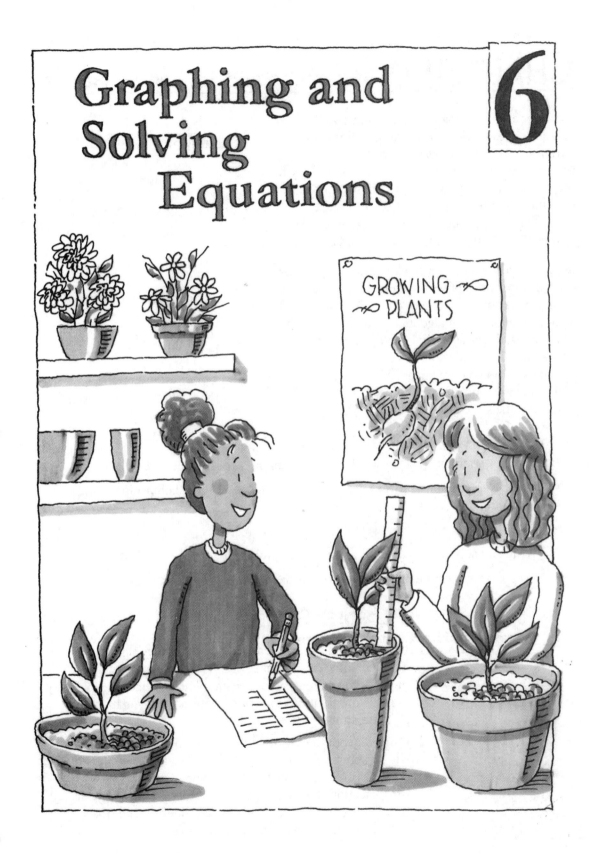

Graphing and Solving Equations

6

CHAPTER 6   Graphing and Solving Equations

In earlier chapters, you used histograms and box-and-whisker plots to answer questions such as *"Are this year's frogs better jumpers than last year's?"* In this chapter, you will develop a way to see if there is a relationship between two different measures for a set of objects. For example, to answer the question, *"If a frog has longer legs, can it jump farther?"* you will use a new tool, called a scatterplot.

In this chapter, you will also extend what you know about comparing expressions to include those cases when expressions are equal. You will build equations on equation mats with algebra tiles as well as write equations with variables and solve them without tiles. This skill will provide a new way to solve word problems without completing a 5-D table. By the end of the chapter you will learn some efficient ways to justify the steps used to solve equations.

Guiding Questions

Think about these questions throughout this chapter:

What would a graph of this data look like?

Can I make a prediction?

Is there a relationship?

How can I represent it?

How can I solve it?

How can I check my answer?

In this chapter, you will learn how to:

➤ Create scatterplots that show relationships among two-variable data.

➤ Identify correlations between sets of data and represent the relationship with a trend line.

➤ Solve for a variable when two expressions are equal.

➤ Write and solve an equation to solve a word problem.

➤ Recognize when an equation has no solution or infinite solutions.

Chapter Outline

Section 6.1 In this section you will create and interpret circle graphs. You will also learn to make graphs that compare two sets of data. Then, you will use scatterplots and linear graphs to make observations and predictions about the data based on correlations.

Section 6.2 Using algebra tiles, you will explore what you can learn when expressions are equal. Solving equations will also provide you an opportunity to develop efficient simplification strategies and learn how to know that your solution is correct. You will also consider special cases, such as when an equation has no solution.

Making Connections: Course 2

6.1.1 How can I represent the data?

Circle Graphs

Data can be found everywhere in the world. When scientists conduct experiments, they collect data. Advertising agencies collect data to learn which products consumers prefer. In Chapter 4 you developed histograms and box-and-whisker plots to represent measures (such as lengths of frog jumps). However, how can you represent data that is non-numerical or that cannot be represented on a number line? Today you will look at a data display that is used for data that comes in categories or groups. As you work, keep these questions in mind:

What portion is represented?

Should I use a fraction or a percent?

Am I measuring in percents or degrees?

6-1.   HUMAN CIRCLE GRAPH

Get a shape card from your teacher. Look at your shape and decide if your shape is a parallelogram, another form of quadrilateral, a triangle, or some other shape. Follow your teacher's directions to create a linear model and circle graph. Then answer the questions below.

a. Your class built a circle graph with your bodies. How can this model be drawn on paper? Work with your team to sketch a picture of your class circle graph showing the portion of your class that held parallelograms, other quadrilaterals, triangles, and other polygons. Be sure to label each section with the category of shape it represents and with an estimated percentage or angle measure.

b. Approximately what portion of the class held triangles? Write your answer as a percent. Then estimate the measure of the central angle on the graph for that portion. A **central angle** is an angle with its vertex at the center of a circle. Its sides are formed by two radii and its measure is a portion of 360°.

c. Was there a section of the circle that had a central angle that was approximately 90°? If so, what type of figure is represented in that section?

6-2.   Nate and Nick are interested in buying a car. According to an ad in the paper, they found that there were 12 cars, 9 pickup trucks, 6 SUVs, and 3 minivans for sale in their price range.

   a.   How many vehicles were in Nate and Nick's price range?

   b.   What portion of the total does each type of vehicle represent?

   c.   On the Lesson 6.1.1B Resource Page, create a circle graph of the vehicles in Nate and Nick's price range. Label each section of the graph with the type of vehicle along with the fraction or percent of the circle it represents.

   d.   Calculate the central angle created by each section in the circle graph.

   e.   Is there another way to represent this data? Are a box-and-whisker plot, stem-and-leaf plot, histogram, or bar graph an appropriate way to display this data? Why or why not?

6-3.   Circle graphs can be used to compare data at different points in time. Analyze the two circle graphs below.

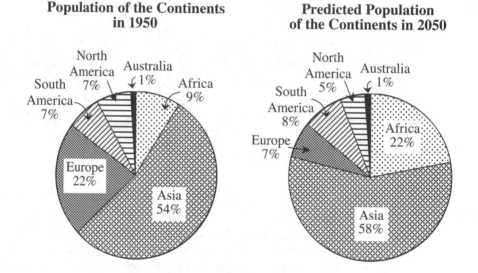

   a.   According to the circle graphs, which continent had the largest population in 1950? Which has the largest predicted population in 2050? Do they represent the same percent of the world's population in both graphs?

   b.   Which continent is predicted to have its percentage of world population increase the most between 1950 and 2050? By how much is its percentage expected to increase?

Problem continues on next page. →

6-3.   *Problem continued from previous page.*

    c.   Which continent is expected to have its portion of the total population shrink the most between 1950 and 2050? By how much will its percentage of world population change?

    d.   Is it reasonable to say that continents with a small percentage of the world population in 1950 will have small percentage of the populatation in 2050? What evidence from the graphs can you provide to **justify** your answer?

6-4.   The world's landmasses are divided into seven continents. The largest continent in terms of landmass is Asia, representing almost 30% of the Earth's land. In contrast, the smallest continent is Australia at about 6% of the Earth's land. Use the circle graph at right to help you make the following comparisons.

Landmass of Continents

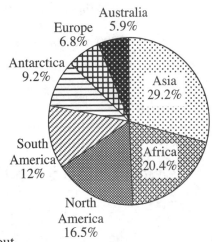

    a.   Which continents are approximately the same size?

    b.   Which continent is about one-half the size of Asia?

    c.   Which continents together make up about half of the world's land mass?

6-5.   The population of the world's people is not evenly divided over the Earth's surface. In 2009, only 0.0002% of the people in the world lived in Antarctica, while 60% of people lived in Asia.

Population of Continents 2000

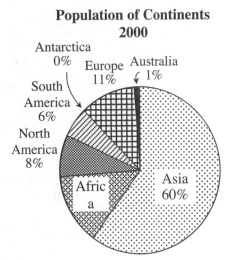

    a.   Where is the portion representing Antarctica's population? Explain.

    b.   What similarities and differences do you notice about the landmass and population circle graphs in problem 6-4 and this problem?

    c.   Is it reasonable to say that larger continents have larger populations? Why or why not?

6-6.   **Additional Challenge:** Take another look at the population graphs from
        problems 6-3 and 6-5.

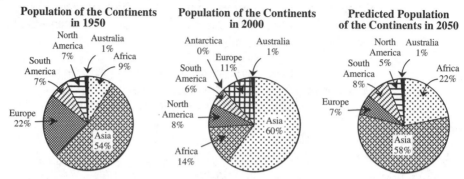

Population of the Continents in 1950

Population of the Continents in 2000

Predicted Population of the Continents in 2050

a.   Note that Asia's population percentage goes from 54% to 60% to 58%.
      Does this mean the population of Asia is expected to shrink between
      2000 and 2050? Why or why not?

b.   What kind of graph could be used so that this misunderstanding would
      not occur?

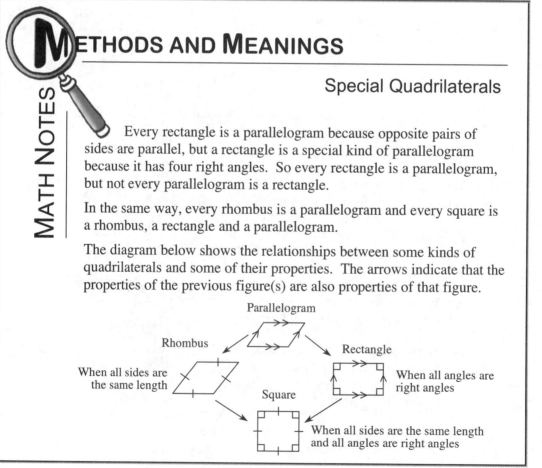

METHODS AND **M**EANINGS

Special Quadrilaterals

MATH NOTES

Every rectangle is a parallelogram because opposite pairs of
sides are parallel, but a rectangle is a special kind of parallelogram
because it has four right angles. So every rectangle is a parallelogram,
but not every parallelogram is a rectangle.

In the same way, every rhombus is a parallelogram and every square is
a rhombus, a rectangle and a parallelogram.

The diagram below shows the relationships between some kinds of
quadrilaterals and some of their properties. The arrows indicate that the
properties of the previous figure(s) are also properties of that figure.

Parallelogram

Rhombus

Rectangle

When all sides are
the same length

Square

When all angles are
right angles

When all sides are the same length
and all angles are right angles

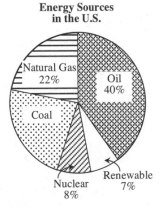

Energy Sources
in the U.S.

6-7. Answer the following questions about the graph
at right.

  a. According to this graph, what percentage of the
     energy in the United States comes from coal?

  b. Which two sources of energy equal about one-
     third of the total energy for the United States?

  c. What combination of energy sources provide
     about half of the total energy for the United
     States?

6-8. If you can travel 156 miles on 4 gallons of gasoline, how far can you travel on
12 gallons? How many miles on 6 gallons? A diagram may help you with your
reasoning. Show your work and explain your thinking.

6-9. Use the Distributive Property to simplify the following expressions.

  a. $4(x+2)$ b. $-5(9+x)$ c. $7(x-3)$

6-10. In 2009, the federal government budget was $3.1 trillion ($3,100,000,000,000).
The government was looking to cut costs.

  a. If it decided to cut 1%, how much did it cut?

  b. If the government reduced the budget by 7%, how much did it cut?

  c. If the government eliminated $93 billion ($93,000,000,000) from the
     budget, what percentage did it cut?

6-11. The diameter of the large circle is 18 cm.

  a. What is the area of the shaded circle?

  b. What steps did you do need to do to find
     the answer?

6.1.2 Is there a relationship?

Organizing Data in a Scatterplot

In previous chapters and Lesson 6.1.1, you have been looking at single data sets, such as world population. Often we need to compare two measurements to answer a question or to see a connection between two types of data. For example, comparing the odometer reading of a car to the price of a car can help determine if these factors are related. In this lesson you will study scatterplots, a new tool for visually presenting data, as a way to relate two sets of measurements. You will be asked to analyze the data to see if you can make predictions or come to any conclusion about the relationships that you find.

As you work with your team today, use these focus questions to help direct your discussion:

How can I organize data?

Can I use this data to make a prediction?

What does a point represent?

Is there a connection between the two factors?

6-12. **HOW MUCH IS THAT CAR?**

Nate and Nick were discussing cars. Nate claimed that cars with lower odometer readings were more expensive than cars with higher odometer readings. His evidence was that his car with 23,000 miles was worth more than Nick's car with 31,000 miles. To investigate Nate's claim, the boys researched several car ads and found the information in the table at right.

Does the information in the table support Nate's claim? That is, do you believe Nate's claim that cars with a lower odometer reading cost more money?

Nate's Data from Car Ads

Odometer Reading (thousands of mi)	Price (thousands of $)
35	$38
55	$16
6	$50
28	$30
50	$26
31	$35
15	$28
99	$10
99	$13

6-13.   Melissa looked at the data from problem 6-12 and said, *"I need to be able to see the data as a picture. I can't tell if there is a relationship from the lists of numbers."* She decided to use a box-and-whisker plot. Her box-and-whisker plots for odometer reading and price are shown below. Do these pictures help you decide if Nate is correct? Why or why not?

Odometer Reading (thousands of miles)   Price (thousands of dollars)

6-14.   Melissa wondered if a coordinate graph could help determine if there was a relationship in Nate's data from problem 6-12.

a.   Follow your teacher's directions to create a scatterplot of the data for Melissa.

- Set up a graph showing Odometer Reading on the *x*-axis and Price on the *y*-axis.

- Label equal intervals on each axis so that all of the data will fit on the graph.

- Plot the data points from problem 6-12.

b.   Describe the scatterplot you just created. What do you notice about how the points are placed on the graph? Do you see any patterns?

c.   Place an additional point on your graph for Nate's car that has an odometer reading of 23,000 miles. Explain your **strategy** for deciding where to put the point.

d.   When a relationship exists, one way to help show a trend in the data is to place a line or curve that in general represents where the data falls. This line (sometimes called a **trend line**) does not need to touch any of the actual data points, but instead shows where the data generally falls. The line is the set of points that represents your predictions for all cars no matter what their mileage or price.

With your team, decide where a trend line could be placed that would best represent the data points. Are there any limits to when the trend line makes sense?

Problem continues on next page. →

6-14.   *Problem continued from previous page.*

e.   Using the trend line, can you predict the price of a car with an odometer reading of 80,000 miles? If so, explain how the trend line helps. If not, explain why it is not helpful.

f.   Based on the scatterplot, would you agree with Nate's claim that cars with a higher odometer reading cost less? Use the scatterplot to **justify** your answer.

6-15.   Sometimes what you know about relationships can help you predict what data will look like when it is graphed. For each situation below:

- Look at the scatterplots and use your experience to decide which statement fits each scatterplot.

- Decide if there is a relationship between the data, that is, as one quantity changes, does the other change in a predictable way?

- If there is a relationship, describe it in a sentence.

- If there is no relationship, explain why you think so.

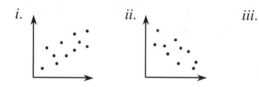

i.   *ii.*   *iii.*   *iv.*

a.   How fast a dog can run and the length of the dog's fur.

b.   A person's age and their body temperature.

c.   The child's age and the size of his or her feet.

d.   Outdoor temperature and the percentage of people wearing long sleeve shirts.

METHODS AND MEANINGS

Circle Graphs

MATH NOTES

A **circle graph** (sometimes called a **pie chart**) is like a bar graph because it deals with categorical data (such as make of car or grade in school) and not continuous data, such as age or height.

Each category of data is put into its own sector of the circle. The measure of the central angle bounding the sector is proportional to the percentage of elements of that type of the whole. For example, if Central Schools has 40% of its students in elementary school, 35% in middle school, and 25% in high school, then its circle graph would have a central angle of 144° (0.4 times 360°) for the sector showing the elementary school, 126° for the sector showing the elementary school, and 90° for the sector showing the high school.

Central

High School: 25 % or 90°

Elementary: 40% or 144°

Middle: 35% or 126°

Review & Preview

6-16.   A class surveyed how students at their school travel to school. The results of the survey are shown in the table at right. Make a circle graph showing the results of the survey using percentages.

Mode of Transportation	Number of Students
Bus	90
Ride Bike	30
Ride in Car	75
Walk	45

6-17.   Simplify the following expressions.

    a. $-5 + 2(8 - 12)$ b. $(-5 + 2)(8 - 12)$ c. $-5 + 2 \cdot 8 - 12$

    d. $\frac{1}{2}(-6)(4 + 10)$ e. $-\frac{2}{3} \cdot 6 + 15 \div (-3)$ f. $(7 - 2)^2 - 5 \div 5$

6-18.   A triangle has a base that is two more than three times the length of its height. The area of the triangle is 400 square cm. What are the base and height of the triangle?

6-19.   Alan wants to convince his parents that he is doing well in math. His test scores are 83, 90, 58, 71, 82, 91, 82, and 64. Should he use the mean, median, or mode to convince them? Explain your **reasoning** and show your work.

6-20.   Find the lengths of the missing sides on the similar shapes at right.

6.1.3 What is the relationship?

Identifying Correlation

When is it reasonable to make a prediction? For example, when you know the height of a tree, can you predict the size of its leaves? Or if you know the outdoor temperature for the day, can you predict the number of glasses of water you will drink during the day?

In Lesson 6.1.2 you found that some data sets were related and others were not. In this lesson you will look at different situations and decide if they show a relationship, and if that relationship allows you to make a prediction. As you work with your team today, use these focus questions to help direct your discussion:

> When one value goes up, what happens to the other one?

> Is there a relationship between one thing changing and the other changing?

> Can I make a prediction?

6-21. Students in a science class have been experimenting with different factors that they think may affect how tall a plant will grow. Each team planted seeds in several pots using different experimental conditions.

With your team, read the questions that the students investigated. Write a team prediction (hypothesis) for the results for each experiment. Assume that all other variables are controlled (meaning that they will not affect the experimental outcome).

a. Does the amount of fertilizer affect the plant height?

b. Does how deep the seed is planted in each pot affect the plant height?

c. Does the number of seeds in each pot affect plant height?

d. Does the size of the pot affect plant height?

e. Does the hours of sunlight per day affect the plant height?

6-22.   After three weeks, the teams measured the heights
of their plants and recorded the data. The Team 1
data chart and the question they investigated are
included below. On graph paper, make a
scatterplot for the data gathered. Be sure that you:

- Clearly label your axes

- Mark the scale at equal intervals

- Title your graph appropriately (such
as with the experimental question)

Team 1: Does the amount of fertilizer affect the plant height?

Amount of fertilizer over 3 week period (ml)	5	10	15	20	25
Height of plant (cm)	9	12	18	24	30

6-23.   Your teacher will assign your team one of the remaining sets of data and will
provide you with poster material. Prepare a scatterplot poster for your assigned
set of data. Be sure your graph has a title and that the axes are correctly labeled.
Also make sure that the points on your graph will be easily seen from across the
room.

Team 2: Does the depth of seed in each pot affect the plant height?

Depth of seed in pot (cm)	3	6	9	12	15
Height of plant (cm)	24	21	18	12	6

Team 3: Does the number of seeds in each pot affect the plant height?

Number of seeds planted in pot	1	2	3	4	5
Height of plant (cm)	21	24	27	21	24

Team 4: Does the size of the pot affect plant height?

Diameter of pot (cm)	6	9	12	15	18
Height of plant (cm)	21	20	19	21	18

Team 5: Do the hours of sunlight per day affect the plant height?

Amount of light per day (hours)	1	3	5	7	9
Height of plant (cm)	3	9	12	24	27

6-24. Examine your scatterplot for Team 1 (from problem 6-22) and the scatterplot posters created by your class. Then answer the following questions.

    a. For each of the graphs of data, does there appear to be a relationship? If so, describe it by completing the sentence:

        As _____ gets larger, then _____ gets _____.

    b. In a scatterplot, if there appears to be no relationship between the variables, then the points in the scatterplot have **no correlation**. But if one variable generally increases as the other variable increases, there is said to be a **positive correlation**. If one variable generally decreases as the other variable increases, there is said to be a **negative correlation**. See some examples below.

       Positive Correlation   Negative Correlation   No Correlation

    Review each of the graphs of the plant experiment data and decide if there is a positive correlation, a negative correlation, or no correlation.

    c. An **outlier** is a piece of data that does not seem to fit into the pattern. Do there appear to be any outliers in any of the scatterplots?

    d. Now go back and look at your team predictions for each question (problem 6-21). Were your predictions accurate? Explain your **reasoning**.

6-25. When there is a correlation, predictions can be made. One way to help make predictions is to draw a trend line or curve for the data.

    a. Find your graph of Team 1's data (from problem 6-22). Work with your team to draw a straight line that represents the trend of the data on this graph. Remember that the line does not need to intersect each of the points.

    b. Now use your trend line to predict the height of the plant when 12 milliliters of fertilizer is given to the plant over a 3-week period.

    c. How much fertilizer would you predict is needed (over the 3-week period) to have the plant grow 26 cm?

6-26. **LEARNING LOG**

In your Learning Log, describe how a graph can help you tell if there is a relationship between two sets of data. That is, what does it look like if there is a correlation? What does it look like if there is no correlation? Title this entry, "Correlations," and label it with today's date.

6-27. **HOW MUCH IS THAT CAR?**

Nate and Nick were talking about cars. Nate claimed that cars with more horsepower were more expensive than cars with less horsepower. His reason was that his 300 horsepower sports car was worth more than Nick's 120 horsepower small economy car. To investigate Nate's claim, the boys looked up information about their friends' cars. The table at right shows their results.

a. Does the information in the table support Nate's claim that cars with more horsepower cost more? Is there a relationship between horsepower and the price of a car?

b. Set up a graph and plot the points from the table. Now do you believe Nick's claim? Explain your **reasoning**.

Nick and Nate's Data

Horsepower	Price (Thousands)
500	$38
160	$16
453	$23
505	$23
228	$30
311	$26
335	$15
197	$40

6-28. Evaluate the inequality $x + 4 < 2x - 3$ for the following values of x. Decide if the given value of x makes the statement true or false. Show all of your work.

a. $x = 4$ b. $x = -2$ c. $x = 7$ d. $x = 9$

6-29. Evaluate the following expressions.

a. $7x + 8$ when $x = 9$ b. $6(y - 11)$ when $y = -6$

c. $45 - 5m + 7$ when $m = -4$ d. $-2t + 9$ when $t = -20$

6-30.   Simplify each expression.

a. $-\frac{4}{5}+\frac{7}{12}$ b. $\frac{5}{9}+(-\frac{1}{4})$ c. $-\frac{3}{7}\cdot\frac{11}{12}$ d. $-1\frac{2}{3}\cdot\frac{4}{5}$

6-31.   Here are the heights (in inches) of hollyhocks (tall, slender flowering plants) that are growing in the park: 10, 39, 43, 45, 46, 47, 48, 48, 49, 50, and 52.

a.   Find the median.

b.   Find the quartiles.

c.   Make a box-and-whisker plot of the data.

6.1.4 What is the relationship?

Introduction to Linear Rules

In Lessons 6.1.2 and 6.1.3, you made scatterplots and examined at how data was related. With your team, you will now explore how some kinds of correlations in scatterplots can be used to help make predictions. So far, the data you have graphed has been a collection of points that you have gathered from the world around you. Today we will begin to collect data from a mathematical situation and attempt to use this data to make predictions. This data, when displayed on a graph, will be like a scatterplot in some ways and different in other ways.

6-32.   COLLECTING DATA

You and a partner will be given a short time to generate a list of number pairs that add to ten. For example, 3 plus 7 equals 10, so the number pair would be $(3, 7)$. Use a table like the one below to record your number pairs.

Number 1												
Number 2												

As you generate your list, think about kinds of numbers you can use.

- Do the numbers have to be positive?
- Do they have to be integers?
- What is the largest number you can use? What is the smallest?
- How many number pairs are possible?

6-33.   ANALYZING THE DATA

Follow the directions from your teacher to create a graph of the data. Then, with your team, discuss the questions below and record your answers.

a.   What do all of the number pairs have in common?

b.   Explain the **strategy** you used to find your number pairs.

c.   How many points could there be on the graph?

d.   How is this relationship different than the scatterplots that you have made in Lessons 6.1.2 and 6.1.3? How is this relationship the same?

6-34.   Now you will play what are known as Silent Board Games. Your teacher will put an incomplete $x \to y$ table on the overhead or board. For each:

- Copy the table, study the input and output values, and look for a relationship.

- Once you know the relationship between x and y, use the relationship to add the missing values to your chart.

- Finally, write the rule in words and symbols that finds each y-value from its x-value.

6-35.   In Chapter 1, your team looked for characteristics that sets of objects had in common. The points below were one of those sets of objects. Use what you learned about finding relationships during the Silent Board Game to describe the relationship between x and y in the points below. Then write a rule of the form $y =$ _____ .

(3, 5)   (98, 100)   (−6, −4)   (11, 13)

6-36. Look for a relationship between the numbers in each table below. Complete the last two entries for each table. Describe any relationships you notice.

a.

Number 1	2	12	6	8	24	–4	1	
Number 2	3	18	9	12	36	–6		30

b.

Number 1	2	–5	7	4	0	–1	3	
Number 2	5	–9	15	9	1	–1		11

c.

Number 1	–3	5	–5	0	2	–2		6
Number 2	1	–7	3	–2	–4	0	2	

METHODS AND MEANINGS

MATH NOTES

Correlation and Trend Lines

In a scatterplot, if one variable increases as the other variable increases, there is said to be a **positive correlation**. If one variable increases as the other variable decreases, there is said to be a **negative correlation**. If there is no relationship between the variables, then the points in the scatterplot have **no correlation**. An example of each situation is illustrated below.

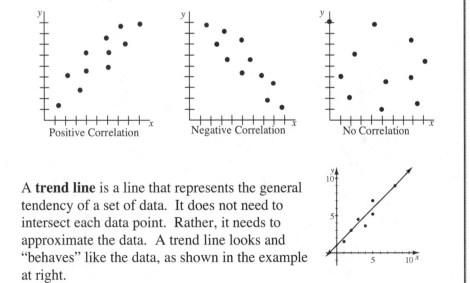

Positive Correlation   Negative Correlation   No Correlation

A **trend line** is a line that represents the general tendency of a set of data. It does not need to intersect each data point. Rather, it needs to approximate the data. A trend line looks and "behaves" like the data, as shown in the example at right.

6-37. Consider the following table.

x	−3	0.5	0	2	4
y	−1	2.5	2	4	6

a. What is the rule for the table?

b. Explain your **strategy** for finding the rule for this table.

6-38. Write an expression for each mat at right.

a. Simplify each mat to determine which expression is greater, if possible.

b. If $x = 3$, would your answer to part (a) change? Explain.

c. If $x = -2$, would your answer change? Explain.

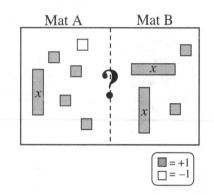

6-39. **Multiple Choice:** Which of the following expressions could be used to find the average (mean) of the numbers k, m, and n?

A. $k + m + n$ B. $3(k + m + n)$ C. $\frac{k+m+n}{3}$ D. $3k + m + n$

6-40. Copy and complete each of the Diamond Problems below. The pattern used in the Diamond Problems is shown at right.

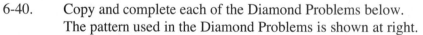

a.   b.   c.   d.

6-41. Find the area of the shaded portion of each circle.

a.   b.

6.1.5 What is the pattern?

Intercepts

In past lessons you looked at data from several situations. Sometimes the data appeared to be random and sometimes it had a predictable pattern. When data has a rule-based pattern, we can make predictions by finding other data points that fit the pattern.

6-42.   SILENT BOARD GAME

Today you will continue to play the Silent Board Game. Your teacher will put an incomplete $x \rightarrow y$ table on the overhead or board. Study the input and output values and look for a pattern. Then write the rule in words and symbols that finds each y-value from its x-value.

6-43.   CLEANING THE TANK, Part One

Roland and Alli work at the Seattle Aquarium. Part of their job is to empty the tank that holds a Giant Pacific Octopus in order to clean the glass and rocks. It is quite a job!

On one cleaning day, Roland carefully transferred the octopus to another tank. He then opened the drain to remove the water. As the water drained, the water level (its height in the tank) lowered at a rate of 2 feet per hour.

When Alli arrived at work that afternoon, she noted that there was still 10 feet of water in the tank.

a. Alli started a table to record the height, as shown below. Copy her table on your paper and complete the missing values. Then graph the data on graph paper.

x (hours after Alli arrived)	−5	−1	0	1	2	3	5	x
y (height in feet)		12	10					$y =$

b. What do the x-values in Alli's table represent? For example, what does $x = 3$ represent? What does $x = -1$ represent?

c. How does the graph tell you what is happening between 2 and 3 hours after Alli got to work? Use the graph to find the water level 2.5 hours after she got to work.

Problem continues on next page. →

6-43.   *Problem continued from previous page.*

   d.   Does it make sense to connect the points? Why or why not?

   e.   What will the height of the water be two hours after Alli gets to work?
        What was the height of the water two hours before she got to work?

   f.   If the water level is 20 feet when the tank is full, how many hours did it
        take to drain it? How many hours before Alli got to work did Roland open
        the drain? Explain how you found your answer.

6-44.   INTERPRETING INTERCEPTS

   The point where a line crosses the *x*- or *y*-axis on a graph often gives useful
   information about a situation. Examine your graph from problem 6-43.

   a.   The point where the line crosses the *x*-axis is called the **x-intercept**. What
        are the coordinates of this point on your graph? What does that point tell
        you about the water in the tank?

   b.   The point where the line crosses the *y*-axis is called the **y-intercept**. What
        are the coordinates of this point? What information does it give about the
        water in the tank?

6-45.   After Alli graphed the data (shown at
   right), she became concerned because
   her graph no longer made a straight line.

   a.   At what *x*-value did Alli make her
        mistake? What *y*-value should she have?

   b.   Explain to Alli how she could have
        recognized her mistake.

Giant Pacific Octopus Tank

6-46.   **Additional Challenge:** Alli's data table from problem 6-43 was based on when
   she arrived at work. However, if Roland had made the data table instead,
   starting with when he opened the drain, his table would have been slightly
   different. Assume that the tank originally was filled to a height of 20 feet.

   a.   On your paper, create a new table that records the height of the water for
        the number of hours after the drain was opened. Start with *x* = 0 hours and
        include each hour until the tank was empty.

   b.   If you graphed Roland's data from part (a), how would this graph be the
        same or different than Alli's graph from problem 6-43? **Visualize.**

   c.   Graph Roland's data from part (a). Compare Roland's graph with Alli's
        graph. Write down your observations.

Making Connections: Course 2

6-47.   LEARNING LOG

In your Learning Log, explain how you can make predictions
with scatterplots and linear graphs. Is one kind of graph
easier to use to make predictions? Can you always make a
prediction with a graph? Label this entry with today's date
and title it "Scatterplot and Linear Graph Predictions."

METHODS AND MEANINGS

Making a Complete Graph

A complete graph has the following components:

- x-axis and y-axis labeled, clearly showing the scale.

- Equation of the graph near the line or curve as a label.

- Line or curve extended as far as possible on the graph.

- Coordinates of special points stated in (x, y) format.

x	–1	0	1	2	3
y	6	4	2	0	–2

Tables can be formatted
horizontally, like the one above,
or vertically, as shown below.

x	y
–1	6
0	4
1	2
2	0
3	–2
4	–4

The graph of
$y = -2x + 4$

y-intercept
$(0, 4)$

x-intercept
$(2, 0)$

origin
$(0, 0)$

$(3, -2)$

Throughout this course, you will
continue to graph lines and other
curves. Be sure to label your
graphs completely.

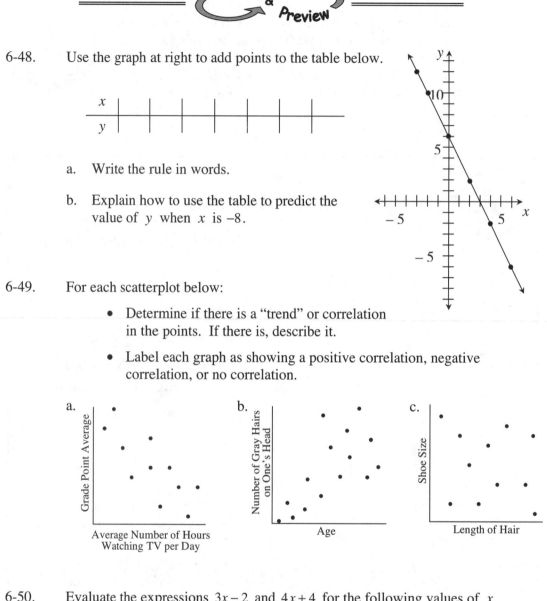

6-48.   Use the graph at right to add points to the table below.

x							
y							

a.   Write the rule in words.

b.   Explain how to use the table to predict the value of y when x is –8.

6-49.   For each scatterplot below:

- Determine if there is a "trend" or correlation in the points. If there is, describe it.

- Label each graph as showing a positive correlation, negative correlation, or no correlation.

a.

Grade Point Average

Average Number of Hours
Watching TV per Day

b.

Number of Gray Hairs
on One's Head

Age

c.

Shoe Size

Length of Hair

6-50.   Evaluate the expressions $3x - 2$ and $4x + 4$ for the following values of x. When you have found the value for each expression, write a statement using $<$, $>$, or $=$ that shows how the two values are related.

a. $x = 0$ b. $x = -6$ c. $x = 5$ d. $x = -2$

6-51.   Draw a trapezoid. Label the top base 6 cm and the height 4 cm. If the area of this trapezoid is 36 square cm, what is the length of the other base? You may find it helpful to use the 5-D Process.

6-52.   Find the area of each shaded portion, called a **sector**, in the circles below.

   a. The diameter is 3 feet.   b. The radius is 12 ft.

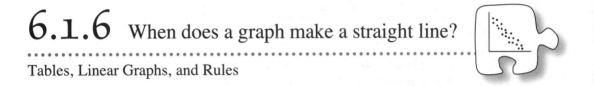

6.1.6 When does a graph make a straight line?

Tables, Linear Graphs, and Rules

In the previous lesson you made a graph showing how the water level in a tank changed as it was being drained at a constant rate. You noticed that the graph made a straight line. Today you will complete a table and graph what happens as the Giant Pacific Octopus tank is being filled. As you work with your team, think about the following questions:

How is the line changing?

What information can we get from a rule?

When does a graph form a straight line? When does it not?

6-53.   SILENT BOARD GAME

Today you will continue to play the Silent Board Game. Your teacher will put an incomplete $x \rightarrow y$ table on the overhead or board. Study the input and output values and look for a pattern. Then write the rule in words and symbols that finds each y-value from its x-value.

6-54. **CLEANING THE TANK, Part Two**

Today Roland and Alli are filling the 20-foot deep octopus tank from problem 6-43. The tank started empty and began filling earlier in the day. When Alli got to work the water level was up to 8 feet. It is being filled at a constant rate of four feet per hour. Alli created the table below. She wants to use a data table to predict when the tank will be full so that she will know when to shut off the water.

x (hours after Alli arrived)	–2	–1	0	1	2	3	x
y (height in feet)			8				$y =$

a. Copy and complete Alli's table on your own paper. Then graph the data on graph paper. Be sure you have a complete graph.

b. What will the height of the water be two hours after Alli gets to work?

c. How long before Alli got to work did the tank begin to be filled? How do you know?

d. How many hours after she got to work did Alli need to turn the water off because the tank was full?

e. The table is set up like a Silent Board Game. What is the rule that describes the data in this table?

6-55. Looking at the x-intercept and the y-intercept on a graph can help you tell the story of the data.

a. What are the coordinates of the x-intercept and what information does that point tell you about the water in the tank?

b. What are the coordinates of the y-intercept and what information does that point tell you about the water in the tank?

6-56.   CLEANING THE TANK, Part Three

The next day Alli started her day's work at the
jellyfish tank that had been cleaned the day before
and was now being refilled. There, she found a
30-foot deep tank that had four feet of water in it.
Alli started filling the tank so that after x hours,
the water level was $y = 3x + 4$ feet high. Alli knew
she could only work for seven hours that day.
After four hours she began to worry that the tank
would not be full before she had to leave.

a.   Using the rule, complete the table and then graph the height of the water in
the tank for the first four hours that Alli was at work.

x (hours)	0	1	2	3	4	x
y (height)						$y = 3x + 4$

b.   Based on your graph, will the tank be full when Alli has to leave work? If
not, how many feet of water still will be needed to fill the tank?

c.   What is the y-intercept and what does this point tell you about this
situation?

6-57.   Look at the following graphs and tell what is happening at each tank. Think
about whether the tank is filling or draining and what the x- and y-intercepts tell
you. Be specific about the water level in the tank.

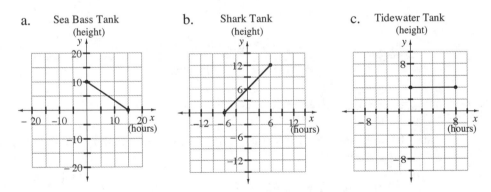

a. Sea Bass Tank
(height)

b. Shark Tank
(height)

c. Tidewater Tank
(height)

6-58.   Complete the table below and draw a graph of the rule $y = -3x + 18$. Check that
your points form a straight line and correct any errors.

x	−3	0.5	−1	6	1	0	3	−2	5
y			21		15				

METHODS AND MEANINGS

When is a Point on the Graph of a Rule?

So far you have drawn several graphs by starting with a rule, substituting x-values, computing y-values, and plotting the points on a set of axes. What if you have the coordinates of a point and want to know if it also belongs on the graph? Use the rule and determine whether the point makes the equation true or false. If the point makes the equation true, it is also on the graph; if it is false, it does not belong on the graph. Here are two examples:

Is (10, 25) on the graph of $y = 2x + 5$?	Is (5, −3) on the graph of $y = -2x - 7$?
Replace x with 10 and y with 25 and determine if the equation is true or false.	Replace x with 5 and y with −3 and determine if the equation is true or false.
Is $25 = 2 \cdot 10 + 5$?	Is $-3 = -2 \cdot 5 - 7$?
$25 = 25$ so yes, the point is on the graph.	$-3 \neq -17$ so no, the point is not on the graph.

6-59.   Make a table and a graph for the following rule: $y = 2x - 4$.

a.   Explain how you know that there are more points than just the ones shown on your graph.

b.   Where would the additional points go on the graph?

6-60.   Determine if each of the numbers below is a solution to the inequality $3x - 2 < 2 - 2x$. Show all of your work.

a.   2   b. $\frac{1}{2}$ c.   −3   d. $\frac{2}{3}$

Making Connections: Course 2

6-61. The school library has 6500 titles in its collection of books, magazines, and reference materials. The librarian is presenting information about the library to the parent association, and she made the graph at right.

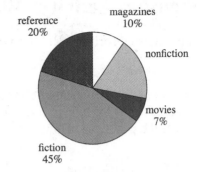

a. According to the graph, what percentage of the collection are nonfiction books?

b. Could the librarian have presented this information in a histogram? Why or why not?

c. How many of the books in the library are fiction?

6-62. Hector has a part-time job at a garage. He gets a paycheck of $820 every four weeks.

a. Hector has to pay 15% of his income in taxes. How much money does he pay in taxes each paycheck? Show your thinking with a diagram and calculations.

b. Hector took a 1-week vacation, so his next paycheck will only be for 3 weeks of work. What percentage of his regular pay should he expect to receive? How much is that?

c. The garage owner is impressed with Hector's work, and is giving him a 10% raise. How much will Hector be paid when he receives his next 4-week paycheck?

6-63. An NBA basketball hoop has an inside diameter of 18 inches. The official NBA basketball has a maximum circumference of 30 inches. What is the difference between the hoop diameter and the diameter of the ball? Show all of your work.

6-64. Red apples cost $1.20 per pound and green apples cost $1.50 per pound.

a. Write an expression to represent the total cost of x pounds of red apples and y pounds of green apples.

b. What is the total cost if you buy 3 pounds of red apples and 2 pounds of green apples?

Extension Activity   What is the relationship?

Finding and Describing Relationships

Today you will become a point on a life-size, human graph. Your teacher will give the class instructions for how to form human graphs. Then you will work in study teams to complete the problems below.

6-65.   HUMAN DATA POINTS

Can you imagine what it is like to be a point on a graph? Today is your chance to find out. Your teacher will direct you to a set of axes and explain how to stand on the graph. As you are doing this problem, think about the different patterns you see. Is there a relationship between them?

6-66.   Your teacher will post the graphs for the points that you and your classmates used to form "human graphs."

a.   Compare the graphs. How are they the same and how are they different?

b.   Look at the graphs that formed scatterplots. Which graphs show a positive correlation? Negative correlation? Did any graph show no correlation?

c.   Were any graphs straight lines? If so, copy the table with all the points next to the graph you made on your resource page. Use the table to find a rule that finds each *y*-value from its *x*-value.

6-67.   LEARNING LOG

Write a paragraph in your Learning Log that describes what you did and what you observed in today's class work. How were the scatterplots different from the linear graphs? How did you identify which kind of graph you had? Put today's date on your entry and title it, "Human Data Points."

6-68.   Simplify each expression.

a. $\frac{73}{100} \cdot (-\frac{2}{7})$ b. $0.4 \cdot 0.3$ c. $-\frac{63}{80} + \frac{7}{10}$

d. $5\frac{1}{9} + 8\frac{2}{5}$ e. $-\frac{9}{17} - \frac{1}{2}$ f. $-1.2 + (-\frac{3}{5})$

6-69.   Graph the following points on a coordinate grid and connect them to make a
         triangle: $(0, 1), (3, 2), (2, 4)$. Then:

- Dilate the shape by multiplying each coordinate by two.

- List the coordinates of the new vertices.

What do you notice about the sides of the two shapes?

6-70.   Sketch the parallelogram shown at right, and
         then redraw it with sides that are half as long.

a.   Find the perimeters of both the
     original and smaller parallelograms.

b.   If the height of the original parallelogram (drawn to the side that is 6 units)
     is 2 units, find the areas of both parallelograms.

6-71.   Simplify each of the following expressions.

a. $32 \div 2 \cdot 4$ b. $3 \cdot 6 \div 2 + 6$ c. $3^2 + 7$

6-72.   Use the 5-D Process to solve the following problem.

Jen, Carrie, and Fran are each thinking of a number. When you add their
numbers together you get 207. Jen's number is 9 more than Carrie's, and Fran's
number is 3 less than Jen's number. What is Fran's number?

6.2.1 What values make expressions equal?

Solving Equations

In Chapter 5, you figured out how to determine what values of x make one expression greater than another. In this lesson you will study what can be learned about x when two expressions are equal. As you work today, focus on these questions:

> What if both sides are equal?
>
> Is there more than one way to simplify?
>
> What value(s) of x will make the expressions equal?

6-73. CHOOSING A PRICE PLAN

Sandeep works at a bowling alley that currently charges a player $3 to rent shoes and $4 per game. However, his boss is thinking about charging $11 to rent shoes and $2 per game.

a. If a customer rents shoes and plays two games, will he or she pay more with the original price plan or the new price plan? Show how you know.

b. If the customer bowls 7 games, which price plan is cheaper?

6-74.   WILL THEY EVER BE EQUAL?

Sandeep decided to represent the two price plans (from problem 6-73) with expressions, where x represents the number of games bowled:

Original price: $4x + 3$ New price: $2x + 11$

a.   Do his new expressions find the same prices? Find both the original and new prices when $x = 2$ and then again when $x = 7$ games. Did you get the same prices as you found in problem 6-73?

b.   Sandeep decided to place his expressions on an Expression Comparison Mat. What steps did Sandeep take to simplify the mat to this point?

c.   Sandeep noticed that for one number of games, a customer would pay the same amount no matter which price plan his boss used. That is, he found a value of x that will make $4x + 3 = 2x + 11$. How many games did that customer bowl? What was the price he paid? Explain.

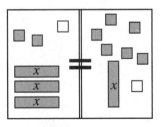

d.   The value of x you found in part (c) is called a **solution** to the equation $4x + 3 = 2x + 11$ because it makes the equation true. That is, it makes both expressions have the same value.

Is $x = 6$ also a solution? How can you tell?

6-75.   SOLVING FOR X

When the expressions on each side of the comparison mat are equal, they can be represented on a mat called an **Equation Mat**. Obtain a Lesson 6.2.1 Resource Page from your teacher. Now the "=" symbol on the central line indicates that the expressions on each side of the mat are "equal."

a.   Build the equation represented by the Equation Mat above on your own mat using algebra tiles.

b.   Record the original equation represented on your Equation Mat on your paper.

c.   Simplify the tiles on the mat as much as possible. Record what is on the mat after each legal move as you simplify each expression. What value of x will make the expressions equal?

6-76.   Amelia wants to solve the equation shown on the
         Equation Mat at right. After she simplified each
         expression as much as possible, she was confused
         by the tiles that were left on the mat.

         a.   What was Amelia's original equation?

         b.   Remove any zero pairs that you find on each
              side of the Equation Mat. What happens?

         c.   What is the solution to this equation? That is, what value of x makes this
              equation true? Explain your **reasoning**.

6-77.   Amelia now wants to solve the equation $2x + 2 + (-3) = 5x + 8$. Help her find the
         value of x that makes these expressions equal. Be sure to:

              • Build the expressions using algebra tiles on your Equation Mat.

              • Draw the mat on your paper.

              • Simplify the mat to help you figure out what value of x makes this
                 equation true.

METHODS AND **M**EANINGS

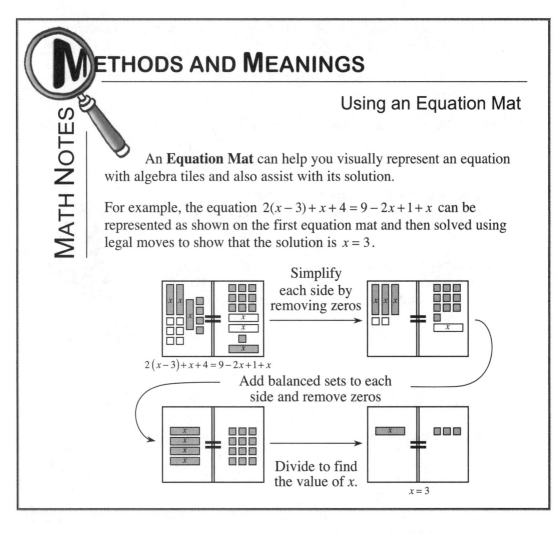

MATH NOTES

Using an Equation Mat

An **Equation Mat** can help you visually represent an equation with algebra tiles and also assist with its solution.

For example, the equation $2(x-3)+x+4 = 9-2x+1+x$ can be represented as shown on the first equation mat and then solved using legal moves to show that the solution is $x = 3$.

Simplify each side by removing zeros

$2(x-3)+x+4 = 9-2x+1+x$

Add balanced sets to each side and remove zeros

Divide to find the value of x.

$x = 3$

Review & Preview

6-78.   Use the legal moves that you have developed to simplify each mat and, if possible, decide which expression is greater.

$\blacksquare = +1$
$\square = -1$

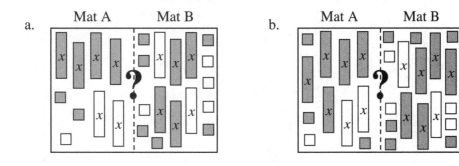

a.   Mat A   Mat B

b.   Mat A   Mat B

6-79.   Victor wants to play "Guess My Number." Use the clues below to figure out his number. Each part is a new game.

   a.   *"When you double my number and subtract 9, you get my original number. What's my number?"*

   b.   *"When you double my number and add 5, you get 17. What's my number?"*

6-80.   To solve the following problem, use the 5-D Process. Define a variable and write an expression for each column of your chart.

In the first three football games of the season, Carlos gained three times as many yards as Alden. Travis gained ten yards more than Carlos. Altogether the three players gained a total of 430 yards. How many yards did Carlos gain?

6-81.   Find the area and perimeter of each shape below. Show your steps and work.

   a.   All angles are right angles.

   b.

6-82.   Copy and complete the table. What is the rule for the table?

x	-2	4	$\frac{1}{2}$	0	7	-4
y	-7			-3	11	

6.2.2 How do I know that it is correct?

· ·

Checking Solutions and the Distributive Property

Sometimes a person's life can depend on the solution of a problem. For example, when skydiving teams jump from airplanes and aim for specific targets on the ground they need to carefully plan their speed and timing. If they are trying to land in a sports stadium as entertainment before a baseball game and they open their parachutes too soon, they may miss the landing area and crash into a building or a tree. If they jump out of the plane too soon, they may run into another skydiver. Even a small miscalculation could be dangerous.

Solving a problem is one challenge. However, once solved, it is important to have ways to know if the solution you found is correct. In this lesson you will be solving equations and finding ways to determine if your solution makes the equation true.

6-83.   Chen's sister was making a riddle for him to solve, *"I am thinking of a number. If you add two to the number then triple it, you get 9."*

a.   Build the equation on an Equation Mat. What are *two* ways that Chen could write this equation?

b.   Solve the equation and show your work by writing the equation on your paper after each legal move.

c.   When Chen told his sister the mystery number in the riddle she said he was wrong. Chen was sure that he had figured out the correct number. Find a way to **justify** that you have the correct solution in part (c).

6-84.   Now solve the equation $4(x + 3) = 8$. Remember to:

- Build the equation on your Equation Mat with algebra tiles.
- Simplify the equation using your legal moves.
- Record your work on your paper.
- Solve for x. That is, find the value of x that makes the equation true.

6-85.   CHECKING YOUR SOLUTION

When you solve an equation that has one solution, you get a value of the variable. But how do you know that you have done the steps correctly and that your answer "works"?

a.   Look at your answer for problem 6-84. How could you verify that your solution is correct and convince someone else? Discuss your ideas with your team.

b.   When Kelly and Madison compared their solutions for the equation $2x - 7 = -2x + 1$, Kelly got a solution of $x = 2$ and Madison got a solution of $x = -1$. To decide if the solutions were correct, the girls decided to check their answers to see if they made the expressions equal.

Finish their work below to determine if either girl has the correct solution.

Kelly's Work	Madison's Work
$2x - 7 \overset{?}{=} -2x + 1$	$2x - 7 \overset{?}{=} -2x + 1$
$2(2) - 7 \overset{?}{=} -2(2) + 1$	$2(-1) - 7 \overset{?}{=} -2(-1) + 1$

c.   When checking, Kelly ended up with $-3 = -3$. Does this mean that her answer is correct or incorrect? And if it is correct, does this mean the solution is $x = -3$ or $x = 2$? Explain.

d.   Go back to problem 6-84 and show how to check your solution for that problem.

6-86.   Kelly solved the equation $4(x + 3) = 8$ from problem 6-84. Her work is shown at right.

$$4(x + 3) = 8$$
$$x + 3 = 2$$
$$x + 3 + (-3) = 2 + (-3)$$
$$x = -1$$

a.   If $4(x + 3) = 8$, does $x + 3$ have to equal 2? Why?

b.   What did Kelly do to remove the 3 unit tiles from the left side of the equation? Does this move affect the equality?

c.   If Kelly were solving the equation $3(x - 5) = 9$, what might her first step be? You may want to build this equation on an Equation Mat to help make sense of her **strategy**.

6-87.　　Now practice this new solving skill by building the equation with tiles, solving for x, and checking your solution for each equation. Record your work.

a.　$4(x+1)+1+(-x)=10+x$　　　　b.　$-1+2x-x=x-8+(-x)$

c.　$5+2(x-4)=4x+7$　　　　　　d.　$9-3x=1+x$

e.　$3x+3-x+2=x+5$　　　　　　f.　$4=3(2x+1)-11$

6-88.　　Show the check for each of these problems and decide if the solution is correct or incorrect.

a.　$5x+8=3x-2$　　　　　　Solution: $x=-5$

b.　$2(x+1)+6=20-3x$　　　　Solution: $x=4$

6-89.　　Consider the Equation Mat at right.

a.　Write the original equation represented.

b.　Simplify the tiles on the mat as much as possible. What value of x will make the two expressions equal?

6-90.　　When Lakeesha solved the equation $3(x+1)=12$ from problem 6-89, she **reasoned** this way:

　　　　"Since 3 groups of $(x+1)$ equals 3 groups of 4, then I know that each group of $(x+1)$ must equal 4."

a.　Do you agree with her **reasoning**? Explain.

b.　How can the result of Lakeesha's **reasoning** be written?

c.　Verify that your answer from problem 6-89 will make the equation you wrote in part (b) true.

6-91.   During this chapter, you will use your new solving skills to solve word
         problems. Think about and use the **strategies** you already have to answer the
         questions below.

   a.   Andy is 4 years older than Eduardo.
         If Andy is x years old, write an
         expression to represent Eduardo's
         age.

   b.   In Eduardo's collection, the number of
         butterflies is 12 more than twice the
         number of moths. If there are x moths,
         write an expression to represent the
         number of butterflies he has.

6-92.   The class advisor was helping students plan an
         end-of-the-year trip. The students were surveyed
         regarding their choices. The results are in the circle
         graph at right.

   a.   What percentage of the students chose the
         water park?

   b.   Which two results are very close?

   c.   Write a recommendation to the class advisor regarding what the next step
         would be?

6.2.3 How can I record it?

Solving Equations and Recording Work

In this lesson, you will continue to improve your skills at simplifying and solving more complex equations. You will develop ways to record your solving **strategies** so that another student can understand your steps without seeing your Equation Mat. Consider the following questions as you work today.

How can I record the steps I use to solve?

How can I record what is on the Equation Mat after each step?

6-93.   Gene and Aidan were using the algebra tiles to solve equations. Aidan was in the middle of a problem when he was called away. Gene picked up Aidan's paper, but he had a hard time figuring out what he should do next.

Help Gene by completing his table on the Lesson 6.2.3 Resource Page.

Mat A	Mat B	Steps taken
$2x + 2(2x+1) + (-3x) + (-6)$	$4x + 3 + (-3) + x + 8$	Original Equation
		1. Distributive Property
$3x + (-4)$	$5x + 8$	2.
		3. Subtract $3x$ from both sides
-12	$2x$	4.
		5. Divide both sides by 2

6-94. Aidan was frustrated that he needed to write so much when solving an equation. He decided to come up with a shortcut for recording his work to solve a new equation.

As you look at Aidan's recording of how he solved $2x + 4 = -12$ below, **visualize** an Equation Mat with algebra tiles. Then answer the questions for each step below.

a. What legal move does writing -4 twice represent?

b. What legal move does circling the $+4$ and the -4 represent?

c. What does the box around the $\frac{2}{2}$ represent?

d. Why did Aidan divide both sides by 2?

e. Check Aidan's solution in the original equation. Is his solution correct?

$$2x \boxed{+ 4} = -12$$
$$\boxed{-4} = -4$$
$$\frac{2x}{2} = \frac{-16}{2}$$
$$x = -8$$

6-95. The method of recording the steps in the solution of an equation is useful only if you understand what operations are being used and how they relate to the legal moves on your Equation Mat.

Find the work shown at right on your resource page for this lesson.

a. For each step in the solution, add the missing work below each line that shows what legal moves were used. You may want to build the equation on an Equation Mat.

b. Check that the solution is correct.

$$x + (-4) + 6x = 3x - 1 + 5$$
$$-4 + 7x = 3x + 4$$
$$7x = 3x + 8$$
$$4x = 8$$
$$x = 2$$

6-96. Gene is confused. He simplified an equation and ended up with the mat shown at right. What is the value of x?

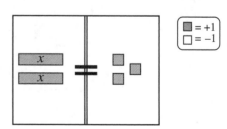

6-97. For each equation below, solve for x. You may build the equation on your Equation Mat. Record your work in symbols using Aidan's method (problem 6-94). Remember to check your solution.

a. $-2x+5+2x-5=-1+(-1)+6x+2$ b. $3(4+x)=x+6$

c. $5x+(-x)-1=11-2x$ d. $3(-x+2)+x-1=-x-3$

6-98. LEARNING LOG

In your Learning Log, explain what it means to solve an equation. What is a solution? Be sure to give an example. Title this entry "Solving Equations and Finding Solutions" and include today's date.

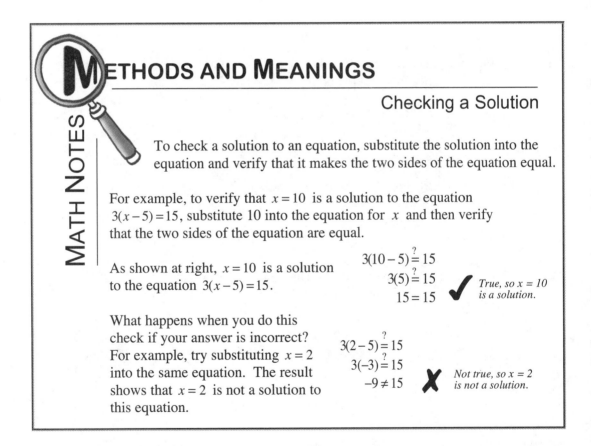

MATH NOTES

METHODS AND **M**EANINGS

Checking a Solution

To check a solution to an equation, substitute the solution into the equation and verify that it makes the two sides of the equation equal.

For example, to verify that $x=10$ is a solution to the equation $3(x-5)=15$, substitute 10 into the equation for x and then verify that the two sides of the equation are equal.

As shown at right, $x=10$ is a solution to the equation $3(x-5)=15$.

$$3(10-5)\overset{?}{=}15$$
$$3(5)\overset{?}{=}15$$
$$15=15 \checkmark$$ *True, so x = 10 is a solution.*

What happens when you do this check if your answer is incorrect? For example, try substituting $x=2$ into the same equation. The result shows that $x=2$ is not a solution to this equation.

$$3(2-5)\overset{?}{=}15$$
$$3(-3)\overset{?}{=}15$$
$$-9\neq15$$ **X** *Not true, so x = 2 is not a solution.*

6-99.   Solve each equation below for x. Check your final answer.

a. $4x = 6x - 14$

b. $3x + 5 = 50$

6-100.   Examine the table below.

x	0.5	0	2	4	5
y	−0.5	−2	4	10	13

a.   What is the rule for the table?

b.   Explain the **strategy** you used to find the rule.

6-101.   Find the area of each shaded **sector** (region) in the circles below. Note that the smaller angles in parts (a) and (c) are 90° angles.

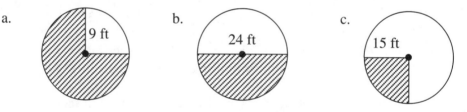

a.   9 ft

b.   24 ft

c.   15 ft

6-102.   Copy and complete each of the Diamond Problems below. The pattern used in the Diamond Problems is shown at right.

a.   13 / 14

b.   16 / −2

c.   −4.2 / −3

d.   0 / 15

6-103.   A cattle rancher gave $\frac{1}{3}$ of his land to his son and kept the remaining $\frac{2}{3}$ for himself. He kept 34 acres of land. How much land did he have to begin with?

6.2.4 How can I represent it?

Using a Table to Write Equations from Word Problems

In the last few lessons you used algebra tiles and Equation Mats to solve problems where variables represented specific numbers. Those tools are related to the processes you have used to solve word problems where a specific value is unknown. Today you will connect these two tools and the expressions you wrote using a part of the 5-D Process to extend your repertoire for solving problems.

6-104.   THE 5-D PROCESS REVISITED

Use the 5-D Process to set up the following problem. Complete only *three* trials. Even if you do not yet know the solution, wait for your teacher's instructions.

The Great Lakes contain the largest amount of fresh water on the surface of the planet. Combined, the five lakes (Superior, Michigan, Huron, Erie, and Ontario) contain 84% of North America's and 21% of the world's surface fresh water!

The amount of water in Lake Superior is 1720 cubic miles more than the amount of water in Lake Michigan. Lake Huron has 330 cubic miles of water less than Lake Michigan. If the total amount of water in the three lakes is 4,930 cubic miles, how much water is in Lakes Huron, Michigan, and Superior?

6-105.   GO FOR THE GOLD

As you saw in problem 6-104,
sometimes organizing your thinking
using the 5-D Process to solve a word
problem involves a lot of work.
Sometimes the tables are very
complicated or the numbers require
many trials to find the answer. How
can your new equation solving skills
help you solve word problems? Read
the following word problem and then
answer the questions below.

While looking at the country of Jamaica's results from the 2008 Beijing
Olympics, Gemma noticed that the number of gold medals Jamaica received
was twice the number of silver medals. She also realized that Jamaica
received 1 fewer bronze medal than silver medals. Altogether, Jamaica
received 11 medals.

a.   Gemma started by setting up the 5-D Process table below. What did she
      define x to represent?

Define			Do	Decide
# Gold	# Silver	# Bronze	Total Number of Medals	11?
$2x$	x	$x - 1$		

b.   How did she represent the number of gold and bronze medals?

c.   Write an equation for the total number of medals.

d.   Solve your equation in part (c). What is the value of x? What does this
      represent?

e.   How many gold medals did Jamaica earn? Explain how you know.

382   *Making Connections*: Course 2

6-106.　Solve the following word problems by writing and solving an equation. You may choose to use the 5-D Process and create a table to help you build your equation. It may be helpful to first do one or two trials with numbers to help establish a pattern. Whatever **strategy** you use, do not forget to define the variable. Check your answer.

    a.   A person's height is positively correlated to their arm span (the distance between the ends of your fingertips as your arms are held out on each side of your body). One of the tallest men in history had an arm span that measured 7 inches more than his height. The combined total of his arm span and height was 221 inches. How tall was this man?

    b.   Have you ever tried to hold your breath? Humans can only hold their breath an average of one minute. However, other animals can hold their breath for much longer.

        A Greenland whale can hold its breath three times as long as a beaver and a hippopotamus can hold its breath five minutes less than a beaver. If you added the time a Greenland whale, beaver, and hippopotamus can hold their breath, you would get 95 minutes! How long can a beaver hold its breath?

6-107.　LEARNING LOG

In Chapter 3 you learned about variables and using the 5-D Process to solve problems. In Chapter 5 you simplified expressions using algebra tiles and in this chapter you focused on solving equations.

In your Learning Log describe how variables and equations can be used to solve word problems. Use an example problem to help make your explanation clear. Title this entry, "Using the 5-D Process to Write and Solve Equations," and label it with today's date.

METHODS AND MEANINGS

Defining a Variable

When you write an equation, it is important to define your variable carefully. You need to be clear about what you are talking about so that someone else looking at your work understands what the variable represents. This step is an important habit to develop because it is an important step in solving many different math problems.

Suppose you have the problem:

> At the neighborhood grocery store, grapes cost $3 a pound. If Belinda spent $5.40 on grapes, how many pounds of grapes did she buy?

One equation you could write would be $3x = 5.4$, if you know what x stands for. The variable x should be clearly defined, such as $x = \text{pounds of grapes}$, rather than just $x = \text{grapes}$. You could also write $g = \text{pounds of grapes}$, since any letter may be used as a variable.

Review & Preview

6-108.   Consider the equation $7 = 3x - 5$.

    a.   Stanley wants to start solving the equation by adding five to both sides, while Terrence wants to first subtract seven from both sides. Will both **strategies** work? Is one **strategy** more efficient than the other?

    b.   Solve $7 = 3x - 5$. Show your steps.

6-109.   The two triangles at right are similar shapes.

    a.   What is the scale factor between shape A and shape B?

    b.   Find the missing sides.

    c.   If you wanted to make shape A smaller instead of bigger, what is a scale factor you could use?

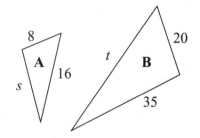

6-110.   Find the area and perimeter of the following figures.

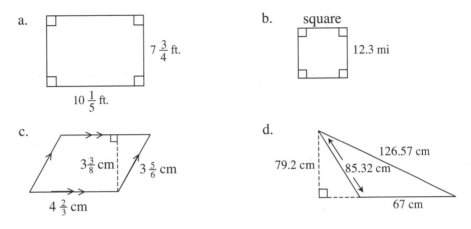

a.

$7\frac{3}{4}$ ft.

$10\frac{1}{5}$ ft.

b.   square

12.3 mi

c.

$3\frac{3}{8}$ cm $3\frac{5}{6}$ cm

$4\frac{2}{3}$ cm

d.

126.57 cm

79.2 cm   85.32 cm

67 cm

6-111.   Graph the following points on a coordinate grid: $(1,1)$, $(4,1)$, and $(3,4)$.

Connect the points, then translate the points three units right and three units up. What are the coordinates of the vertices of the new triangle?

6-112.   Find the value of the expression $2x+6$ for the given values of x.

a. $x=6$ b. $x=-2$ c. $x=0$ d. $x=5$

6.2.5 How can I model it?

Writing and Solving Equations

Engineers investigate practical problems to improve people's quality of life. To investigate solutions to problems they often build models. These models can take various forms. For example, a structural engineer designing a bridge might build a small replica of the bridge. Civil engineers studying the traffic patterns in a city might create equations that model traffic flows into and out of a city at different times.

In this lesson you will be building equations to model and solve problems based on known information. As you work today keep the following questions in mind:

What does x represent in the equation?

How does the equation show the same information as the problem?

Have I answered the question?

6-113.   Today your team will be responsible for solving a problem and sharing your solution with the class. It is important that your poster communicates your thinking and **reasoning** so that people who look at your poster understand how you solved the problem. Your poster should include:

- Connections between the words in the problem and the relationships in your chart and/or equation. Connections can be made with arrows, colors, symbols, and labels.

- Variables that are defined completely.

- An equation to represent the problem.

- Your solution to the problem.

- The answer declared in a sentence.

Begin by solving one of the problems below and writing an equation. Make sure to define the variable you use and answer the question(s) being asked. Using the 5-D Process, including numerical trials, may be helpful.

a.   Hong Kong's tallest building, Two International Finance Center, is 88 stories tall. The former Sears Tower in Chicago is eight stories taller than the Empire State Building in New York City. If all of the buildings were stacked on top of each other, the combined heights would have 300 stories. How many stories does the Sears Tower have?

b.   Have you ever driven or walked across a suspension bridge? There are many suspension bridges in the world of different lengths that allow people to travel across rivers, bays and lakes.

The Mackinac Bridge in Michigan is 1158 meters long. The Tsing Ma Bridge in Hong Kong is 97 meters longer than the Golden Gate Bridge in California. Together, all three bridges have a length of 3815 meters. How long is the Tsing Ma Bridge?

Problem continues on next page. →

Making Connections: Course 2

6-113.   *Problem continued from previous page.*

c.   Elevations found in the United States range from California's Death Valley at 282 feet below sea level to Alaska's Mount McKinley at 20,320 feet above sea level.

The highest elevation in Delaware is 106 feet higher than the highest elevation in Florida. Louisiana's highest elevation is 190 feet higher than Florida's highest elevation. If you climbed from sea level to the highest points in Delaware, Florida, and Louisiana, you would only climb 1331 feet. How high is the highest elevation in each of the three states?

d.   Most states in the United States are divided into counties. Some counties are very large and some are very small, and different states have different numbers of counties. Pennsylvania has five less than twice as many counties as Oregon. Florida has one less county than Pennsylvania. All together, the three states have 169 counties. How many counties does Florida have?

e.   A train from Washington, D.C. to Chicago first stops in Pittsburg and then in Cleveland. The distance from Washington, D.C. to Pittsburg is 30 miles less than twice the distance from Pittsburg to Cleveland. The distance from Cleveland to

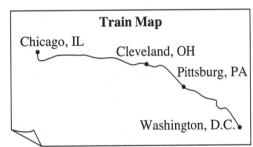

Chicago is 220 miles more than the distance between Pittsburg and Cleveland. If the entire train ride is 710 miles, how far is the train ride from Cleveland to Chicago?

6-114.   On graph paper, graph the rule $y = 4x - 6$. Determine the value of y when $x = \frac{1}{2}$.

6-115.   Solve the following equations using any method. Show your work and check your solution.

   a. $2x + 16 = 5x + 4$ b. $3x - 5 = 2x + 14$ c. $5x - 5 = x + 15$

6-116.   Janet lit a 12-inch candle. She noticed that it was getting an inch shorter every 30 minutes.

   a.   Is the correlation between the time the candle is lit and the height of the candle positive or negative?

   b.   In how many hours will the candle burn out? Support your answer with a **reason**.

6-117.   Write the expression as shown on the expression mats, then simplify by making zeros and combining like terms.

$$\square = +1$$
$$\square = -1$$

   a.

   b.

6-118.   Whole pizzas are described by the length of their diameters. For example, a 12-inch pizza has a diameter of 12 inches.

   Stan the Pizza Man told a customer that a 12" medium pizza costs $10 and an 18" large pizza costs $16. Which pizza is the better deal for the customer (that is, which one costs less per square inch)? You may use a calculator, but you must show your work.

Making Connections: Course 2

6.2.6 Is there always a solution?

Cases With Infinite or No Solutions

Are all equations solvable? Are all solutions a single number? Think about this: Annika was born first and her brother William was born 4 years later. How old will William be when Annika is twice his age? How old will William be when Annika is exactly the same as his age?

In this lesson you will continue to practice your **strategies** of combining like terms, removing zeros and balancing to simplify and compare two expressions, but you will encounter unusual situations where the solution may be unexpected. As you work today, focus with your team on these questions:

What if both sides are not equal?

Are there many values of x that will make the expressions equal?

Is there always a solution?

6-119. Many students believe that every equation has only one solution. However, in the introduction to this lesson you might have noticed that if Annika was four years older than her brother, William, they could never be the same age. There are sometimes situations that have "one solution," or, "no solution," or "all numbers" as solutions.

For each of the following equations, **reason** with your team to decide if there is "One solution," "No solution," or "All numbers are solutions." If there is a single number solution, write it down. If you are not sure how many solutions there are, have each member of your team try a number to see if you can find a value that makes the equation work.

a. $x = x$

b. $x + 1 = x$

c. $x = 2x$

d. $x + x = 2 + x$

e. $x + x = x - x$

f. $x + x = 2x$

g. $x \cdot x = x^2$

h. $x - 1 = x$

6-120.   Use the 5-D Process to write an equation for the problem below. Then, answer the question.

Kelly is 6 years younger than her twin brothers Bailey and Larry. How old will Kelly be when the sum of their ages is 12 more than three times Kelly's?

6-121.   SPECIAL CASES – Part One

Use the equation $8 + x + (-5) = (-4) + x + 7$ to complete parts (a) through (c).

a.   Build the equation on your Equation Mat and simplify it as much as possible. Record your steps and what you see when you have simplified the equation fully. Draw a picture of your final mat.

b.   Have each member of your team test a different value for x in the original equation, such as $x = 0$, $x = 1$, $x = -5$, $x = 10$, etc. What happens in each case?

c.   Are there any solutions to this equation? If so, how many?

6-122.   SPECIAL CASES – Part Two

Use the equation $x + x + 2 = 2x$ to complete parts (a) through (c).

a.   Build the equation on your Equation Mat and simplify it as much as possible. Record your steps and what you see when you have simplified the equation fully. Draw a picture of your final mat.

b.   Have each member of your team test a different value for x in the equation, such as $x = 0$, $x = 1$, $x = -5$, $x = 10$, etc. What happens? Is there a pattern to the results you get from the equation?

c.   Did you find any values for x that satisfied the equation in part (a)? When there is an imbalance of units left on the mat (such as $2 = 0$), what does this mean? Is $x = 0$ a solution to the equation?

6-123. Keeping these special cases in mind, continue to develop your equation solving **strategies** by visualizing and solving each equation below. Remember to build each equation on your mat, simplify as much as possible, and solve for x. Identify whether one number is the solution, any number is the solution, or there is no solution. Record your steps.

a. $-x + 2 = 4$

b. $-3 + x = 2(x + 3)$

c. $5x + 3 + (-x) = 2x + 1 + 2x + 3$

d. $3x + 7 + (-x) + -2 = 2x + 5$

e. $4 + -3x = 2$

f. $3x + 3 = 4 + x + (-1)$

MATH NOTES

METHODS AND MEANINGS

Solutions to an Equation With One Variable

A **solution** to an equation gives the value(s) of the variable that makes the equation true. For example, when 5 is substituted for x in the equation at right, both sides of the equation are equal. So $x = 5$ is a solution to this equation. Some equations have several solutions, such as $x^2 = 25$, where $x = 5$ or -5.

$$4x - 1 = 2x + 9$$
$$4(5) - 1 = 2(5) + 9$$
$$19 = 19$$

Equations may also have no solution or an infinite (unlimited) number of solutions.

Notice that no matter what the value of x is, the left side of the first equation will never equal the right side. Therefore, we say that $x + 2 = x + 3$ has **no solution**.

Equation with no solution:
$$x + 2 = x + 3$$
$$2 \neq 3$$

However, in the equation $x - 2 = x - 2$, no matter what value x has, the equation will always be true. So all numbers can make $x - 2 = x - 2$ true. Therefore, we say the solution for the equation $x - 2 = x - 2$ is **all numbers**.

Equation with infinitely many solutions:
$$x - 2 = x - 2$$

6-124. Copy and simplify the following expressions by combining like terms, making zeros, and using the Distributive Property. Using algebra tiles may be helpful.

a. $(-1) + 4x + 2 + 2x + x$

b. $-8x + 4 + (-3) + 10x$

c. $(-4) + 1x^2 + 3x + 4$

d. $2(3x - 2)$

6-125. Simplify and solve each equation below for x. Show your work and record your final answer.

a. $24 = 3x + 3$

b. $12 + x = 2x - 2$

6-126. Consider the following table.

x	-3	0.5	0	2	4
y	9	2	3	-1	-5

a. What is the rule for the table?

b. Explain your **strategy** for finding the rule for this table.

6-127. Show the "check" for each of these problems and write whether the solution is correct or incorrect.

a. For $3x + 2 = x - 2$, does $x = 0$?

b. For $3(x - 2) = 30 + x - 2 - x + 2$, does $x = 12$?

6-128. Some steps in solving an equation are more efficient than others. Complete parts (a) through (d) to determine the most efficient first step to solve the equation $34 = 5x - 21$.

a. If both sides of the equation were divided by 5, then the equation would be $\frac{34}{5} = x - \frac{21}{5}$. Does this make the problem simpler? Why or why not?

b. If we subtract 34 from both sides, the equation becomes $0 = 5x - 55$. Does this make the equation simpler to solve? Why or why not?

c. If we add 21 to both sides, the equation becomes $55 = 5x$. Does this suggestion make this a problem you can solve more easily? Why or why not?

d. All three suggestions are legal moves, but which method will lead to the most efficient solution? Why?

6.2.7 Which method should I use?

Choosing a Solving Strategy

The 5-D Process and algebra tiles are useful tools for solving problems. Today you will practice writing equations from word problems and solving them using any of the tools you know. We are developing an efficient set of tools to solve any word problem. Having a variety of methods will allow you to choose the one that makes sense to you and ultimately makes you a more powerful mathematician.

6-129.   Nick tried to use the symbolic **visualization** shortcut for $3x - 6 = 27$, but may have made a mistake. His work is shown at right. If he did, on which step did he first make a mistake and what was his mistake? If he did not make a mistake, check his solution and write "all correct."

6-130.   Nick represented the equation $3(2x + 4) = -6$ on the Equation Mat at right.

a.   Choose a strategy to solve for x. You may continue to use algebra tiles or may use numbers and variables.

b.   Check your answer. If your answer does not make the equation true, try solving the equation using a different strategy.

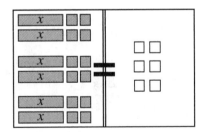

6-131. Read the problem below, then answer the questions in parts (a) and (b).

Cisco and Misty need to construct a chicken coop for their famous egg-laying hens. The hens need at least 108 square feet of living space. The space available allows Cisco and Misty to make the length of the coop 3 feet longer than the width and to create exactly 108 square feet of area. What are the dimensions of the coop?

a. Laura tried to use an Equation Mat for this problem but got stuck and decided to use a different **strategy**. Why do you think she decided not to use the Equation Mat?

b. Choose a different method, such as the 5-D Process or writing and solving an equation to solve this problem. Even if you solve an equation and do not use the chart from the 5-D Process, you still need to define how you are using variables and remember to write a sentence answer. Check your answer.

6-132. Here is a problem started in a 5-D table.

Describe/Draw:

We want to find the side lengths so the perimeter is 35.

	Define			Do	Decide
	Side 1	Side 2	Side 3	Perimeter	Target: 35 ft
Trial 1	5	$5+2=7$	$7+4=11$	$5+7+11=23$	23 *Too small*
	x	$x+2$	$(x+2)+4$	$x+(x+2)+(x+2+4)=35$	

a. Write the word problem that could have accompanied this 5-D table.

b. What is your preferred method to solve this problem: algebra tiles, an equation, or the 5-D Process?

c. Decide on a method to solve this problem, use your method to find your answer, and write a Declare statement for your answer.

6-133. Apiologists (scientists who study bees) have found that the number and types of bees in a hive is based on the amount of nectar and pollen available. Within a hive there are three types of bees that help the queen. They are workers, drones, and nurses.

In a recent study of a hive it was found that, not including the queen, there were a total of 4,109 bees. There were thirty-three more nurses than drones. The number of workers was twelve more than six times the number of drones. How many of each type of bee was in the hive?

Choose a method to solve this problem such as the 5-D Process or writing and solving an equation. Even if you solve an equation and do not use the chart from the 5-D Process, you still need to define how you are using variables and remember to Declare your answer in a sentence.

6-134. Use any method to solve the following equations. Show your work.

a. $3x + 4 = -5$

b. $3(x + 4) = -3$

c. $3(x + 4) = x + 2(x + 6)$

d. $3x + 4 = 3x - 4$

6-135. Beth is filling a small backyard pool with a garden hose. The pool holds 300 gallons of water. After 15 minutes the pool is about one-fourth full.

a. Assuming that the water is flowing at a constant rate, about how much water is going into the pool each minute?

b. About how long will it take to fill the pool?

6-136.   One way of thinking about solving equations is to work to get the variable terms on one side of the equation and the constants on the other side. Consider the equation $71 = 9x - 37$.

a.   As a first step you could subtract 71 from both sides, or divide both sides by 9, or add 37 to both sides of the equation. Does one of these steps get all of the variable terms on one side of the equation and the constants on the other?

b.   Solve $71 = 9x - 37$ for x. Show your steps.

6-137.   Make a table and a graph for the following rule: $y = 3x - 2$.

a.   Explain how you know that there are more points than just the ones shown on your graph.

b.   Where would the additional points go on the graph?

6-138.   For each equation below, solve for x. Sometimes the easiest **strategy** is to use mental math.

a. $x - \frac{2}{3} = \frac{1}{3}$ b. $4x = 6$ c. $x + 4.6 = 12.96$ d. $\frac{x}{7} = \frac{3}{7}$

6-139.   Explain what the following graphs would look like. You may write your answer in words or sketch a graph.

a.   Scatterplot with a negative correlation.

b.   Scatterplot with no correlation.

c.   Scatterplot with a positive correlation.

Chapter 6 Closure   What have I learned?

Reflection and Synthesis

The activities below offer you a chance to reflect about what you have learned during this chapter. As you work, look for concepts that you feel very comfortable with, ideas that you would like to learn more about, and topics with which you need more help. Look for connections between ideas as well as connections with material you learned previously.

①   SUMMARIZING MY UNDERSTANDING

In this chapter you have used algebra tiles and an equation mat as tools for solving equations, and you have represented your solution steps on an equation mat and with algebraic symbols. Today you will use what you have learned about equations in this chapter to show connections between all of these methods. To start, consider this problem:

Jamee is working to solve an equation. She did the work shown below. With your team, answer the following questions:

Jamee's work: Original problem: $3(2x - 4) = 2(2x + 5)$

Step 1: $6x - 12 = 4x + 10$

Step 2: $2x = -2$

- Explain what Jamee did at each step.

- What is her solution?

- Was her solution correct? **Justify** your answer. If it was not, find her error and the correct answer.

Problem continues on next page. →

① *Problem continued from previous page.*

Obtain a Chapter 6 Closure Resource Page (shown at right) from your teacher. Follow the directions below to demonstrate your understanding of solving equations with an equation mat, algebraically (with numbers and symbols), and in words.

Part 1: Sketch the equation on the mat on the resource page. You might also want to build it with algebra tiles.

Part 2: Complete each step to solve the equation. Represent each step on the mat, in symbols, and in words. As you work, ask questions to clarify your thinking and understanding. Make sure you can give reasons for each step.

Part 3: Color code the matching steps in each representation. For example, if your second step is to combine like terms, label this step with green in the symbols, on the mat, and in words. Use a new color to code each step.

② WHAT HAVE I LEARNED?

Working the problems in this section will help you to evaluate which types of problems you feel comfortable with and which ones you need more help with.

Solve each problem as completely as you can. The table at the end of this closure section has answers to these problems. It also directs you to additional help and other similar practice problems.

CL 6-140. Ruthie did a survey among her classmates comparing the time spent playing video games to the time spent studying. The scatterplot of her data is shown at right.

a. What correlation can you make from her data?

b. Use an ordered pair (x, y) to identify any outliers.

Playing Video Games

Making Connections: Course 2

CL 6-141. Consider the equation mat at right.

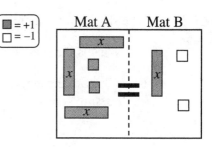

a. Write the original equation represented.

b. Simplify as needed. Record all steps of your work. What value of x will make the two sides equal?

c. Check your solution.

CL 6-142. Make a table with at least 6 entries and a graph for the following rule: $y = 3x - 5$.

a. If you added four more entries to your table and plotted the points, where would the points be on the graph?

b. Is there a limit to the number of points you could put in your table? Explain how you know.

CL 6-143. Find the area and perimeter or circumference of the following figures. Approximate π as 3.14.

a.

6.8 m

4.84 m

3.2 m

6.6 m

b.

$\frac{1}{2}$ cm

CL 6-144. Write the expressions for the expression mats on the right.

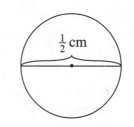

a. Simplify each mat to determine which side is greater.

b. If $x = 4$, would your answer to part (a) change? Explain.

CL 6-145. Serena found the spinner at the right. Help her find the value of the missing portion.

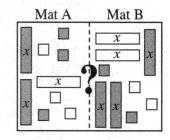

$\frac{1}{3}$

$\frac{1}{6}$

$\frac{2}{5}$

CL 6-146. The shapes at right are similar.

a. What is the scale factor?

b. What are the lengths of the missing sides?

CL 6-147. Solve this problem using the 5-D Process or writing and solving an equation. No matter which you method you use, be sure to define your variable and write an equation to represent the relationship.

A rectangle has a perimeter of 30 inches. Its length is one less than three times its width. What are the length and width of the rectangle?

CL 6-148. For each of the problems above, do the following:

- Draw a bar or number line that represents 0 to 10.

- Color or shade in a portion of the bar that represents your level of understanding and comfort with completing that problem on your own.

If any of your bars are less than a 5, choose *one* of those problems and do one of the following tasks:

- Write two questions that you would like to ask about that problem.

- Brainstorm two things that you DO know about that type of problem.

If all of your bars are a 5 or above, choose one of those problems and do one of these tasks:

- Write two questions you might ask or hints you might give to a student who was stuck on the problem.

- Make a new problem that is similar and more challenging than that problem and solve it.

③   WHAT TOOLS CAN I USE?

You have several tools and references available to help support your learning – your teacher, your study team, your math book, and your Toolkit, to name only a few. At the end of each chapter you will have an opportunity to review your Toolkit for completeness as well as to revise or update your Toolkit to better reflect your current understanding of big ideas.

The main elements of your Toolkit should be your Learning Log, Math Notes, and the vocabulary used in this chapter. Math words that are new appear in bold in the text. Refer to the lists provided below and follow your teacher's instructions to revise your Toolkit, which will help make it useful for you as you complete this chapter and as you work in future chapters.

Learning Log Entries

- Lesson 6.1.3 – Correlations
- Lesson 6.1.5 – Scatterplot and Linear Graph Predictions
- Extension Activity – Human Data Points
- Lesson 6.2.3 – Solving Equations and Finding Solutions
- Lesson 6.2.4 – Using the 5-D Process to Write and Solve Equations

Math Notes

- Lesson 6.1.1 – Special Quadrilaterals
- Lesson 6.1.2 – Circle Graphs
- Lesson 6.1.4 – Correlation and Trend Lines
- Lesson 6.1.5 – Making a Complete Graph
- Lesson 6.1.6 – When Is a Point on the Graph of a Rule?
- Lesson 6.2.1 – Using an Equation Mat
- Lesson 6.2.3 – Checking a Solution
- Lesson 6.2.4 – Defining a Variable
- Lesson 6.2.6 – Solutions to an Equation With One Variable

Mathematical Vocabulary

The following is a list of vocabulary found in this chapter. Some of the words have been seen in the previous chapter. The words in bold are the words new to this chapter. Make sure that you are familiar with the terms below and know what they mean. For the words you do not know, refer to the glossary or index. You might also want to add these words to your Toolkit for a way to reference them in the future.

circle graph	**Equation Mat**	**negative correlation**
no correlation	**outlier**	**positive correlation**
solution	scatterplot	**trend line**
x-intercept	**y-intercept**	

Process Words

The list of words below are problem solving strategies and processes that you have been involved in throughout the course of this chapter. Make sure you know what it means to use each of them. If you are not sure, look through your book for problems when you were asked to think in the following ways.

choose a strategy	compare	describe
explain your reasoning	generalize	justify
predict	reason	simplify
solve	test your prediction	visualize

Answers and Support for Closure Activity #2
What Have I Learned?

Problem	Solution	Need Help?	More Practice
CL 6-140.	a. Negative: when the time playing video games increases, the time spent studying decreases. b. (100, 140)	Lessons 6.1.2, 6.1.3, and 6.1.4 Math Notes box in Lesson 6.1.4 Learning Logs (problems 6-26 and 6-47)	Problems 6-14, 6-15, 6-24, 6-25, 6-26, and 6-49
CL 6-141.	a. $3x + 2 = x - 2$ b. $x = -2$ c. $3(-2) + 2 = -2 - 2$ $-6 + 2 = -4$ $-4 = -4$	Lessons 6.2.1, 6.2.2, and 6.2.3 Math Notes boxes in Lessons 6.2.1, 6.2.3, and 6.2.6 Learning Log (problem 6-98)	Problems 6-75, 6-76, 6-77, 6-87, 6-89, 6-97, 6-99, 6-115, 6-125, 6-130, and 6-134
CL 6-142.	<table><tr><td>x</td><td>4</td><td>-3</td><td>0.5</td><td>0</td><td>2</td></tr><tr><td>y</td><td>7</td><td>-14</td><td>-3.5</td><td>-5</td><td>1</td></tr></table> a. The points would follow the rule $y = 3x - 5$ and would fall on the same line. b. There are an infinite number of points possible, because we can choose any value for x.	Lessons 6.1.2, through 6.1.6 Math Notes boxes in Lessons 6.1.5 and 6.1.6 Learning Log (problem 6-47)	Problems 6-37, 6-43, 6-48, 6-56, 6-59, 6-114, and 6-137
CL 6-143.	a. $A = 26.532$ m^2, $P = 21.44$ m b. $A \approx 0.196$ cm^2, $C \approx 1.571$ cm	Lessons 2.3.2, 2.3.5, 5.3.3, and 5.3.4 Math Notes box in Lesson 5.3.4 Learning Logs (problems 2-150 and 5-124)	Problems CL 2-163, CL 3-111, CL 4-116, 5-127, 5-129, and 6-11

Problem	Solution	Need Help?	More Practice
CL 6-144.	a. $x = x$, The mats are equal in value. b. No, the mats will be equal for any value of x.	Lessons 5.2.1, 5.2.2, and 6.2.1 through 6.2.6 Math Notes boxes in Lessons 5.1.2, 6.2.1, 6.2.3, and 6.2.6 Learning Log (problem 5-54)	Problems CL 5-134, CL 5-136, 6-38, 6-74, 6-75, 6-76, 6-78, and 6-117
CL 6-145.	$\frac{1}{10}$	Lessons 1.2.4 and 1.2.5 Math Notes box in Lesson 1.2.4 Learning Log (problem 1-107)	Problems CL 1-140, CL 2-160, CL 3-114, 4-45, and 5-12
CL 6-146.	a. Multiply by $\frac{1}{4}$ (or you can divide by 4 moving from shape A to shape B or multiply by 4 moving from shape B to shape A). b. On Shape A, the missing sides are 10 and 8 units; on shape B, the missing sides are 2 and 1.5 units.	Lessons 4.3.1 through 4.3.4 Math Notes boxes in Lessons 4.3.1 and 4.3.4 Learning Log (problem 4-76)	Problems CL 4-119, 5-10, 5-48, and 6-109
CL 6-147.	The length is 11 in. and the width is 4 in. If x = width, one possible equation would be $x + (3x - 1) + x + (3x - 1) = 30$.	Lessons 3.2.3, 3.2.4, 3.2.5, 5.1.2, 5.1.3, 6.2.5, and 6.2.7 Math Notes boxes in Lessons 3.2.3 and 5.1.2 Learning Log (problems 5-32 and 6-107)	Problems CL 5-135, 6-97, 6-105, 6-113, 6-131, 6-132, and 6-133

Puzzle Investigator Problems

PI-11.   GRAPHING MADNESS

On graph paper starting at $(0, 0)$, carry out the following moves:

Move Number	Directions
1	Right 1 unit
2	Up 2 units
3	Left 3 units
4	Down 4 units
5	Right 5 units

Continue moving counter clockwise using this pattern, increasing the length 1 unit each move.

a.   What patterns can you find in the figure on the graph? For example, find the coordinates of each point in the design. How are the coordinates changing? How is the quadrant where each point is located changing with the addition of each new point?

b.   In which quadrant will the 79th move land? What will be the coordinates` of this point? Explain how you can find your answer without listing 79 moves.

c.   For **any** move, name which quadrant it will be in and what its coordinates will be. Explain the method you are using.

PI-12.   CONSECUTIVE SUMS

A consecutive sum is an addition sequence of consecutive whole numbers.

Examples: $2+3$

$8+9+10+11+12+13$

$7+8+9+10$

a.   Write the first 35 counting numbers (1 through 35) with as many consecutive sums as possible. The number 15 can be written as $7+8$ or $4+5+6$ or $1+2+3+4+5$. Make sure you organize your work in order to find patterns.

b.   Describe as many patterns as you find. For example, are there any numbers that have no consecutive sums? Which numbers can be written as a sum of two consecutive numbers? Which can be written as a sum of three consecutive numbers?

c.   Ernie noticed a pattern with the numbers that can be written as a sum of three consecutive numbers. He wants to understand why the pattern works. He thinks it might help to represent the consecutive numbers as x, $x+1$, and $x+2$.

i.   Why do these expressions represent consecutive numbers?

ii.   Find the sum of x, $x+1$, and $x+2$. How does this sum help make sense of the pattern?

Slopes and Rates of Change

7

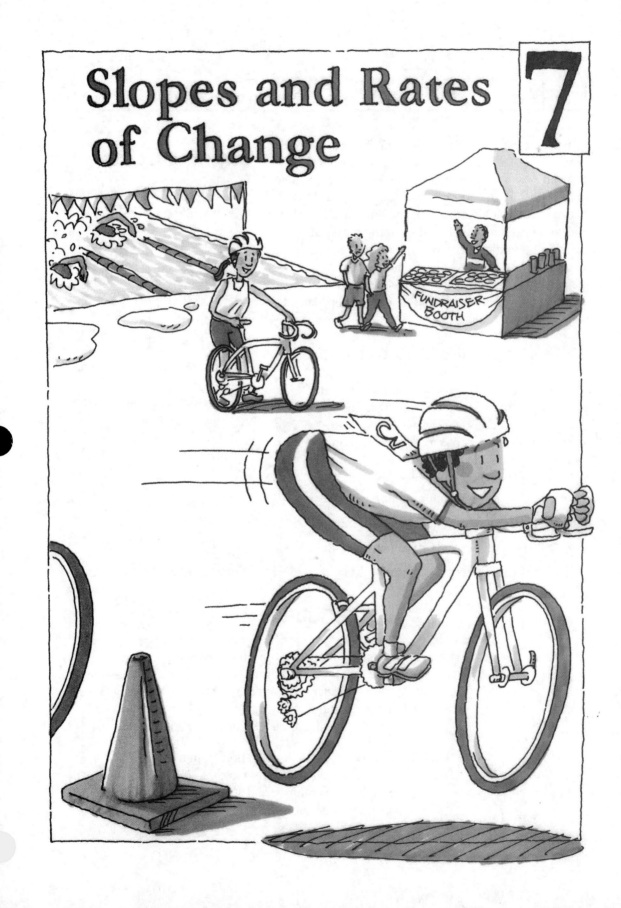

CHAPTER 7   Slopes and Rates of Change

In Japan, speed limit signs on the highway say, "Speed Limit 100." Does this mean people in Japan are allowed to drive faster than people in the United States? In Section 7.1, you will explore questions involving rate, as well as look at how to find unit rates in order to make comparisons. You will examine races called "triathlons" to discover when rates are be the same and also different. You will also explore rate through the concept of slope, a measure of the steepness of lines, and examine multiple representations of slope such as situations, tables, and graphs.

In Section 7.2, you will explore new situations to consider when expressions are the same, called systems of equations. You will use some of the events at a county fair to practice working with systems of equations and use what you have learned about expressions to help solve them.

In this chapter, you will learn how to:

> ➤ Calculate rates, including unit rates.

> ➤ Compare ratios and rates with different units.

> ➤ Measure the steepness of a line using slope.

> ➤ Compare equations to determine when they have the same solution.

Guiding Questions

Think about these questions throughout this chapter:

What is being compared?

What does the comparison tell me?

How else can I represent it?

How can I find the solutions?

When are the solutions the same?

Chapter Outline

Section 7.1 You will compare ratios and rates using different representations including numbers, tables, and graphs. You will learn ways to rewrite ratios so that they can be compared more easily, and you will find out how to measure the steepness of a line on a graph.

Section 7.2 You will evaluate information from different expressions on graphs, in tables, and in words. You will learn how to compare and solve equations to determine when the solution is the same for more than one equation.

7.1.1 How can I compare rates?

Comparing Rates

Whenever you are trying to describe how fast or slow something occurs, you are describing a **rate**. However, to describe a rate, you need to provide two pieces of information. For example, if two people each walk 10 miles, it may seem like they are doing the same thing. But if you find out that one person walked the whole distance in 3 hours, while another person took 8 hours, then it becomes clear that they were traveling at different speeds. In this lesson you will be describing how things change in comparison to each other.

7-1. The seventh graders at Shasta Middle School are planning a class trip to Washington, D.C. They need to raise enough money for all 140 seventh graders to travel, so they have a lot of work to do! The class officers have collected the data below about different kinds of fundraisers. They want your help in choosing a fundraising activity.

Type of Fundraiser	Time	Expected Profit
Cookie sales	3 weeks	$500
Car washes	4 weeks	$700
Recycling	$\frac{3}{5}$ week	$85
Yardwork	2 weeks	$320

a. How much will the class earn if they spend 6 weeks doing yardwork? How much will they earn if they spend six weeks having car washes? Be prepared to explain your **reasoning**.

b. How much money would the class earn if it recycled bottles and cans during the next 3 weeks of school?

7-2.   MAKING MONEY

The class president has decided that
the students will either sell cookies
or hold car washes. The rest of the
officers need your help to compare
the profit from cookie sales to the
profit from car washes.

Your task: Discuss with your team ways that you could compare the two
fundraising **strategies** to recommend which one to use. Use the data in problem
7-1 and the questions below to start your discussion. Then write a note to the
class officers recommending which fundraising activity they should do. Be sure
to **justify** your recommendation with details about rates.

Discussion Points

What can we compare?

Which fundraising activity raises money faster? Which raises money slower?

Further Guidance

7-3.   Isabelle decided to see how long it would take to earn $5000 with each kind of
fundraiser.

   a.   For how many weeks would the class need to sell cookies in order to earn
        $5000?

   b.   For how many weeks would the class need to have car washes to earn
        $5000?

   c.   How can this help Isabelle decide which way will earn more money?

7-4.   Liam thinks that the class could earn $175 each week by washing cars.

   a.   Is this **reasonable**? How could he have figured out this amount? Discuss
        his claim with your team and record your ideas.

   b.   How much could the class earn during one week of cookie sales? Show
        your work.

7-5.   Nicolette decided to see what the class could earn from each activity in the same number of weeks. She decided to see how much they could earn in 12 weeks.

   a.   Why do you think Nicolette chose 12 weeks?

   b.   How much could they earn from each activity in 12 weeks?

   c.   Write a pair of equivalent ratios for each of the relationships in parts (a) and (b) above.

7-6.   Which fundraising activity raises money the fastest: selling cookies or washing cars? Write a note to the class officers recommending the fastest fundraising activity. Be sure to **justify** your recommendation with how you know it will raise money the fastest.

--- *Further Guidance* ---
section ends here.

7-7.   The eighth grade class was also looking at the data from problem 7-1. They had information about another fundraiser: they could earn $65 every two days selling lemonade. Assume all of the fundraising activities happen only on school days, and that there are 5 days in a school week.

   a.   Which activity will raise money faster: selling lemonade or selling cookies? The rate for selling cookies was $500 every 3 weeks. Be sure to **justify** your answer.

   b.   Trinh described the profit from lemonade sales as earning at a **rate** of "$325 in two weeks." A **rate** is a measure of how one quantity changes in comparison to another.

   Is Trinh's rate of $\frac{\$325}{2 \text{ weeks}}$ the same as earning money at a rate of $\frac{\$65}{2 \text{ days}}$? Why or why not?

7-8. Eliza is saving her allowance to buy a new computer so she can email her pen pals around the world. She currently saves $45 every 4 weeks.

   a. If her brother saves $39 every 3 weeks, who saves at a faster rate? Explain your **reasoning**.

   b. Instead of using dollars and cents, money in Armenia is called "drams." One American dollar is worth the same as 360 drams. Eliza's pen pal in Armenia saves 2880 drams from her allowance every week. Work with your team to determine who is saving money faster, Eliza or her pen pal. Explain your **reasoning**.

   c. Eliza's pen pal in Laos is also saving money. He is saving 17000 kips (Laotian money) per week. Can you determine who is saving at a faster rate? Determine the rate or write a question that you would need answered in order to determine it.

7-9. Solve the equations below for the variable. Be sure to check your answer.

   a. $3(2x - 1) + 2 = 5x$ b. $600x + 200 = 500x$

7-10. Adam earns $36 for every four hours of work. If he continues to be paid at the same rate:

   a. How long will it take him to earn $144? Show and explain your **reasoning**.

   b. How long will it take him to earn $222? Show and explain your **reasoning**.

   c. How could you describe his rate for a 40-hour work week? For an 8-hour day? Show and explain your **reasoning**.

7-11. A college has a 2:3 ratio of men to women in its student body.

   a. What is the ratio of women to men?

   b. What is the ratio of women to total students?

   c. What percent of the college is men?

   d. What fraction of the college is women?

7-12. Complete the table below by following the rule $y = 10 - 2x$. Then graph the relationship on graph paper.

x	−3	−2	−1	0	1	2	3	4
y								

7-13. Use $<$, $>$, or $=$ to compare the number pairs below.

a. 0.183 _____ 0.18

b. −13 _____ −17

c. 0.125 _____ $\frac{1}{8}$

d. −6 _____ −4

e. 72% _____ $\frac{35}{30}$

f. −0.25 _____ −0.05

7.1.2 How can I find the rate?

Comparing Rates with Graphs and Tables

Rates are used in many situations to describe and compare information. When purchasing a car you might compare the gas mileage of vehicles, that is, how many miles each car can travel per gallon of gas. When determining the print quality of a printer the number of dots per square inch is important. The percent of interest earned per dollar, or interest rate, is important when saving money in a bank.

Today you will focus on different ways to display rates in tables and graphs as a way to compare information. As you work with your team, ask each other these questions:

Which quantities can we compare?

Are the ratios equivalent?

How else can the ratio be expressed?

7-14. The local news station is selecting this week's female student for "Athlete of the Week." Wendy and Yoshie, sprinters on the track team, are both finalists and they are trying to decide who is fastest based on recent race data. Wendy's times are represented in the table at right.

Yoshie can run 70 meters in 11 seconds, which can be expressed by the rate $\frac{70 \text{ meters}}{11 \text{ seconds}}$.

Wendy's Data

Time (seconds)	Distance (meters)
5	30
10	60
15	90
25	
35	210
45	
55	330
x	

a. Copy the table and use the relationship to complete the table for Wendy. How can you use the table to find Wendy's running rate?

b. Based on the information in the table, are the two runners traveling at the same speed? How can you tell? Explain your **reasoning**.

c. To compare the two runners, the news station made a graph of the two runners' rates. Identify points (time, distance) on the graph at right and determine which line represents each runner. Based on the graph, who is running faster? **Justify** your answer.

d. Use the same graph to find two additional data points (time, distance) for each runner.

e. The graph at right shows information for Vanessa, last week's Athlete of the Week. What is Vanessa's rate? If she were to race Yoshie and Wendy, who would win?

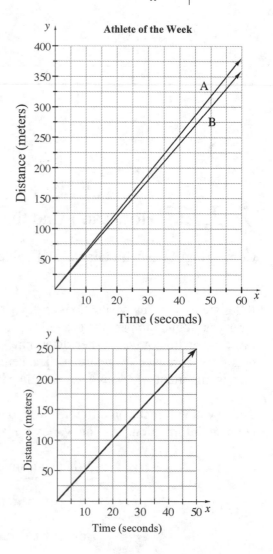

7-15.   TRAINING FOR THE TRIATHLON

A triathlon is a race where participants swim, bike, and run specific distances. Participants start by swimming, then jump out of the water, get dressed as fast as they can, and ride a bicycle. After they complete the biking section, the participants finish the race by running several miles.

Diane has been taking swimming lessons, riding her bike, and running to prepare for her first triathlon. She used the graph at right to analyze one of her practice sessions. Use the graph on the Lesson 7.1.2 Resource Page to help you answer the questions below.

a.   During which segment of the race (a, b, or c) did Diane go the fastest? Explain your **reasoning**.

b.   Use the graph to determine the distance traveled during each segment of the race.

c.   How much time did it take Diane to complete each segment of the race?

d.   Write a rate (in miles per minute) for each segment of the race.

e.   How can you show a rate on a graph? Work with your team to find a way to show the rates from part (d) on the resource page.

7-16.   Edgar is training to be on the high school cross-country running team. Edgar has training runs that are two different lengths. One trail is 4 miles, and he usually completes that run in 0.5 hours (30 minutes). If he runs the 10 mile trail, it usually takes him 1.25 hours (75 minutes).

a.   Graph points for the length and time of Edgar's run on a graph. Does it make sense to connect the points? Where could you add a point to show how far he has traveled after 0 minutes?

b.   Helena is a long-distance runner. Once a week she does a 16-mile training run that usually takes her 2 hours. Does she run slower or faster than Edgar? How do you know?

7-17.   Match each situation in parts (a) through (d) with its graph below, and state the rate in miles per minute.

a.   Family A travels 30 miles in 25 minutes.

b.   Family B travels 60 miles in an hour.

c.   Family C travels 50 miles in an hour.

d.   Family D travels 60 miles in $1\frac{1}{2}$ hours.

e.   One graph below was not matched with a situation from parts (a) through (d). Describe the rate of travel for Family E if they are represented by the unmatched graph.

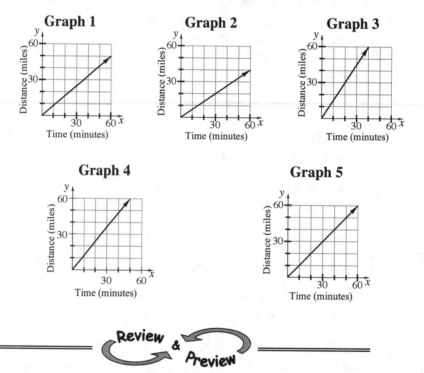

Review & Preview

7-18.   Beth and Amy are racing to see who can ride a tricycle the fastest.

a.   Graph the data about Beth's travel that is recorded in the table at right.

Time (sec)	5	10	15	20
Distance (ft)	11	22	33	44

b.   What is Beth's rate of travel?

c.   If Amy travels at a rate of 75 feet per 30 seconds, would the line representing her distance and time be steeper or less steep than the graph of Beth's rate? Explain your **reasoning**.

Making Connections: Course 2

7-19.   Write an equation to represent the situation below and answer the question. You may use the 5-D Process to help you.

Andrew just opened a new office supply store. He has been keeping track of how many customers visit his store. During his second week, he had 18 more customers than he did the first week. The third week, he had four less than twice as many customers as he had during the second week. In his fourth week of business he had 92 customers. If he had 382 customers in total during his first four weeks of business, how many customers did he have during the second week?

7-20.   For each equation below, solve for x. Sometimes the easiest **strategy** is to use mental math.

a. $x - \frac{3}{5} = 1\frac{2}{5}$ b. $5.2 + x = 10.95$

c. $2x - 3.25 = 7.15$ d. $\frac{x}{16} = \frac{3}{8}$

7-21.   Simplify each expression.

a. $-\frac{9}{5} \cdot \frac{8}{15}$ b. $\frac{1}{5} + (-\frac{2}{15}) - (-\frac{4}{9})$ c. $-\frac{4}{8} \cdot \frac{3}{7} \cdot (-\frac{2}{5})$

d. $\frac{3}{5} \cdot (-\frac{2}{7}) + (-\frac{5}{7})(\frac{3}{10})$ e. $-8\frac{1}{9} + 3\frac{5}{6}$ f. $2\frac{1}{2} \cdot 4\frac{1}{5}$

7-22.   In one week the museum had attendance as shown in the table at right.

a.   Find the mean, the median, and mode for the daily attendance.

b.   The museum management needs to tell the staff their work schedule a week in advance. The museum wants to have approximately one staff member for every 150 visitors. How many staff members should be scheduled to work each week? Explain your **reasoning**.

Day	Attendance
1	870
2	940
3	731
4	400
5	861
6	680
7	593

7.1.3 How can I find the rate?

Unit Rates

News reports use rates to provide important information. For example, when there is a sudden heavy rain, reporting the rate at which the local river is rising gives people a sense of how quickly it might flood. Sometimes rates are reported in words, such as *"The pitcher struck out the batter after throwing the ball 92 miles per hour."* Other times the rate is provided in a graph or a table, such as the price of food over time or how rapidly a disease is spreading.

Today your team will develop **strategies** to find a rate in new contexts using tables and graphs.

7-23.   MAXIMUM MILES

The graph at right compares how many miles are traveled to how many gallons of gas are used for two different cars. Use the Lesson 7.1.3 Resource Page or copy the graph at right on graph paper and answer the following questions.

a.   Which car can travel the farthest on 5 gallons of gas? Which one travels the shortest distance using 5 gallons of gas? How is this found on the graph?

b.   Does car A travel the same number of miles with every gallon of gas? How can you tell?

c.   A third car (Car C) uses 6 gallons of gas to travel 120 miles. Make a table for the car listing at least four equivalent ratios of gallons and miles, and add those points to the graph.

d.   Manufacturers often advertise the miles per gallon, or mpg, for the cars they make. This measurement is a **unit rate**, because it is the mileage for one gallon (unit) of gasoline. Calculate the unit rate (mpg) for each car. List cars in order from highest mpg to lowest.

e.   How can the graph help us compare the miles per gallon of the different cars? List the cars in order from the one with the steepest line to the one with the least steep line. Which car goes farthest for each gallon of gas it uses?

f.   How can you use the graph to figure out which car has the best gas mileage (the highest number of miles per gallon)?

7-24. Tamika and Lois like to knit and have decided to knit a scarf using the same pattern. Tamika started knitting the scarf last week, but Lois is just starting now. The tables at right show information about the number of inches of scarf knitted per hour after Lois joins Tamika.

Tamika

Time (in hours)	Length (in inches)
0	5
1	7
2	9
3	
x	

Lois

Time (in hours)	Length (in inches)
0	
1	
2	
3	
x	$3x$

a. Copy and complete each table to show the amount of time each girl has been knitting and the number of inches that have been knitted.

b. At what rate does Tamika knit? How can you use the table to find her rate?

c. At what rate does Lois knit? Explain how you found your answer.

d. If you graphed the data (so that x is the number of hours and y is the number of inches) for both Tamika and Lois on the same graph, which line would appear steeper? Explain why it would be steeper.

7-25. Olivia was curious about how fast she knits. She decided to measure how much she could knit in 10 hours. She already had a scarf started and recorded her data in the table at right.

If Olivia knits at a constant rate, what is Olivia's knitting speed in inches per hour? Discuss with your team and be prepared to explain your **reasoning**.

Olivia

Time (in hours)	Length (in inches)
0	12
10	67

7-26. A wheel for a Wheel of Winning game makes one revolution in 4 seconds. What is the unit rate in terms of revolutions per minute? Use diagrams or words to explain your **reasoning**.

7-27.   LEARNING LOG

Think about what you have learned so far about rate.
Write a Learning Log entry that explains how to find a
rate from a table. How can you compare rates using a
graph? Be sure to include an example. Title this entry
"Rates, Tables, and Graphs" and include today's date.

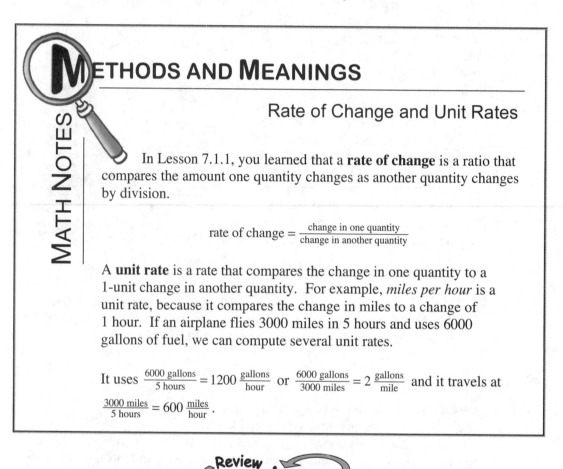

MᴇTHODS AND Mᴇᴀɴɪɴɢꜱ

MATH NOTES

Rate of Change and Unit Rates

In Lesson 7.1.1, you learned that a **rate of change** is a ratio that
compares the amount one quantity changes as another quantity changes
by division.

$$\text{rate of change} = \frac{\text{change in one quantity}}{\text{change in another quantity}}$$

A **unit rate** is a rate that compares the change in one quantity to a
1-unit change in another quantity. For example, *miles per hour* is a
unit rate, because it compares the change in miles to a change of
1 hour. If an airplane flies 3000 miles in 5 hours and uses 6000
gallons of fuel, we can compute several unit rates.

It uses $\frac{6000 \text{ gallons}}{5 \text{ hours}} = 1200 \frac{\text{gallons}}{\text{hour}}$ or $\frac{6000 \text{ gallons}}{3000 \text{ miles}} = 2 \frac{\text{gallons}}{\text{mile}}$ and it travels at

$\frac{3000 \text{ miles}}{5 \text{ hours}} = 600 \frac{\text{miles}}{\text{hour}}$.

Review & Preview

7-28.   Which company offers the lowest unit rate per minute? Show how you decided.

Company	Price	# of minutes
AB & C	$19.95	100
Berizon	$24.95	150
Cinguling	$9.95	60
DWest	$14.75	100

7-29.   The graph at right shows the cost per pound of strawberries at four different stores.

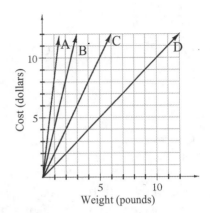

a.   At which store are strawberries about $2 per pound?

b.   What is the rate of cost of strawberries at store B?

c.   Which store has the most expensive strawberries? How can you tell?

7-30.   Solve the following equations using any method. Show your work and check your solution.

a. $5x + 20 = 3x + 4$ b. $7x - 4 = 3x + 8$ c. $2x + 6 = x - 9$

7-31.   Felipe knew that he was 60 inches tall and that his sister Maria was 5 feet tall.

Felipe said, *"Hey, I'm 12 times as tall as you, since 5 times 12 equals 60."* At first, Maria was puzzled, but then she said, *"That's not true, and I know why."*

Explain in a complete sentence what Maria realized.

7-32.   Look at the similar shapes shown at right.

a.   What is the scale factor from shape A to shape B?

b.   Find the lengths of the missing sides.

c.   Sketch a new shape C that is similar to shape A and has a scale factor of 1. What do you know about the measures of the angles and sides on this new shape? Label them on your picture.

d.   When two shapes are similar and have a scale factor of one, what are they called?

7.1.4 How does y change with respect to x?

Slope

Can you imagine swimming 1.5 km (just less than a mile), getting dressed as fast as you can, hopping on a bicycle to race 40 km (almost 25 miles), then getting off your bike to run 10 km (just more than 6 miles)? Athletes who compete in Olympic distance triathlons do exactly that! In the 2008 Summer Olympic Games, Jan Frodeno of Germany won the gold medal by finishing the triathlon in 1 hour, 48 minutes and 53.28 seconds. Frodeno did not finish the swimming section in first place, though. In fact, he was not even one of the first ten people to finish that part of the race. While Frodeno may not have been the fastest swimmer, what mattered most was his overall rate.

As you compare rates today, you will learn a new way to describe the rate of change of a line called **slope**. As you investigate rates of change, use the following questions to focus mathematical discussions with your team:

> How can I use the graph to figure out which racer is faster?
>
> How can we find the unit rate for each racer?
>
> What if the line does not pass through $(0, 0)$?

7-33.   BIKING THE TRIATHLON

The second part of the triathlon is a bicycle race. Since participants do not start the bicycle race until they complete the swimming portion, the bicyclists have varying starting times.

The graph at right shows information about four bicyclists during a 20-minute portion of a race.

a.   Based on the graph, list the bicyclists from slowest to fastest. How can you tell?

Problem continues on next page. →

Making Connections: Course 2

7-33. *Problem continued from previous page.*

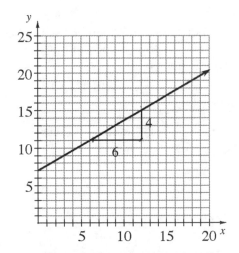

b. Lydia wants to describe each bicyclist's rate as a number of kilometers per minute for an article in the school paper. To do this, she sketched triangles like the one for line A on the graph at right.

Where do the 4 and 6 come from on Racer A's triangle? What do they represent?

c. These numbers can be written as a rate to describe the distance the bicyclist rides as time passes. The fraction $\frac{4}{6}$ represents how the graph of the line goes up 4 units for every 6 units that it moves to the right. The number $\frac{4}{6}$ is called the **slope** of the line.

On the Lesson 7.1.3 Resource Page, find the slope of each of the other three lines.

d. Did the slopes in part (c) confirm your ranking from slowest to fastest in part (a)? If not, review your slopes and your comparison of rates based on the graph to find any mistakes.

7-34. While comparing the rates from problem 7-33, a study team is struggling to decide how to tell which athlete is moving faster.

• Leo thinks that because athlete A's line is highest on the graph, he is traveling faster.

• Linda disagrees. *"He starts first, but racer B is moving faster."*

Which person do you agree with? Look at the graph of bicyclists A and B at right and discuss this with your team. Be prepared to explain your **reasoning** to the class.

7-35. Mr. Regnier's class has been struck with hiccups! Three of the students track their number of hiccups over time. Assume each student hiccups at a constant rate.

Student I

Time (in min)	Number of Hiccups
2	8
4	16
7	28

Student II

Student III

a. Which student has the most hiccups per minute? **Justify** your answer.

b. Find the slope that describes the rate of hiccups for each student. What does the slope tell you about each student?

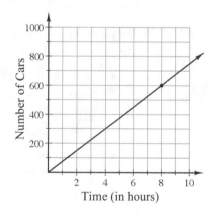

c. If you graphed a line for the student who hiccups 4 times per minute, would the line be steeper, less steep, or the same steepness as the line in the graph for Student II? Explain your **reasoning**.

7-36. **Additional Challenge:** CHANGING LINES

Lupe is a manager of an assembly line at a manufacturing company that makes cars. The speed at which the cars are usually built is represented by the graph at right.

Lupe has decided to increase the number of cars built each day and has written directions for her employees. Which of her directions below would increase the number of cars built each day? Explain how you know.

a. Build 200 cars every 4 hours.

b. Build 75 cars every hour.

c. Build 500 cars every 5 hours.

d. Decrease the time it takes to make each car.

7-37.   Compare the graphs of lines A, B, and C at right.

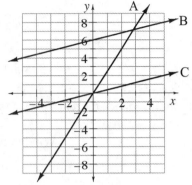

   a.   Which line has the greatest slope? **Justify** your answer.

   b.   What is the *y*-value of line A when $x = 2$?

   c.   Compare the slopes of lines B and C.

7-38.   Lydia drew a graph of four athletes in the final part of the triathlon, the 10 km run. She found the slope of each runner's line. Her results are listed below.

   Runner A: slope $= \frac{2}{6}$ Runner B: slope $= \frac{3}{7}$

   Runner C: slope $= \frac{5}{12}$ Runner D: slope $= \frac{4}{10}$

   List the runners from slowest to fastest.

7-39.   If a car is parked on the side of the road and not moving, what is its speed? What would it look like on a graph of time and distance?

7-40.   Find the missing measure(s) of each circle.

   a.   diameter = ?   b.   diameter = ?
        circumference = ?   radius = ?

   $r = 12$ cm $C = 188.5$ cm

7-41.   Write an equation to represent this problem and find the unknown side lengths. You may use the 5-D Process to help you organize your thinking and to define your variables.

   A trapezoid has a perimeter of 117 cm. The two shortest sides have the same length. The third side is 12 cm longer than one short side. The final side is 9 cm less than three times one short side. How long is each side of the trapezoid?

7.1.5   How can I find the slope ratio?

Slope in Different Representations

In Lesson 7.1.4, you learned about how to describe the steepness of a line with a number. Today, you will work with different representations of lines and look for how the slope can be found in each representation. As you work with your study team today, keep these questions in mind:

> What is being compared to find the slope ratio?

> What would it look like in another representation?

7-42.   A planting manual printed the graphs below so that gardeners could predict the height of trees after planting. Jill wants to figure out how fast each tree will grow. She remembers that **slope** is a ratio of the vertical change to the horizontal change between any two points on a line. Finding the slope for each graph will allow her to compare the change in height to the change in time.

   a.   On a Lesson 7.1.5 Resource Page, draw and label a slope triangle on the line in graph (*i*). Then write the slope ratio. How fast does tree *i* grow?

   b.   Can you find the slope on graph (*ii*) just by looking at the line? Why or why not? When it is difficult to read the slope on a graph, look for points where the line appears to pass through **lattice points** (where the grid lines intersect). Then use those points to create a slope triangle and find the slope.

Slope Triangle

   c.   On the resource page, draw a slope triangle for lines (*iii*) and (*iv*) using lattice points. Then label each slope triangle with its dimensions and calculate the slope ratio.

i.

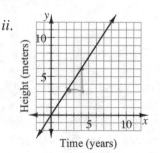

ii.

Problem continues on next page. →

7-42.   *Problem continued from previous page.*

iii.

iv.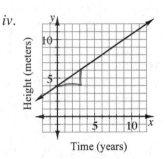

7-43.   Three different students looked at the line graphed at right and each drew a different slope triangle as shown.

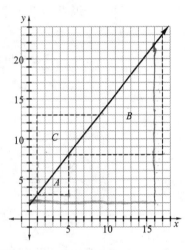

   a.   Find each slope using the slope triangles on the Lesson 7.1.5 Resource Page.

   b.   The numbers in the slope ratios found by the students are all different. Does this mean that the slope of the line changes depending on which points you pick? Discuss this with your team and be ready to share your **reasoning** with the rest of the class.

   c.   Another student said her slope triangle goes up 20 units for every 16 units to the right. Where could her slope triangle be? Draw a possible slope triangle for this student.

   d.   Simplify each of the four slope ratios and compare them. Describe what you find.

7-44. IS SEEING BELIEVING?

Did you know that a bank will pay you
money (called **interest**) when you place
your money in a savings account? The
amount you receive is a portion of the
amount you deposit and the interest rate
often varies with each bank.

Thomas and Ryan have each invested the same amount of money in different
bank accounts that earn **simple interest**, which means the same amount of
interest is added each week. They decided to compare their earnings by
graphing how much interest each of them has earned over time, shown below.

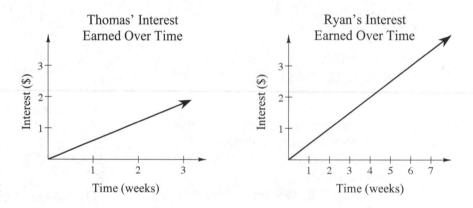

a. When you look at the graphs, which investment seems to be growing
    fastest? Explain how you decided.

b. The tables for
    Thomas and Ryan's
    accounts are shown
    at right. Which
    table reflects
    Thomas' interest?
    Which one reflects
    Ryan's interest?
    How do you know?

Time (in weeks)	Interest Earned ($)	Time (in weeks)	Interest Earned ($)
1	0.60	2	1.00
4	2.40	3	1.50
7	4.20	6	3.00
10	6.00	12	6.00

c. Use the tables to find the rate of *interest earned (in dollars)* to *time (in
    weeks)* for each of them. Whose money is growing faster?

d. Did your answers from parts (a) and (c) agree? If not, compare the tables
    and graphs with your team to find out why the line that is less steep actually
    represents the bank account that grows faster. Be ready to share your ideas
    about why the graphs look the way they do.

Making Connections: Course 2

7-45.   The students in a study team are now arguing about who has graphed the steepest line. Assume that they set up their axes with the same scale. Here is some information about their lines:

Lucy: slope = $\frac{7}{5}$ Bree: slope = $\frac{5}{7}$

Cliff: slope = $\frac{14}{10}$ Geetha: slope = $\frac{12}{10}$

equal

Can you use the slopes of their lines to **visualize** how each of them would look on a graph? Discuss their lines with your team, and then settle their argument without graphing. Explain completely who has the steepest line and who has the least steep line.

7-46.   Which lines on the graph at right and on your resource page appear to have the same slope? Which line or lines are steepest? Make a prediction, then check your prediction by finding the slope of each line in the graph on the Lesson 7.1.5 Resource Page.

7-47.   LEARNING LOG

What is slope? How is it calculated? In your Learning Log, sketch a graph of a line and explain how to find its slope. How would the slope be different if the line was steeper? Explain as completely as you can. Title this entry "Slope and Steepness" and include today's date.

7-48.   There are 36 green gumballs, 18 red gumballs, 22 white gumballs, 30 purple gumballs, and 14 blue gumballs in the gumball machine. Find the probability for each of the following outcomes and write it as a percent. Assume that the gumball machine is always full and that gumballs are released from the machine randomly. Show work to support your answer.

a.   Getting a purple gumball.

b.   Getting either a purple or a green gumball.

c.   *Not* getting a green gumball.

d.   Getting either a purple or a white gumball.

7-49. Graph the points in the table at right and draw a line. Then, find three different ratios to describe the slope of this line.

x	y
0	1
2	6
5	13.5
−2	−4
−4	−9

7-50. Find the slope of each line below.

a.

b.

c.

7-51. For each equation below, solve for x. Show the process you use to check your answer.

a. $2\frac{1}{2} = x - 1\frac{1}{4}$

b. $5x = 2x + 12$

c. $x - 14.6 = 8.02$

7-52. Use the hundredths grids at right to answer the following questions.

a.   Give three names for the largest shaded area.

b.   Give three names for the smallest shaded area.

c.   What are two other names for 120%? Can you show 120% on a single hundreds grid? Explain your thinking.

7.1.6 What else can slope tell us?

More about Slope

In recent lessons you have learned to find the slope of a line and how slope describes the rate of change and the steepness of a line on a graph. In this lesson you will learn about other information that slope can tell you.

7-53.   Will a line with a slope of $\frac{2}{5}$ or $\frac{5}{2}$ be steeper? How do you know? Explain.

7-54.   Compare the two lines in the graph at right.

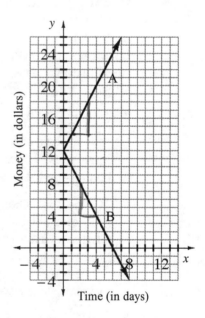

a.   How are the two lines the same? How are they different?

b.   Each line on this graph describes how much money a person has in her wallet over time (in days). Explain what is happening to the amount of money each person has. Be specific.

c.   To describe how person A's amount of money is changing, the unit rate (slope) represents the amount that is added each day. Since the value of money is increasing, the slope is positive. But what should we do when the value is decreasing? How should the decrease be reflected in the rate (slope)? Discuss this with your team.

d.   Remember that the slope ratio compares how the change on the *y*-axis compares to the change on the *x*-axis. Lines that go up from left to right show positive rates of change, or **positive slopes**, while lines that go down from left to right show negative rates of change, or **negative slopes**.

Find the slope of each line in the graph.

7-55. **WHAT IF IT DOESN'T GROW?**

The graph at right shows 3 different lines.

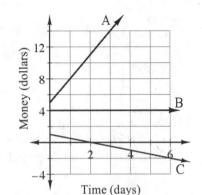

a. Describe each line in words. Is it increasing or decreasing? Quickly or slowly?

b. Line B is different from the other two lines. As the x-value increases, what happens to y?

c. Slope is a comparison of $\frac{\text{change in } y}{\text{change in } x}$. Pick two points on line B. How can you represent the change in y between these two points with a number? Use this number or the change in y to write a slope ratio for line B.

7-56. **PERSONAL TRAINER**

To prepare for biking long distances, Antoine has been trying to keep a steady pace as he bikes. However, since his hometown has many hills, he ends up biking faster and slower during different parts of his ride.

In order to track his distance and time when he trains for the triathlon, Antoine has purchased a special watch that tells him how far he has traveled at specific time intervals. He can set it to record data whenever he decides to push a button and then get a list of the data at the end of his workout.

a. On his first bike ride around town, he recorded several times and distances. These measures are shown in the table at right. Based on the table, does he appear to be traveling at a constant rate? Explain your **reasoning**.

b. Draw and label a graph that extends to 40 minutes on the x-axis and at least to 15 miles on the y-axis. Plot Antoine's distance and time data on the graph. What type of graph is this?

Antoine's Data

Time (minutes)	Distance (miles)
3	0.5
5	1
8	2
12	3
16	4.5
19	6

c. Draw a trend line that best represents Antoine's data. Then extend it to predict about how long it will take him to bike 10 miles (his normal long distance workout).

d. What is Antoine's **general** rate during his bike ride? Find the slope (rate of change) of the trend line you drew in part (c) to determine his **general** rate.

METHODS AND MEANINGS

Slope of a Line

The **slope of a line** is the ratio of the change in y to the change in x between any two points on the line. We compute the *ratio* that indicates how y-values are changing with respect to x-values. In essence, slope is the **unit rate of change** because it measures how much y increases or decreases as x changes by one unit. If the slope is positive (+), the y-values are increasing, and if it is negative (–), the y-values are decreasing. The graph of a line goes up for positive slopes and down for negatives slopes as the line moves across the graph from left to right.

$$\text{slope} = \frac{\text{vertical change}}{\text{horizontal change}} = \frac{\text{change in } y\text{-values}}{\text{change in } x\text{-values}}$$

Some textbooks write this ratio as $\frac{\text{rise}}{\text{run}}$.

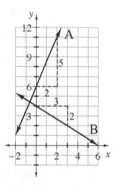

In the graph at right, the slope of line A is $\frac{5}{2}$ because for every 2 units the line increases horizontally, the line increases 5 units vertically, so y increases by $\frac{5}{2}$ units when x increases by 1 unit.

To find the slope of line B, notice that when x increases by 3, y *decreases* by 2, so the vertical change is –2 and the slope is written as $-\frac{2}{3}$.

It is important to notice that horizontal lines do not increase or decrease vertically, and so are described with a slope of 0. The slope of a vertical line is undefined because the horizontal change is 0, which would result in a slope of $\frac{y}{0}$, which is undefined.

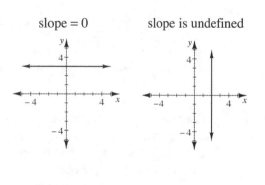

slope = 0   slope is undefined

7-57.   For each pair of slope ratios, decide if they are equivalent (=), or if one slope is greater. If the slopes are not equal, use the greater than (>) or less than (<) symbol to show which is greater.

a. $\frac{6}{7}$, $\frac{5}{6}$ b. $\frac{3}{2}$, $\frac{15}{10}$ c. $\frac{12}{10}$, $\frac{7}{5}$

7-58.   Make a table and graph for the rule $y = -3x + 1$.

7-59.   Lynne took a taxicab from her office to the airport. She had to pay $3 per mile plus a $5 flat fee.

a.   How much would she need to pay to go a distance of 2 miles? How much to travel 8 miles?

b.   Her total cost was $23. Represent the cost of her trip with an equation. How far did she travel? Show your work.

7-60.   Forty percent of the students at Pinecrest Middle School have a school sweatshirt. There are 560 students at the school. Draw a diagram to help you solve each problem below.

a.   How many students have a school sweatshirt?

b.   If 280 students have school t-shirts instead of sweatshirts, what percentage of the school has a t-shirt?

c.   What percentage of the school does not have a t-shirt or a sweatshirt?

7-61.   Ella and her study team are arguing about the slope of the line in the graph at right. They have come up with four different answers: $\frac{3}{4}$, $-\frac{4}{3}$, $-\frac{3}{4}$, and $\frac{4}{3}$. Which slope is correct? **Justify** your answer.

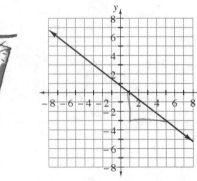

7.2.1 When are they the same?

Systems of Equations

During the summer, county fairs are held all over the country. People from around the county attend the fairs to play carnival games and listen to music. Some people raise animals (such as pigs) that they take to the fair to show and be judged. Today you will use several of the skills you have learned in this course to solve problems in which two factors in a relationship are compared.

7-62.   It is almost time for the county fair! Juanita is looking forward to seeing the animals and enjoying the rides at the carnival on the fairgrounds. She lives near three different county fairs and has to decide which fair she will attend.

The Morgan County Fair charges ten dollars to get in the gate. There is also an additional charge of three dollars per ride at the carnival. The Larimer County Fair charges fifteen dollars to get in the gate, but only two dollars per ride.

Juanita cannot decide which of the two fairs would be cheaper. Help her answer this question by completing the tables on the Lesson 7.2.1 Resource Page and drawing a graph of the cost for each fair.

Morgan County Fair

Gate fee: ___

# of rides	Total cost

Larimer County Fair

Gate fee: ___

# of rides	Total cost

7-63.   Once Juanita estimated the number of rides she wanted to take, she realized that it did not matter which county fair she attended because the cost would be the same.

   a.   How many rides does she plan to ride? How is this shown on the graph?

   b.   How much should Juanita plan to pay? How is this shown on the graph?

7-64. While trying to decide which fair would be cheapest, Juanita considered another fair, the Weld County Fair. She made a table, shown at right, to figure out the costs for this fair.

a. Use the information in the table to add a line for the Weld County Fair on the resource page.

b. What is the cost to get in the entrance gate at the Weld County Fair? What is the cost per ride?

Weld County Fair

# of rides	Total Cost ($)
0	6
1	6 + 5
2	6 + 5 + 5
3	6 + 5 + 5 + 5

7-65. How do the costs at the three county fairs compare? Look at the graph and tables on your Lesson 7.2.1 Resource Page to answer the following questions.

a. Which county fair costs most per ride? How is this shown on the graph?

b. Which county fair has the highest entry fee? How is this shown on the graph?

c. For how many rides do the Morgan County Fair and the Larimer County Fair cost the same total amount of money? How can you see that on the graph? How can you see that in the table?

d. Is there any amount of rides for which all three county fairs have the same cost? Explain.

7-66. Graphs are ways to tell stories without using many words. If you look at them carefully you can get a lot of information. Use the graphs to answer the following questions.

a. The graph below shows Mica and Joel's progress as they are walking. How can you tell when Joel and Mica will pass each other? When and where will that happen?

b. The graph below shows Mica and Joel walking for 15 minutes on a different day. If they both continue at the same rate, will they ever be the same distance from school at the same time? How do you know?

7-67.   For each equation below, solve for x. Show the process you use to check your answer.

   a. $x - \frac{2}{5} = 1\frac{3}{5}$ b. $5x = 0$ c. $x - 14.6 = 2.96$

7-68.   Use the graph shown at right to enter the ordered pairs in the table below.

   a.   Write the rule in words.

   b.   Explain how to use the table to predict the value of y when x is -7.

7-69.   Evaluate the inequality for the listed values of x. Decide if the value makes the statement true or false. Show your work.

$$3x - 3 \geq 2x + 3$$

   a. $x = -3$ b. $x = 9$ c. $x = 6$ d. $x = 10\frac{1}{2}$

7-70.   Mr. Takaya can eat three slices of pizza in five minutes. If he continues to eat at the same rate, how long will it take him to eat the whole pizza (twelve slices)? How many slices could he eat in half of an hour?

7-71.   Use the similar shapes at right to answer the questions below.

   a.   What is the scale factor from shape A to shape B?

   b.   What is the scale factor from shape B to shape C?

   c.   How are these scale factors related?

   d.   What do you know about shape A and shape C?

7.2.2 Where is the solution found?

Solving Systems of Equations

In the previous lesson, you looked at tables and graphs to compare several relationships. Today, you will learn a new method of comparing to help you figure out when two relationships are the same.

7-72. In problem 7-64, Juanita made a table like the one at right to figure out the cost to attend the Weld County Fair. Find the table you made on the Lesson 7.2.1 Resource Page. Add Juanita's expressions for total cost to your table and add the next two entries.

Weld County Fair	
# of Rides	Total Cost ($)
0	6
1	6 + 5
2	6 + 5 + 5
3	6 + 5 + 5 + 5
4	
5	
x	

a. Is there a shorter way to write the expression for total cost? For example, for 10 rides, how could you calculate the total cost without adding $5 ten times?

b. Add one more entry in the table by writing a variable expression for the cost of x rides.

7-73. In Lesson 7.2.1, you used a graph to find out when two of the county fairs cost the same amount of money for the same number of rides. Another way to find out this information is to use expressions for each county fair.

a. A table for the total costs to attend the Morgan County Fair is shown at right. Find the table you made on the Lesson 7.2.1 Resource Page. If you have not done so already, add the entries shown at right, as well as two more entries. Then write a variable expression for the total cost for x rides at the Morgan County Fair.

Morgan County Fair	
# of Rides	Total Cost ($)
0	10
1	10 + 3
2	10 + 3 + 3

Problem continues on next page. →

Making Connections: Course 2

7-73. *Problem continued from previous page.*

    b. Since the Larimer County Fair has a $15 entry fee and charges $2 for a ride, what would its table look like? Add to your table on the resource page and write a variable expression for the Larimer County Fair.

    c. How can you use what you know about comparing expressions to find the number of rides for which the Larimer and Morgan County Fairs will cost the same amount? What is that cost?

    d. Look at the graph on the Lesson 7.2.1 Resource Page. Where is your answer from part (c) found on the graph? What does the answer represent?

7-74. When will the Weld County Fair and Larimer County Fair cost the same amount? Set up an equation using the expressions from the Weld County Fair and the Larimer County Fair. Make sure your answer includes both the number of rides and the total cost. Verify that this shared point is the same on your graph.

7-75. Emilie and her sister Robin are excited because they have both been raising pigs to show at the county fair. When they first got their pigs, Emilie was worried because her pig was 5.5 pounds lighter than Robin's pig. Emilie knew weight was not the only factor on which her pig would be judged, but it was one of the more important factors.

As the pigs began to grow, Emilie decided to keep track of both pigs' weight so she could see when her pig would weigh as much as Robin's pig. Emilie recorded her data in the tables at right.

Emilie's Pig		Robin's Pig	
Time (weeks)	Weight (lbs)	Time (weeks)	Weight (lbs)
0	49.5	0	55
1	60	1	65.5
2	70.5	2	76
3	81	3	86.5
4	91.5	4	97

    a. Write a variable expression for the weight of each pig in which x represents the number of weeks.

    b. When will Emilie's pig weigh as much as Robin's pig? Explain your answer.

7-76.   The graph at right shows the
results of the weight for Emilie
and Robin's pigs from problem
7-75. Does the graph **justify**
your answer from that problem?
Why or why not?

MATH NOTES

METHODS AND MEANINGS

Systems of Linear Equations

You know how to solve equations like $3x - 4 = 14$. The solution is $x = 6$, since $3(6) - 4$ is $18 - 4$, which is 14. You also know that for the equation $y = 3x - 4$, you can create a table of xy-coordinates and represent the equation with a straight line on a graph.

A **system of linear equations** is a set of two or more linear equations in two variables that are considered together (simultaneously). In problem 7-73, you represented the cost of admission and x rides for Larimer County as $3x + 10$ dollars and Morgan County as $2x + 15$ dollars. If y represents the cost, we can write $y = 3x + 10$ and $y = 2x + 15$. The graphs of these two equations are shown at right.

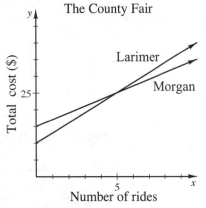

One way to **solve a system of linear equations** is to find the **point of intersection** (that is, where they cross – if they do) for the graph. The lines intersect at $(5, 25)$, which means that the cost, $25, is the same at both county fairs when you go on 5 rides.

A second way to find the point of intersection is to use what you know about comparing expressions. Since we want to know how many rides cost the same, y must have the same value in both equations, so we can set the two expressions in x equal to each other and solve the resulting equation.

$y = 3x + 10$ (Larimer)
$y = 2x + 15$ (Morgan)

$3x + 10 = 2x + 15$ $x = 5$ rides

Then you can replace x with 5 in either equation to find the cost for 5 rides: $3(5) + 10 = \$25$ or $2(5) + 15 = \$25$, so the **solution** is 5 rides that cost $25.

7-77.   Pierre was walking toward school at a rate of two miles per hour. He started six miles from school. Dom left school and walked toward Pierre at a rate of four miles per hour. When and how far from school will the boys pass each other?

7-78.   Graph the rule $y = -6x + 4$. Use the graph to predict the value of y when $x = \frac{1}{3}$. Use the rule to check your prediction.

7-79.   Sketch each angle below on your paper, and label each one with its measure in degrees.

  a.   Identify whether each angle is an acute, obtuse, or right angle.

  b.   Which angles could form a complementary pair?

  c.   Which angles could form a supplementary pair?

7-80.   Simplify each expression.

  a. $\dfrac{2(5+3)}{4}$

  b. $\frac{1}{2}(15+3) - 10 \div 2$

  c. $5\frac{1}{2} - 2\frac{1}{4} + \frac{3}{8}$

  d. $3 + \frac{3}{5} \cdot \frac{1}{4}$

  e. $-2 + (-5+6)^2$

  f. $\frac{3}{4} \cdot \frac{1}{4} + \frac{5}{8} \cdot \left(-\frac{3}{2}\right)$

7-81.   Alex has a job delivering newspapers. He puts 20% of his earnings each week into his college savings account. Each week he puts $16 into the account.

  a.   Draw a diagram to represent this situation. How much money does Alex earn each week?

  b.   Alex spends 10% of his earnings on snacks each week. How much does he spend?

  c.   When Alex has worked for one year, he will get a raise that is equal to 15% of his current earnings. How much more money will he earn each week?

Making Connections: Course 2

7.2.3 Is there always a solution?

More Solving Systems of Equations

One of the most common events at the county fair is showing animals to a group of judges to win a "Best of Show" award. Many people compete with animals such as cows, pigs, sheep, goats, and even chickens! There are also many displays so that people can learn about these animals.

7-82. Emilie was looking at two tables that recorded the weekly weights of two lambs. She thinks she sees a way to tell where two lines on the graph will intersect without having to draw the graph.

She told her friend, Sterling, that the answer was nineteen because that number was in both tables, shown at right.

Sterling looked at what Emilie had done and said, *"I don't think 19 is the answer."*

x	y
0	3
1	7
2	11
3	15
4	⑲
5	23
6	27

x	y
0	10
1	13
2	16
3	⑲
4	22
5	25
6	28

a. Did Emilie make a mistake? Explain.

b. If both tables represent lines, when will the lines intersect? Write the intersection as a point in the form (x, y) and state what it tells you about the lambs.

[handwritten notes: 7 30, 7 31, 8 33, 8 35, 9]

7-83. Juanita is enjoying the Morgan County Fair. However, she noticed that the temperature is getting colder. When she arrived at the fair (when the fair opened), the temperature was 81°. However, due to an approaching storm, the temperature has dropped 3° per hour.

Meanwhile, the fair in Larimer County has had better luck with the weather. It opened at the same time and the temperature was 72°. It has only dropped 1° per hour.

Problem continues on next page. →

7-83.   *Problem continued from previous page.*

When Juanita called her friend at the Larimer County fair, she found out that both counties had the same temperature. How long has Juanita been at the fair?

a.   Discuss which representation your team would like to use to find the solution. Think about these questions as you discuss your ideas:

* Are these numbers easy to graph accurately?

* Is a table convenient?

* Would an equation be faster?

Be ready to share your **reasoning** with the class.

b.   Solve the problem using the representation your team chose in part (a). What does the solution represent?

7-84.   Answer the questions below based on the graph at right.

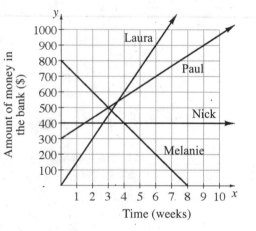

a.   Who is saving money the fastest and how can you tell?

b.   Who is not spending or saving? How can you tell?

c.   When did Paul and Melanie have the same amount of money?

d.   Will anyone run out of money? How can you tell?

7-85.   LEARNING LOG

In your Learning Log, explain how to find the intersection between two lines using graphs, tables, and equations. Use pictures, symbols, or words and give specific examples. Title this entry, "Systems of Equations," and label it with today's date.

7-86.   Mimi is saving money. She already has $30 and earns an additional $10 per week. Alexis already has $80, but she is not spending or saving any additional money. When will the girls have the same amount of money and how much money will they have?

7-87.   Four pieces of taffy cost 25 cents. Complete the table below.

Taffy (# of pieces)	4	16	8	80	24	32	40
Cost (in dollars)							

7-88.   Simplify each expression below.

a. $2\frac{3}{10} - 1\frac{2}{5}$ b. $\frac{9}{3} \cdot \frac{4}{5}$ c. $\frac{3}{4} + 5\frac{7}{8}$

d. $\frac{2}{9} \cdot (-\frac{3}{7}) \cdot (\frac{14}{5})$ e. $-\frac{9}{15} - (-\frac{26}{45})$ f. $5\frac{1}{6} \cdot (-\frac{7}{9})$

7-89.   Richard's **strategy** to change a percent to a decimal is to put the decimal point in front of the percent number. On the right is an example of his work. Do you agree with Richard's method? Explain your **reasoning**.

$8\% = 0.8$
$80\% = 0.80$
$800\% = 0.800$

7-90.   Find the area and perimeter of each shape below. Show your steps and work.

a.

b.

Chapter 7 Closure   What have I learned?

Reflection and Synthesis

The activities below offer you a chance to reflect about what you have learned during this chapter. As you work, look for concepts that you feel very comfortable with, ideas that you would like to learn more about, and topics you need more help with. Look for connections between ideas as well as connections with material you learned previously.

① SUMMARIZING MY UNDERSTANDING

This section gives you an opportunity to show what you know about certain math topics or ideas.

Obtain both of the Chapter 7 Closure GO Resource Pages (the slope page is pictured at right) from your teacher. (GO is short for Graphic Organizer.) Follow the directions below to demonstrate your understanding of similar shapes and slope.

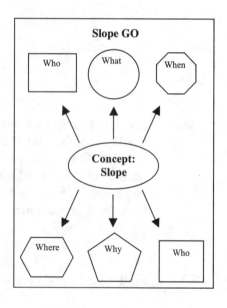

Part 1: Answer the question provided in each section of the Similar Shapes GO. Be ready to share your ideas about similar shapes with your team.

Part 2: Now, use the same format to create your own Slope GO. On the resource page, work with your team to write six "Who, What, When Where, Why, How?" questions about slope.

Part 3: Follow your teacher's directions to pair up with students in another team and trade GO questions to answer.

Part 4: Be ready to contribute your team's ideas to a class discussion. On your own paper, make note of new ideas about slope.

Working the problems in this section will help you to evaluate which types of problems you feel comfortable with and which ones you need more help with. This section will appear at the end of every chapter to help you check your understanding.

Solve each problem as completely as you can. The table at the end of this closure section has answers to these problems. It also tells you where you can find additional help and practice on problems like them.

CL 7-91. Annika is saving money for a trip. She is able to save $75 a week. Her friend from Iceland, Eva, is also saving money. Eva is able to save 9000 Kronas (Icelandic money) each week. If $4 is equal to 509 Kronas, who is saving at a greater rate?

CL 7-92. A breakfast cereal is made of oats, nuts, and raisins. The advertisements boast that 30% of the cereal in each box is raisins.

    a.   What portion of each box is not raisins?

    b.   If each box contains 8 cups of cereal, how many cups of raisins are in each box? Draw and label a diagram to represent the problem.

    c.   If the box contains 2 cups of nuts, what percentage of each box is nuts?

CL 7-93. Clay and his friend Lacey are making cookies for the school dance. Clay started early and has already made 3-dozen cookies. He can make an additional two-dozen cookies an hour. Lacey has not started making cookies yet, but she has a bigger oven and can make four-dozen cookies an hour. If Lacey starts baking her cookies right away, how long will it take for her to have made as many cookies as Clay and how many cookies will they each have made?

CL 7-94. Complete the table and find the rule.

x	6	$\frac{1}{2}$	−6	8	−12	3	$\frac{2}{3}$
y				18		3	

CL 7-95. For the following examples, tell whether there is positive correlation, negative correlation, or no correlation.

a. The number of inches of rain per hour and the height of water in a reservoir.

b. Amount of food a person eats and how many pets they have.

c. The height of a tree and the amount of nutrients it gets.

d. Number of hours spent hiking in the mountains and the amount of water left in your water bottle.

CL 7-96. Use the following graph to complete the table and find the rule.

0	1	2	3	4	5	x
						$y =$

CL 7-97. Use the rule $y = 4x + 2$ to complete a table like the one in problem CL 7-96 and then draw a graph.

CL 7-98. Solve the following equations.

a. $3x - 2 = 4x + 6$

b. $6x - 12 = -x + 2$

c. $3(x + 2) - 3 = 3x - 2$

d. $5(x - 1) = 5(2x - 3)$

CL 7-99. For each of the problems above, do the following:

- Draw a bar or number line that represents 0 to 10.

- Color or shade in a portion of the bar that represents your level of understanding and comfort with completing that problem on your own.

If any of your bars are less than a 5, choose *one* of those problems and do one of the following tasks:

- Write two questions that you would like to ask about that problem.

- Brainstorm two things that you DO know about that type of problem.

If all of your bars are a 5 or above, choose one of those problems and do one of these tasks:

- Write two questions you might ask or hints you might give to a student who was stuck on the problem.

- Make a new problem that is similar and more challenging than that problem and solve it.

③   WHAT TOOLS CAN I USE?

You have several tools and references available to help support your learning – your teacher, your study team, your math book, and your Toolkit, to name only a few. At the end of each chapter you will have an opportunity to review your Toolkit for completeness as well as to revise or update it to better reflect your current understanding of big ideas.

The main elements of your Toolkit should be your Learning Log, Math Notes, and the vocabulary used in this chapter. Math words that are new to this chapter appear in bold in the text. Refer to the lists provided below and follow your teacher's instructions to revise your Toolkit, which will help make it a useful reference for you as you complete this chapter and as you work in future chapters.

Learning Log Entries

- Lesson 7.1.3 – Rate, Tables, and Graphs
- Lesson 7.1.5 – Slope and Steepness
- Lesson 7.2.3 – Systems of Equations

Math Notes

- Lesson 7.1.3 – Rate of Change and Unit Rates
- Lesson 7.1.6 – Slope of a Line
- Lesson 7.2.2 – Systems of Linear Equations

Mathematical Vocabulary

The following is a list of vocabulary found in this chapter. Some of the words have been seen in the previous chapter. The words in bold are the words new to this chapter. Make sure that you are familiar with the terms below and know what they mean. For the words you do not know, refer to the glossary or index. You might also want to add these words to your Toolkit for a way to reference them in the future.

constant rate	**horizontal change**	**intersect**
negative slope	**positive slope**	**ratio**
rate	**slope**	**steep**
unit rate	variable expression	**vertical change**

Process Words

These words describe problem solving strategies and processes that you have been involved in throughout the course of this chapter. Make sure you know what each of these words means. If you are not sure, you can talk with your teacher or other students or look through your book for problems in which you were asked to do these things.

analyze	compare	explain
interpret	justify	predict
visualize		

Answers and Support for Closure Activity #2
What Have I Learned?

Problem	Solution	Need Help?	More Practice
CL 7-91.	Annika is saving at a faster rate because she saves $75 a week and Eva saves about $71 a week.	Lessons 7.1.1, 7.1.2, and 7.1.3 Math Notes boxes in Lessons 4.1.1 and 7.1.3 Learning Log (problem 7-27)	Problems 7-8, 7-28, 7-35, 7-36, and 7-44
CL 7-92.	a. 70% is not raisins. b. 2.4 cups of raisins. c. 25% is nuts.	Lessons 4.1.1 and 4.1.2 Math Notes box in Lesson 4.1.2	Problem CL 4-112

Problem	Solution	Need Help?	More Practice
CL 7-93.	In $1\frac{1}{2}$ hours they will each have made 72 cookies.	Lessons 7.1.3, 7.2.1, 7.2.2, and 7.2.3 Math Notes box in Lesson 7.2.2 Learning Log (problem 7-85)	Problems 7-73, 7-75, 7-77, 7-83, and 7-86

| CL 7-94. | | | | | | | | Lessons 6.1.4, 6.1.5, and 6.1.6 | Problems 6-36, 6-37, 6-43, 6-54, 6-82, 6-100, 6-126, and 7-68 |

6	$\frac{1}{2}$	−6	8	−12	3	$\frac{2}{3}$
12	−4.5	−24	18	−42	3	−4

$y = 3x - 6$

Problem	Solution	Need Help?	More Practice
CL 7-95.	a. positive correlation b. no correlation c. positive correlation d. negative correlation	Lessons 6.1.2 and 6.1.3 Math Notes box in Lesson 6.1.4 Learning Logs (problems 6-26 and 6-47)	Problems 6-15, 6-24, 6-49, 6-116, 6-139, and CL 6-140

CL 7-96.

0	1	2	3	4	5
10	12.5	15	17.5	20	22.5

$y = 2.5x + 10$

Lessons 6.1.4, 6.1.5, and 6.1.6

Problems 6-48, 6-79, and 7-68

CL 7-97.

0	1	2	3	4	5
2	6	10	14	18	22

$y = 4x + 2$

Lessons 6.1.4, 6.1.5, and 6.1.6

Problems CL 6-142, 7-12, and 7-58

CL 7-98.

a. $x = -8$
b. $x = 2$
c. no solution
d. $x = 2$

Lessons 6.2.1, 6.2.2, and 6.2.3

Math Notes boxes in Lessons 6.2.1, 6.2.3, 6.2.4, and 6.2.6

Learning Log (problem 6-98)

Problems 6-87, 6-88, 6-97, 6-115, 6-125, 6-134, 7-9, and 7-30

Puzzle Investigator Problems

PI-13.   GOING BANANAS!

This year's harvest from a small, remote banana plantation consists of 3000 bananas. The farmer's camel can carry up to 1000 bananas at a time. The market place where the bananas are sold is 1000 miles away. Unfortunately, the camel eats one banana each and every mile she walks.

Your task: Of the three thousand bananas harvested, what is the greatest number of bananas the farmer can get to market?

PI-14.   WITH OR WITHOUT FROSTING

Mr. Hamada baked a cake for his class that was in the shape of a big cube. As he carried the cake over to the frosting table, he slipped and the cake fell into a large tub of frosting!

Amazingly, the cake stayed in one piece, but all 6 sides were now frosted. One student suggested the cake be cut into cube-shaped pieces, all the same size.

a.   There are 32 students in Mr. Hamada's class and he does not want more than 100 pieces of cake. If Mr. Hamada cuts the cake into cube-shaped pieces, all the same size, how many pieces of cake should he cut so that everyone could have a piece? (Note: You might want to use small blocks to explore this question.)

b.   A student noticed that some pieces have no frosting, while others have 1, 2, or 3 sides frosted. How many of each type of piece can Mr. Hamada offer?

c.   There were many students that wanted a piece with frosting on 3 sides, so Mr. Hamada changed his mind and decided to cut the cake into 125 cube-shaped pieces, all the same size. Did this increase the number of pieces with frosting on 3 sides? Why or why not?

Percents and More Solving Equations 8

CHAPTER 8 Percents and More Solving Equations

When traveling in a car, have you ever asked, *"When are we going to get there?"* Did you know that you could use mathematics to answer that question? In Section 8.1, you will use diagrams, like the ones you used for percents, to find the relationship between rate, time, and distance. You will also learn to compare quantities that are very different.

You will revisit scale factor in Section 8.2 and connect it to percents. You will learn to take difficult problems and make them simpler by rewriting equations to remove fractional and decimal coefficients. Finally, you will investigate how to find the percent increase, percent decrease, and simple interest.

Guiding Questions

Think about these questions throughout this chapter:

How is it changing?

What is the relationship?

What is the connection?

How can I represent it?

What **strategy** should I use?

In this chapter, you will learn how to:

➢ Solve problems involving distance, rate, and time.

➢ Convert units so that they are the same, then use them to compare rates.

➢ Solve equations that have fractional or decimal coefficients.

➢ Find the whole amount if you only know a percentage of it.

➢ Calculate simple interest.

Chapter Outline

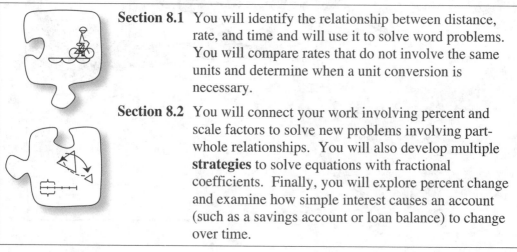

Section 8.1 You will identify the relationship between distance, rate, and time and will use it to solve word problems. You will compare rates that do not involve the same units and determine when a unit conversion is necessary.

Section 8.2 You will connect your work involving percent and scale factors to solve new problems involving part-whole relationships. You will also develop multiple **strategies** to solve equations with fractional coefficients. Finally, you will explore percent change and examine how simple interest causes an account (such as a savings account or loan balance) to change over time.

8.1.1 What is the relationship?

Distance, Rate, and Time

Throughout this course you have been developing skills for writing equations to describe relationships in tables, in graphs, and in situations. You have used the 5-D Process, diagrams of percentage problems, and geometric relationships to organize information for those equations. Today you will use your equation writing skills to represent the relationships between rate, time, and distance.

8-1.   Axel is getting his pig ready for the pig races at the county fair. During the race, four juvenile pigs run around a track, trying to be the first pig to get to a cream-filled chocolate cookie. His pig, Hammy, can run at a rate of 11 feet per second.

   a.   At this speed, how far will Hammy run in 3 seconds? In 5 seconds? In 1 minute (that is, in 60 seconds)?

   b.   Write an expression that represents how far Hammy will run in x seconds.

   c.   The race track at the fair is 150 feet long.

   • Draw a diagram that shows how long it will take Hammy to finish the race.

   • Write an equation to represent this situation.

   d.   About how long it will take Hammy to finish the race?

8-2.   A.J. and her sister are entering a 200-mile bike race on their bicycle built for two. On a training ride, they traveled 60 miles in 2.5 hours. They want to use this information to find out how long it will take them to finish the bike race. Draw a diagram for this situation and be ready to explain how you found your solutions to the questions below.

   a.   What is their bicycling rate? What is their unit rate (per hour)?

   b.   How far can they go in three hours? In six hours? Explain how you can use the rate of travel and the time to find the distance.

Problem continues on next page. →

8-2.   *Problem continued from previous page.*

    c.   If they bicycle ten miles, how long will it take them? Explain how the
         distance and rate helped you find the time.

    d.   If they bike at this same rate for the entire race, how long will it take them
         to finish the 200 mile race?

    e.   Summarize in words the relationship between the distance the girls travel,
         their rate of travel, and how long they ride (the time).

8-3.   A new high-speed train travels 300 miles in 1.2 hours. Luis and Omar are
         trying to figure out how they can find the distance the train has traveled after
         any number of hours. Omar decided to draw a diagram to help figure out the
         problem. He drew the diagram below.

    a.   Find a unit rate (in miles per hour) for the train. Then copy and change
         Omar's diagram to show the unit rate.

    b.   How far will the train travel in 5 hours? Write an equation to represent how
         to use the picture to find out how far the train will go in miles (d miles)
         after t hours.

    c.   Work with your team to write an equation to show the relationship between
         distance (d), rate (r), and time (t). Is there more than one way to represent
         this relationship in an equation? Explain.

8-4.   In problem 8-3 you wrote an equation to relate
         distance to rate of travel and time traveled. What
         if the rate does not involve distance? Use the
         situation below to investigate this question.

         Fred was filling bags of food for families in need
         at the neighborhood food pantry. Fred could fill
         6 bags in 15 minutes. Draw a diagram for this
         situation and be ready to explain how you found
         your solutions.

    a.   How many bags could Fred fill in two hours?

    b.   How many bags can Fred fill in $\frac{5}{6}$ of an hour? What **strategy** did you use
         to find this answer?

Problem continues on next page. →

Making Connections: Course 2

8-4.   *Problem continued from previous page.*

    c.   Write a rule to **generalize** the relationship between the number of bags Fred can fill and the amount of time that he works. Be sure to define your variables.

    d.   Use your equation from part (c) to find the number of bags Fred will fill during a week (assuming he fills bags at a constant rate and that Fred works 36 hours in a week).

8-5.   Claudia and her cousin Brian often ride their bikes to meet each other. They live 16 miles apart. Claudia can bike at a speed of 8.5 mph, and Brian can ride 11 mph. If they leave their homes at the same time and bike towards each other for half an hour, will they meet?

METHODS AND MEANINGS

MATH NOTES

Distance, Rate, and Time

    Distance (*d*) equals the product of the **rate of speed** (*r*) and the **time** (*t*). This is usually written as $d = r \cdot t$. We use the units of distance (such as feet or miles) and units of time (such as seconds or hours) to write the units of rate (feet per second or miles per hour).

One way to make sense of this relationship is to treat rate as a unit rate that equals the distance covered in one hour (or minute) of travel. Then $r \cdot t$ is *t* sets of *r* lengths, which is *rt* long. For example, if someone travels for 3 hours at 5 miles per hour, we could represent this situation by the following diagram.

| 5 miles | 5 miles | 5 miles |

| 1 hour | 1 hour | 1 hour |

We can also use the same equation to find either rate or time if we know the other two variables. For example, if you need to travel 200 miles and need to be there in 4 hours, you have the equation
$200 \text{ mi.} = r \frac{\text{mi.}}{\text{hr.}} \cdot 4 \text{ hrs.}$, so $r = 50 \frac{\text{mi.}}{\text{hr.}}$.

8-6.   If a train travels at an average rate of 40 miles per hour, how long will it take the train to travel 110 miles? Be sure to show all of your work.

8-7.   The graph at right represents this situation: Cara jogs every morning. After 30 minutes, Cara has run 3.5 miles.

a.   How is Cara's speed represented on the graph?

b.   Write a rule for Cara's distance if t represents the number of hours.

c.   If Cara continues to run at this rate, predict how far she will run in 4 hours.

8-8.   Solve each equation.

a. $3(x+4) = -42$ b. $90 = 5 - (2x+1)$

c. $5(3+x) = 3x$

8-9.   Consider the three similar shapes at right.

a.   Find the lengths of the sides labeled with variables.

b.   What is the scale factor between shapes A and B?

c.   What do you know about shapes A and C? **Justify**.

8-10.   Find the area of each shaded **sector** (region) in the circles below. Write an exact answer in terms of π and an approximate answer as a decimal.

a.

b.   Each sector has equal area.

8.1.2 How can I compare them?

Comparing Rates

Have you ever heard someone use the expression, "They are like apples and oranges"? Usually the person talking means that the two things they are talking about are so different that they are hard to relate to each other. For example, it is very hard to decide which is heavier, a million feathers or 1000 bricks. The information you have does not describe their weight, and the two kinds of objects are so different that trying to **reason** about which is heavier is very difficult.

In order to compare two things, it is useful to find ways to relate them to each other. Often, quantities cannot be compared without doing some calculations or rewriting them in equivalent forms. As you work today, think about the quantities that you are comparing and what you need to do to be able to make a good comparison.

8-11. Rob and Marla are going for a run. They typically run an average of five miles in one hour, as represented in the diagram at right. Today, they plan to run for 40 minutes.

a. Estimate how far Rob and Marla run in 40 minutes. Remember that an estimate can be done with only simple mental calculations, and does not need to be an exact answer. Be ready to share your **reasoning**.

b. Marla said, *"I know that in order to find distance, I need to multiply rate times time. Multiplying five by 40 gives me the answer 200 miles."* Do you agree with how she organized the problem? If not, explain what you think she did wrong, and what you think the actual distance should be.

8-12. Wei and Jinfai like to let their pet gerbils run on a small track. Wei thinks her gerbil can run faster than Jinfai's gerbil, but Jinfai disagrees. They decide to take some measurements and compare them. Wei's gerbil runs two yards in 20 seconds. Jinfai's gerbil runs 20 feet in one minute.

Your task: Work with your team to determine whose gerbil is fastest. Use a diagram to **justify** your answer and record your calculations carefully so that they are clear enough for someone else to understand.

Discussion Points

How can you represent the situation for each gerbil with a diagram?

How can you compare the rates?

How can you compare measures that are in different units?

Further Guidance

8-13. Why is it that Wei and Jinfai cannot compare the rates for their gerbils directly from the measurements that they took? That is, what makes it difficult to compare two yards per 20 seconds and 20 feet per minute to find out which gerbil is faster?

8-14. One way to begin changing the rates so that they can be compared is to make the time measurements have the same units. The times for the gerbils are given in minutes or seconds. Knowing that there are 60 seconds in a minute, decide if you want to use minutes or seconds and convert both measurements to the same units.

8-15. Jinfai has decided to change both of the time measurements into minutes. He started the diagram at right to find the rate for Wei's gerbil.

a. Why did Jinfai label the diagram with $\frac{1}{3}$ of a minute?

b. Can you use the diagram to figure out Wei's gerbil's rate and compare it to Jinfai's gerbil to decide which is fastest? If not, what do you still need to do?

Making Connections: Course 2

8-16.   If you have not done so already, use the fact that three feet are equal to one yard to modify the diagram in problem 8-15 to show how many feet Wei's gerbil travels in one minute. Then decide whose gerbil travels faster.

—————— *Further Guidance* ——————
section ends here.

8-17.   Use your understanding of the relationship between distance, rate, and time to find the following:

   a.   Jinfai and Wei let their gerbils run for 90 seconds. How far does each gerbil run?

   b.   If Jinfai and Wei let their gerbils run for 30 seconds, how far apart will they be and whose gerbil will be in the lead?

   c.   If Jinfai and Wei race their gerbils across a room that is 12 feet long, by how much time will the faster gerbil win?

8-18.   A professional speed walker who is training for the Olympics can walk two miles in 16 minutes. Calculate the following rates. Refer to the Math Notes box following this lesson if you need help with unit conversions.

   a.   What is the athlete's minutes per mile rate?

   b.   What is the athlete's miles per minute rate?

   c.   What is the athlete's feet per minute rate?

   d.   What is the athlete's feet per second rate?

8-19.   Use the relationship between distance, rate, and time to write an equation for the following problem. Then solve the equation to find the missing information.

   Henry knows it takes approximately 4 hours to drive from Madison to Des Moines, a distance of about 275 miles. What must his average speed be to drive the distance in 4 hours? If the highway speed limit is 65 miles per hour, can he make it in this amount of time without breaking the law?

METHODS AND MEANINGS

Equivalent Measures

When you need to compare quantities, it is often helpful to write them using the same units. Here are some common units of measurement and their relationships:

Length	Volume	Weight
12 inches = 1 foot	8 ounces = 1 cup	16 ounces = 1 pound
36 inches = 1 yard	16 ounces = 1 pint	2,000 pounds = 1 ton
3 feet = 1 yard	2 pints = 1 quart	
5,280 feet = 1 mile	4 quarts = 1 gallon	

Time

60 seconds = 1 minute	24 hours = 1 day
60 minutes = 1 hour	7 days = 1 week

One year is closely approximated as 365.25 days, or a bit more than 52 weeks and 1 day. Two commonly used approximations based on these figures are:

365 days ≈ 1 year   52 weeks ≈ 1 year

Review & Preview

8-20.   Mr. Benesh is in charge of facilities at Walt Clark Middle School. He is organizing a project to paint all 36 classrooms during the school's summer break. He estimates that it will take one person five hours to paint each classroom.

a.   How many total hours would it take for one person to paint all of the classrooms?

b.   Mr. Benesh has a team of four workers he is planning to assign to the job. Assuming they all paint at the same rate of five hours per classroom, how many hours would it take the team to do the painting?

c.   Mr. Benesh realized that he needs the painting to be finished in nine hours so that a different team can come in to wax the floors before school starts. How many people will he need to assign to do the painting in order to do this?

8-21.   Convert the following data and write equivalent measurements. Use the information in the Math Notes box to help you.

   a.   How many inches are in 6 feet?

   b.   How many inches are in 5 feet, 2 inches?

   c.   How many minutes are in 7.5 hours?

   d.   How many hours are in 2 days?

   e.   How many days are in 3168 minutes?

8-22.   Maia was serving five pizzas at the weekly meeting of the student council. She wanted to divide the pizzas into slices that were each $\frac{1}{8}$ of a whole pizza.

   a.   How many slices will she have?

   b.   Represent this problem using a mathematical sentence. Can you find more than one way to do this?

8-23.   Think of a standard deck of playing cards that has four suits in two colors: diamonds and hearts are red; clubs and spades are black. Each suit has 13 cards: an ace, the numbers two through ten, a jack, a queen and a king (the last three are called "face" cards). What is the probability of drawing:

   a.   A black 9 or 10?   b.   A red face card?   c.   A card less than 5?

8-24.   Copy the diagram below on your paper. Use the given information to fill in all of the missing labels.

8-25.　　Use the graph at right to answer the questions below.

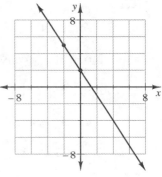

a.　Create a table of values for the line on the graph such as the one started below. Include at least 5 entries.

x	-2	
y	5	

b.　What is the slope of the line?

c.　Write an equation (rule) for the line.

8.2.1　How can I make it smaller or bigger?

Scaling Quantities

In Chapter 4 you learned how to find the percent of a number by making a diagram to relate the part to the whole and find the desired portion. This calculation is fairly straightforward if the percent is a multiple of 10, like 40%, or can be thought of as a fraction, like $\frac{1}{4} = 25\%$. However, it can be more challenging if the percent is something like 6.2% or 87.5%.

Today you will connect what you have learned previously about:

- The relationship between distance, rate, and time.

- How to use a scale factor to find the corresponding lengths of similar figures.

You will use these connections to develop a new method for calculating percents. They will add a powerful new tool to your collection of problem solving **strategies**.

8-26.　　Dana is training for a bicycle race. He can ride his bike 25 miles per hour.

One day, when he had been riding for $\frac{3}{5}$ of an hour, he had to stop and fix a flat tire. How many miles had he ridden when he stopped? The diagram below may be useful.

8-27. Matt thought about problem 8-26 and drew the diagram at right. Look at Matt's drawing and decide how he is thinking about this problem.

a. Write an equation that uses the scale factor to find x.

b. What connection is Matt making between finding a distance using the rate and time (as you did in problem 8-26) and using a scale factor with similar figures? How are the situations alike and how are they different?

8-28. In the two previous problems, $\frac{3}{5}$ is used in two ways – as *time* in the rate problem $\frac{25 \text{ miles}}{1 \text{ hr}} \cdot \frac{3}{5}$ hrs and as the *scale factor* in the similar triangle problem used to find three-fifths of 25 miles. Both of these situations resulted in an equivalent calculation: $25 \cdot \frac{3}{5} = 15$. How else could this be written?

a. Using the Portions Web (shown at right), work with your team to find two other ways to write the equation $25 \cdot \frac{3}{5} = 15$. For example, one way might be $25 \cdot \frac{6}{10} = 15$.

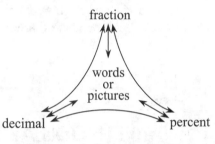

b. If you did not already find it, what percent would be equivalent to $\frac{3}{5}$? Use this percent to write a statement in words and symbols that is equivalent to $25 \cdot \frac{3}{5} = 15$.

Representations of a Portion

c. Use the idea of scaling to find the following values. Write an expression using either a fraction or a percent, then find the result.

i. 90% of 25 miles   *ii.* 8% of $75   *iii.* 25% of 144

8-29. Josea went out to dinner at an Indian restaurant. The total bill was $38. She wanted to leave a 15% tip.

a. If we use the idea of scaling to find the tip amount, what would she need to multiply by? As you talk about this with your team, consider:
- How could you represent this multiplier as a fraction?
- How could you represent it as a decimal?
- Does it make a difference which representation, fraction or decimal, you use to solve this problem?
- Which do you think will be easier?

b. How much should Josea leave for the tip? Show your calculations.

c. If Josea changes her mind and wants to leave a 20% tip instead, how much will this be?

8-30. While shopping for a computer game, Isaiah found one that was on sale for 35% off. He was wondering if he could use $\frac{35}{100}$ as a multiplier to scale down the price to find out how much he would have to pay for the game.

a. If Isaiah uses $\frac{35}{100}$ as a scale factor (multiplier), will he find the price that he will pay for the game? Why or why not?

b. There is scale factor (multiplier) other than 35% that can be used to find the sale price. What is it? Draw a diagram to show how this scale factor is related to 35%. Label the parts of your diagram "discount" and "sale price" along with the relevant percents.

c. How much will Isaiah have to pay for the game if the original price is $40? Show your **strategy**.

MᴇᴛHODS AND Mᴇᴀɴɪɴɢs

Scale Factor

One way to increase or decrease a quantity is to use a **scale factor**, which can also be called a **multiplier**. A scale factor compares the sizes of the part and whole in a proportional relationship. You learned about scale factors when you dilated shapes in Chapter 2 and compared similar shapes in Chapter 4. Scale factors can also be used to increase and decrease quantities that are not side lengths.

For example, if you want to scale down (reduce) a recipe that makes six servings so that it makes only two servings, you would need to multiply the quantity of each ingredient by $\frac{1}{3}$. This could be written:

$$\text{scale factor (multiplier)} = \frac{(2 \text{ servings})}{(6 \text{ servings})} = \frac{1}{3}$$

8-31.   Ameena's boat travels 35 miles per hour. The best fishing spot in the lake is
        27 miles away from her starting point.

   a.   If she drives her boat for $\frac{2}{3}$ of an hour will she make it to the best fishing
        spot on the lake?

   b.   How long will Ameena need to drive to get to the best fishing spot on the
        lake? Express your answer in both a portion of an hour and in minutes.

8-32.   Use the triangles at right to answer the questions
        that follow. You may want to reread the Math
        Notes box for this lesson before you begin.

   a.   What is the scale factor change from A to B?

   b.   What is the scale factor change from B to A?

   c.   What is the relationship of the scale factors?

8-33.   Trina planted 43 plants in her garden last week. She planted twice as many
        cucumbers as zucchini and eight more tomatoes than cucumbers. Write and
        solve an equation to find the number of each kind of plant in her garden. Be
        sure to clearly identify your variable.

8-34.   Andre and Leticia plan to meet at the mall. Use
        the graph at right to answer these questions.

   a.   Who left first to go to the mall?

   b.   Who will arrive at the mall first?
        Explain how you know.

8-35.   Copy the diagram at right on your paper. Then
        use the diagram to answer the questions below.

   a.   Name two pairs of angles that are supplementary.

   b.   Name one pair of complementary angles.

   c.   Name two right angles.

   d.   Name one obtuse angle.

8.2.2 Which multiplier should I use?

Solving Problems Involving Percents

As you have seen many times in this course, there is usually more than one way to solve a problem. When a problem uses portions (fractions, decimals, or percents), there are different ways to write the numbers and different solving **strategies** to choose from. Today, you will look at the different multipliers that can scale a quantity and see what each of them will help you find. As you work with your team today, consider the questions:

What multiplier (scale factor) should I use?

How can I write an equation?

8-36. Hugo and his family were shopping and they purchased a new bed. The bed was a great deal at 60% off of the original cost. The bed originally cost $245.

a. Draw a diagram for this situation.

b. If Hugo scales (multiplies) the original price of the bed by 60%, what will his result represent?

c. What should Hugo scale (multiply) the original price by to find the new price of the bed?

d. Work with your team to find the sale price of the bed in two different ways, that is, using two different multipliers (scale factors). How do your answers from your two methods compare?

Making Connections: Course 2

8-37.   Hugo's older sister, Sandra, had the same summer job for the past two years. Last year she worked the entire summer and was paid a salary of $3,000. This summer she is going to get a 6% raise in pay. In order to figure out how much she will make, Sandra drew the following diagram.

a.   Copy the diagram on your paper and fill in the missing information.

b.   Since Sandra's salary is increasing, does it make sense that her scale factor (multiplier) should be less than 1, equal to 1, or more than 1? Why?

c.   The diagram shows Sandra's original salary and the amount of the increase. What is the scale factor (multiplier) between her original salary and her new salary? That is, what number could Sandra multiply the original salary by to get the new salary?

d.   Show two ways that use different scale factors (multipliers) that Sandra can use to compute her new salary.

8-38.   Miranna teaches gymnastics lessons at summer camp. She is paid $12 per hour.

a.   If Miranna were offered a raise of 100% per hour, what would her new hourly rate be? What percent of her original pay would she be paid?

b.   Miranna is offered a raise of 75% of her hourly rate to teach a private lesson. How much per hour would she be paid for the private lesson? What percent of her original pay would she get?

c.   What is the relationship between the percent raise that Miranna gets and her new pay as a percent of her original pay? How is this related to the scale factor (multiplier) between her original pay and her new pay?

8-39.   Liam was working on a problem and drew a diagram like the one below. He then wrote the equation $(\$72)(0.14) = x$. Does his equation agree with his diagram?

- If you agree, then solve his equation for x.

- If you disagree, write and solve a new equation that will find x in his diagram.

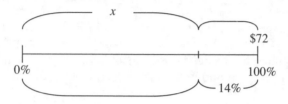

8-40.   **Additional Challenge:** Ramon went to the corner store and bought some more notebook paper to do his homework. The cost for the paper was \$7.50 but he also had to pay the 8.2% sales tax. How much will the notebook paper cost Ramon? If Ramon gives the clerk \$10 how much change should he receive?

8-41.   LEARNING LOG

In your Learning Log, describe how you scale a quantity. For example, how do you know what multiplier (scale factor) to use? How can you tell if your multiplier should be more than one? Title your entry "Scaling Quantities" and include today's date.

8-42.   A homeowner must reduce the use of the home's electricity. The home currently consumes 25 kwh (kilowatt hours) of electricity per day and the homeowner must reduce the use by 20%. Find the amount of electricity that will be used after the reduction in two different ways, using two different scale factors.

Making Connections: Course 2

8-43.   Copy the Diamond Problems below and complete each of them.
         The pattern used in the Diamond Problems is shown at right.

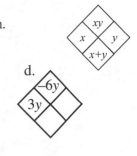

a. $3a$ | 7

b. $12x$ / $3x$

c. $2y$ / $2y-6$

d. $-6y$ / $3y$

8-44.   Study the following division problems and the diagrams that represent them.
         Answer the question below each diagram.

a. $8 \div \frac{1}{3}$ b. $8 \div \frac{1}{4}$

          How many thirds?   How many fourths?

8-45.   The table at right shows speed
         limits in some foreign
         countries in kilometers per
         hour. One kilometer is equal
         to 0.6 miles. What are these
         speed limits in miles per hour?

Speed Limits in km per hour

Country	Country Roads	Motorways
Australia	100	110
South Africa	100	120
Great Britain	96	112
Turkey	90	90

8-46.   Lue is rolling a random number cube. The cube has six sides, and each one is
         labeled with a different number one through six. What is the probability he will
         roll a 5 or a 3 on one roll?

8-47.   Simplify each expression.

a. $(-\frac{3}{4}+\frac{1}{8})^2$ b. $\frac{2}{3}(9-6)+40$ c. $15 \div 5 + \frac{1}{2} \cdot \frac{-4}{7}$

d. $-\frac{7}{10}+(-\frac{5}{12})-(\frac{1}{4})$ e. $\frac{1}{4}(\frac{9}{14}-\frac{1}{7})+\frac{2}{3}\cdot(-\frac{6}{8})$ f. $\frac{7}{8}-(-\frac{1}{10})+(-\frac{3}{5})$

8.2.3 How can I solve it?

Equations with Fraction and Decimal Coefficients

Throughout this course you have worked with quantities represented in multiple ways. You have seen that $\frac{12}{16}$, 0.75, 75%, and $\frac{3}{4}$ each represent the same portion even though they *look* different. In your work with algebra tiles you **visualized** and described perimeters in different ways. For example, the perimeter of the algebra tiles at right can be described by the expressions $3x+2+x$, $x+1+x+1+x+x$, or $4x+2x+2-2x$ units.

In this lesson, you will develop **strategies** to solve a new type of equation: equations with coefficients that are fractions. Recall that coefficients are the numerical part of a term, such as the 5 in $5x$ and the $\frac{2}{3}$ in $\frac{2}{3}x^2$. You will choose between different **strategies** based on how the problem is represented, what diagram you draw or whether you represent the situation with an equation. As you explore solving **strategies** today, keep the following questions in mind:

How can I represent it?

How are the representations related?

What is the best approach for this equation?

8-48. **ARE WE THERE YET?**

The Sutton family took a trip to visit the mountains in Rocky Mountain National Park. Linda and her brother, Lee, kept asking, *"Are we there yet?"* At one point, their mother answered, *"No, but what I can tell you is that we have driven 100 miles and we are about $\frac{2}{5}$ of the way there."*

Linda turned to Lee and asked, *"How long is this trip, anyway?"* They each started thinking about whether they could determine the length of the trip from the information they were given.

Linda's Method

Lee's Method

Problem continues on next page. →

8-48.   *Problem continued from previous page.*

   a.   Explain how both Linda's and Lee's work illustrate the situation described by their mother. What does x represent in each diagram?

   b.   What equation could represent this situation? Use the scale factor (multiplier) to represent this situation in an equation. Let x represent the total distance in miles.

   c.   Is the answer going to be more or less than 100 miles? Explain your thinking.

8-49.   Linda had never seen an equation like this before. She wondered, *"When I look at my diagram I see that the total distance is two and a half times the distance we've driven."*

   a.   Do you agree? How can you add labels to Linda's diagram to show $2\frac{1}{2}$ times the distance?

   b.   How long is the trip? Show how you know.

8-50.   Lee thinks what he knows about similar triangles can help.

   a.   Review problem 8-32, which involved similar triangles. What was the relationship of the two scale factors?

   b.   How can the relationship of the scale factors between similar shapes help Lee? Find the missing scale factor in his diagram at right. That is, what could he multiply 100 by to solve for x?

   c.   Use the new scale factor to find x. Does your answer agree with the one you found in problem 8-49?

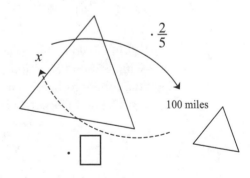

8-51.   As Linda and Lee were talking about the problem (from problem 8-48), their mother overheard and offered them another **strategy**. *"Here is how I would start solving the problem."* She showed them the work at right.

$$\frac{2}{5}x = 100$$

$$\frac{\frac{2}{5}x}{\frac{2}{5}} = \frac{100}{\frac{2}{5}}$$

a.   *"I see a Giant One!"* exclaimed Lee. Where is the Giant One? Help rewrite the left side of the equation.

b.   One way of making sense of $\dfrac{100}{\frac{2}{5}}$ is as $100 \div \frac{2}{5} = ?$. This could be read, *"How many two-fifths are in one-hundred wholes?"* With your team, find one way to explain how you could figure out how many two-fifths are in 100.

8-52.   Lee began to wonder how his diagram could help him solve his mother's equation (from problem 8-51). He showed his work below.

$$\frac{2}{5}x = 100$$

$$\frac{5}{2}\left(\frac{2}{5}x\right) = \left(100\right)\frac{5}{2}$$

a.   How does Lee's work relate to the similar triangles diagram? What is $\frac{5}{2}\left(\frac{2}{5}x\right)$ equal to?

b.   Finish Lee's work to solve for x. Then check your solution.

8-53.   Linda and Lee wondered how these new equation-solving **strategies** would work with different equations. They made up more equations to try to solve. Copy the equations below on your paper and solve each one using either of the **strategies** from this lesson. How did you decide which **strategy** to use?

a. $\frac{9}{2}x = 27$ b. $12 = \frac{2}{7}x$ c. $-\frac{3}{4}x = 21$

476   *Making Connections*: Course 2

ETHODS AND MEANINGS

MATH NOTES

Scaling

When a quantity is increased or decreased by a specific proportion of the original amount, it is changed by a specific scale factor (also called a multiplier). Quantities are **scaled up** when they are increased by multiplying by a number greater than one or **scaled down** when they are decreased by multiplying by a number less than one.

For example, if a music system is on sale for 25% off its original price of $500, the discount can be found by multiplying by 25%:

$$\text{discount} = 0.25(\text{original price}) = 0.25(\$500) = \$125$$

The full price (100%) minus the discount (25%) would result in the sale price, which in this case is 75% of the original. The sale price can also be found by scaling:

$$\text{sale price} = 0.75(\text{original price}) = 0.75(\$500) = \$375$$

Scaling can be used to enlarge and reduce side lengths of similar shapes, or to increase or decrease times, distances, and other related quantities.

Review & Preview

8-54. Mr. Anderson's doctor has advised him to go on a diet. He must reduce his caloric intake by 15%. He currently eats 2800 calories per day. Calculate his new daily caloric intake rate in two different ways, using two different multipliers.

8-55.   Last year a bonsai lemon tree grew half as much as a dwarf lemon tree. A full
         size lemon tree grew three times as much as the dwarf lemon. Together the
         three trees grew 9 inches. Write and solve an equation to determine how much
         each tree grew. Make sure you clearly identify your variable.

8-56.   Would you expect a scatter plot that compares "speed of a car" and "time it
         takes to drive 10 miles" to show a "positive correlation," a "negative
         correlation," or "no correlation?" Explain your thinking.

8-57.   Enrique is saving money to buy a graphing calculator. So far he has saved $30.
         His math teacher told him he has saved 40% of what he will need. How much
         does the calculator cost?

8-58.   Sao can text 1500 words per hour. He needs to text a message with 85 words.
         He only has 5 minutes between classes to complete the text. Can he do it in
         5 minutes?

8-59.   Simplify each expression.

   a. $3\frac{1}{4} + \frac{2}{5}$ b. $2\frac{3}{8} - 1\frac{5}{7}$ c. $4.25 - 7.06$ d. $18 \div \frac{3}{4}$

   e. $-\frac{4}{7} \cdot (-\frac{2}{3})$ f. $10 \div \frac{1}{2}$ g. $-5\frac{1}{8} \cdot 1\frac{2}{3}$ h. $-\frac{3}{11} + \frac{1}{2} - \frac{3}{4}$

8.2.4 How can I eliminate the fractions?

Creating Integer Coefficients

Often, one of the best ways to deal with a challenging task is to find a way to make the task easier. For example, lifting a heavy weight can often be made easier with a lever or pulley. Mathematical problems are very similar; often a challenging problem can be changed to create a new problem that is much easier to solve. In this lesson, you will develop **strategies** to rewrite a complicated equation into an equivalent equation that is more familiar and easier to solve.

8-60.   COMMUNITY SERVICE

The community service club at North Middle School is planning to paint apartments at the local senior citizen center next week. The club needs your help to determine how many apartments they should be able to paint in a day. Earlier in the year, when only $\frac{4}{7}$ of the students worked, they painted 9 apartments in one day. Next week all of the students are available.

a.   Assume that all of the workers contribute equally to the work. If x represents the number of apartments that can be painted by all of the students in the club, use a multiplier and your understanding of scaling to represent this situation as an equation.

b.   **Choose a strategy** to solve your equation in part (a). What does your answer represent? Be ready to share your **strategy**.

8-61.   HOW CAN I MAKE WHOLES?

Janice, the club's president, began to
think about how she could **visualize**
$\frac{4}{7}x$ to help her solve her equation
(from problem 8-60). She recalled
using algebra tiles to represent x.
In her mind, she **visualized** the
diagram at right.

a.   Does this Equation Mat represent your equation from problem 8-60?
     Why or why not?

b.   Janice recognized that these
     numbers were not easy to work
     with, since she did not have whole
     tiles. After working on her paper
     for some time she said, *"Maybe I
     can make whole tiles using more
     than one set of partial tiles."* She
     drew the diagram shown at right.

     What is her new equation as represented in this picture?

c.   With your team or class, discuss Janice's **strategy** for solving this equation.
     During your discussion, answer the following questions (in any order):

     • What made Janice's **strategy** different than what you did in
       Lesson 8.2.3?

     • How many sets of $\frac{4}{7}x$ did Janice use to get a whole number of
       algebra tiles?

     • Why did the right hand side of the equation change?

     • How does the number of sets Janice used relate to the equation you
       wrote in part (a)?

8-62.   Will the **strategy** of turning fractions into integers from problem 8-61 work
         with other equations, such as $\frac{2}{3}x = 8$? Consider this question as you answer
         the questions below.

a.   How many sets of $\frac{2}{3}x$ would make a whole number of x-tiles?

b.   Solve for x using Janice's method from problem 8-61. How could you
     record your work on your paper?

c.   Show how your solution is also the number of two-thirds in 8 wholes
     (written $8 \div \frac{2}{3}$).

Making Connections: Course 2

8-63.　Janice wondered if the method of creating whole number x-terms would work with decimals. Suppose an item was marked 15% off and the sale cost was $36.21. Could this **strategy** help to find the original price? She wrote the equation below:

$$0.85x = 36.21$$

a.　Is there a number she can multiply both sides of the equation by to get an integer coefficient (so there is no decimal)? If so, list at least one. If not, explain why not.

b.　Use Janice's **strategy** to solve the equation. What was the original price of the item?

c.　Does this method work for all equations with decimal coefficients? What if you wanted to solve the equation $1.2x = 14$? What about $0.999x = 71.2$? Discuss these equations with your team and write down your conclusion.

8-64.　Solve each equation below by changing the number that x is being multiplied by (the coefficient of x) to an integer. Check your answer.

a.　$\frac{5}{6}x = 4$　　　　b.　$0.8x = 19$　　　c.　$\frac{5}{3}x = 12$　　　　d.　$0.12x = 1$

8-65.　LEARNING LOG

In your Learning Log, summarize at least two **strategies** to solve an equation with fractional (or decimal) coefficients. Provide an example for each **strategy** and include a diagram. Title this entry, "Solving Equations with Fractional Coefficients" and include today's date.

8-66.　If $\frac{1}{4}$ of x is 16, what is $\frac{3}{4}$ of x? **Justify** your answer in more than one way.

8-67.　LuAnn talked on her cell phone for 180 minutes, using $\frac{3}{7}$ of her total monthly minutes. Find out how many total minutes LuAnn gets to talk in one month using at least two different methods.

8-68.   Jeffrey and Liz are each saving money for college.
         Their savings are shown in the graph at right.

         a.   Based on the graph, who is saving money
               fastest? **Justify** your answer.

         b.   What is the slope of each line? What does
               the slope tell you about this situation?

8-69.   Write the inequality represented by each graph.

         a.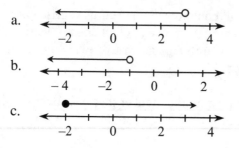

         b.

         c.

8-70.   In the circle at right, the shaded sector is $\frac{1}{8}$ of the circle.

         a.   What is the area of the unshaded region of the
               circle? Write your answer in terms of π and as
               a decimal approximation.

         b.   What is the area of the shaded region? Write your
               answer in terms of π and as a decimal approximation.

         c.   In a few sentences explain each of the steps you
               followed to answer parts (a) and (b).

8-71.   Daniella has $210 in the bank and her balance is growing at a rate of $3 each
         month. Lori has $187 in the bank but her balance is growing at a rate of $4.50
         each month. Choose a graph, a table, or an equation to find when the girls will
         have the same amount of money. Explain your solution choice and show all
         your work.

8.2.5 Percent of what?

Percent Increase and Decrease

Perhaps you have heard an adult say something like, *"When I was growing up, it only cost a dime to go to the movies!"* The rate at which prices increase over a period of time, called **inflation**, is one of the many things that mathematics can help us to understand. In this lesson, you will be using diagrams and computations to calculate the way quantities (like cost or height) change.

As you work today, keep the following questions in mind:

Is it increasing or decreasing?

What is it changing from?

By how much did it change?

8-72.   WHAT IS THE PERCENT INCREASE?

Several years ago Joe started a lawn care business. Due to rising costs, he needs to raise his prices. He is concerned, however, because he has heard that if he raises his rates more than 33%, he might lose business. At right is a letter he sent to his clients.

Joe began to wonder about how the increase in his fees could be expressed in terms of a percent.

> *Dear Valued Customer,*
>
> *After several years of business, Mowcare is increasing its price for lawn service. Since the cost of gas and other supplies has increased, we need to raise our prices. Our prices will increase from $12.50 per hour to $15 per hour. We hope you continue to be happy with the quality of our work.*
>
> *Sincerely,*
> *Joe*

a. Joe wants to determine the scale factor (multiplier) for the price increase and wrote the following equation:

$$12.50x = 15$$

Explain how this expression represents this situation. What does x represent?

b. Solve the equation above to determine the scale factor for his change in fees. Represent this multiplier (scale factor) as a fraction, decimal, and percent.

Problem continues on next page. →

8-72.   *Problem continued from previous page.*

    c.   How could this situation be represented with a line diagram? With your team, copy and complete the diagram below.

        • Which portion of the diagram corresponds to the original price? Circle and label this part "original."

        • Which portion of the diagram corresponds to the change in price? Circle and label this part "change."

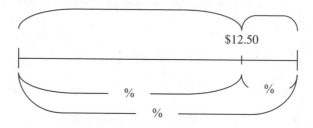

    d.   When Joe raised his rates, what was the **percent increase**? That is, what percent of the original price did the price change? Should Joe expect to lose business?

8-73.   Paige needs your help! She wants to convince her grandmother to let her sign up for a rock climbing class. The class normally costs $50, but the school is offering a special price of $34. Paige's grandmother wants to know what percent of the cost of the class she would save.

    a.   Without calculating, estimate the percent of the discount.

    b.   With your team, determine the percent change in the price of the class. Use the prompts below to help guide your team's discussion.

        • Draw a diagram that represents the situation.

        • What is the original (whole) value? Show this on your diagram.

        • What is the percent of the change? Show this on your diagram.

        • Does this situation represent an increase or decrease?

8-74.   The **percent change** is a comparison of the amount of change to the original amount. If a number increases from the original amount it is called **percent increase**, while if the number decreases from the original it is called a **percent decrease**.

   a.   What is the percent change from $30 to $33? Is this a percent increase or decrease? To answer this question:

   • Draw a diagram to represent the problem.

   • Determine if it is a percent increase or decrease.

   • Calculate the percent change.

   b.   What is the percent change from $33 to $30? Is this a percent increase or decrease? To answer this question:

   • Draw a diagram to represent the problem.

   • Determine if it is a percent increase or decrease.

   • Calculate the percent change.

   c.   If both parts (a) and (b) above have a change of $3, why are the percent changes different? Explain.

8-75.   To attract new customers, a shoe company called Shoe Fits will raise their prices 10% and then offer a 10% off coupon.

   a.   Without doing any calculations, consider the following question: If a coupon is used, do you think the final price will be more than, less than, or the same as the original price? Discuss this with your team and be ready to share your thinking with the class.

   b.   Akari wants to use a coupon to buy a pair of shoes that originally cost $46. What will the increased price be? What will be the price after the 10% coupon is used? Show all calculations. Does this result confirm your answer to part (a)?

   c.   Akari had assumed that after the price increased 10%, and then he received a 10% discount, it would return to the original price. Explain why this did not happen.

MᴇTHODS AND Mᴇᴀɴɪɴɢꜱ

Percent Increase or Decrease

A **percent increase** is the amount that a quantity has increased represented as a percent of the original amount. A **percent decrease** is the amount that a quantity has decreased written as a percent of the original amount. We can write an equation to represent a percent change that is an increase or decrease using a scale factor or multiplier:

amount of increase or decrease = (% change)(original amount)

Example 1: A loaf of bread increased in price from $0.29 to $2.89 in the past 50 years. What was the percent increase?

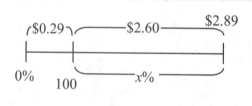

increase = $2.89 − $0.29
= $2.60

$2.60 = (x)($0.29)

$\frac{\$2.60}{\$0.29} = x$

$x \approx 8.97$ or 897%

Example 2: Calculator prices decreased from $59 to $9.95. What was the percent decrease?

decrease = $59 − $9.95
= $49.05

$49.05 = (y)($59)

$\frac{\$49.05}{\$59} = y$

$y \approx 0.83 = 83\%$

8-76.   Joe wanted to know more about how the cost of fertilizer for his lawn care business was changing. The cost of a bag of fertilizer just increased from $8 to $15. What is the percent increase of the price? Represent the change as a fraction, percent, and a decimal.

8-77.   Solve each equation. Show all work.

   a. $0.85x = 200$ b. $\frac{7}{6}x = 140$

8-78.   Ellen is building a scale model of the space shuttle. A space shuttle is approximately 122 feet long and has a wingspan of 78 feet.

   a.   How many inches long is the space shuttle?

   b.   If Ellen builds her model so that 1 cm on the model represents 10 inches on the space shuttle, how many centimeters long will her model be?

   c.   What will her model's wingspan be (in centimeters)?

   d.   Remember that 1 inch is approximately equal to 2.54 cm. How many inches long will her model be?

8-79.   Graph the rule $y = 2x - 6$. Create a table if it will help.

8-80.   Use the drawing at right to answer the questions below. Assume the figure is drawn to scale.

   a.   Identify three types of triangles in the drawing.

   b.   What do you know about the angles labeled x and y?

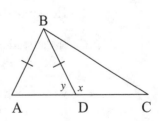

8.2.6   How does it change over time?

Simple Interest

When banks lend money, they charge **interest**, which is a fee for letting the borrower use the money. Interest is usually expressed as a percent of the amount borrowed, and is added to the amount that the borrower owes. For example, a bank might charge someone an 8% annual (yearly) interest rate for borrowing $500. In addition, if you have money in a savings account, banks generally pay interest to you on the money in the account. So by leaving your money in a bank you are earning more money.

There are different ways of calculating interest, and each one creates different patterns of growth. As you work with your team to investigate one kind of interest called **simple interest**, ask these questions to focus your discussion:

> What patterns do you see?

> How can you show the connection?

8-81.   RENTING THE HALL

> The student council is planning a spring celebration. Unfortunately, to rent a hall for the event, they will need to pay a deposit in advance of the event. Since they have not started selling tickets yet, they asked the Parent-Teacher Association for a loan of $825 for the hall rental. The PTA agreed, but said they would charge 2% simple interest each week until the loan is paid back.

> Ms. Becker, the student council advisor, explained to the students that the amount of the loan ($825) is called the **principal** amount. Until the loan is paid back, 2% (called the **weekly interest rate**) of the principal amount will be added to the amount owed each week.

> a.   How much interest will the PTA charge each week?

> b.   If the student council borrows $825, how much will it owe after 1 week? After 3 weeks? Show your calculations.

> c.   How much would the student council owe two months (8 weeks) from now? Be prepared to **justify** your **strategy**.

Making Connections: Course 2

8-82. The Student Council members realized that they would also need funds before the event to pay the DJ and photographer a deposit. They will need a second loan of $1000 to pay for these two expenses.

    a. If the PTA also charges them 2% weekly simple interest for this loan, how much will be added to this loan each week?

    b. The PTA has decided that to cover its costs it only needs to earn $18 interest each week. What percent weekly interest should they charge the Student Council for this loan? Be prepared to share your **strategy**.

8-83. A loan agreement between the Student Council and the PTA has finally been reached, but the PTA will not loan the full $1825 requested. To make sure everyone understands the agreement, the PTA created the table below.

Number of Weeks	Calculations	Total Loan Amount
0	$1250	$1250
1	$1250 + $18.75	$1268.75
2	$1250 + $18.75 + $18.75	$1287.50
3		
4		

    a. Based on this table, how much will the Student Council borrow? What is the percent interest?

    b. How much will the Student Council owe after 3 weeks? After 4 weeks? Show your calculations.

    c. How is the amount of money that the Student Council owes changing each week? Show how this change can be found in your table.

    d. The president wants to be able to quickly know how much the Student Council owes at any point. Use your table to write a variable expression that shows the amount of money the club owes the PTA after any number of weeks. Make sure to define your variable.

    e. The president figured out that if the Student Council does not pay off the loan by the end of the school year, it would owe $1500. How many weeks of school are left? Use your expression from part (d) to write and solve an equation to answer this question.

8-84.   SHOPPING AROUND

The treasurer of the Student Council decided to look into some other funding options for the DJ and the photographer. With your team, examine how each loan would grow and find a way to compare them. (Assume that a month is 4 weeks). Then find answers to the questions below.

| The local bank offered to loan the Student Council $955 for 1% weekly simple interest. | The Math Club offered to loan the Student Council $940 for 4.5% monthly simple interest. | The Booster Club offered to loan the Student Council $960 and would add $36 interest each month. |

a.   Which loan would grow more quickly? That is, which has the most interest added each month?

b.   What is the monthly interest rate the Booster Club is offering? Show how you got your answer.

c.   For which loan would the Student Council owe the most money overall after 3 months? **Justify** your answer.

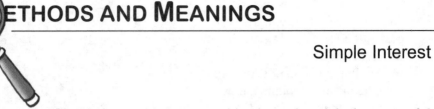

METHODS AND MEANINGS

Simple Interest

MATH NOTES

Simple interest is interest paid only on the original amount of the principal at each specified interval (such as annually, or monthly). The formula to calculate simple interest is:

$$I = Prt \quad \text{where} \quad \begin{aligned} P &= \text{Principal} \\ I &= \text{Interest} \\ r &= \text{Rate} \\ t &= \text{Time} \end{aligned}$$

Example: Theresa invested $1425.00 in a savings account at her local bank. The bank pays a simple interest rate of 3.5% annually. How much money will Theresa have after 4 years?

$$I = Prt \quad \Rightarrow \quad I = 1425(0.035)(4) = \$199.50$$
$$\Rightarrow \quad P + I = \$1425 + \$199.50 = \$1624.50$$

Theresa will have $1624.50 after 4 years.

8-85.   Ida wants to buy a car, but she does not currently have any money. The car she wants costs $2500. Consider her two options and decide which loan she should take.

a.   She could borrow $2500 at a monthly interest rate of 4% simple interest and pay the total after 12 months. Write a simple interest expression and calculate what she would owe at the end of 12 months.

b.   She could borrow $2500 at a weekly interest rate of 1% simple interest and pay the total after 12 months. Show calculations and a written explanation to **justify** your answer.

8-86.   The Jones family wants to remodel
their kitchen. They have saved
$23,000 in the last two years. Their
contractor says the remodel will
cost $40,000. They can borrow the
difference at a monthly interest rate
of 2% simple interest. If they pay
the loan off in six months, how
much will they have paid?

8-87.   Graph the following points on a coordinate grid: $A(-3,-3)$, $B(3,0)$, $C(3,6)$,
$D(-3,6)$. Connect the points as you plot them. Then connect point A to
point D.

   a.   Describe the shape you have created.

   b.   Identify the angles at points C and D.

   c.   Record the coordinates of the new points if you were to translate the
original points three units left and five units up.

8-88.   Martha is saving money to buy a new laptop computer that costs $1800. She
received $200 for her birthday and has a job where she makes $150 each week.

   a.   Make a table and a graph for this situation.

   b.   Explain how you can use the table or graph to predict how many weeks it
will take Martha to earn enough money to pay for the new computer.

8-89.   Simplify each expression.

   a. $\frac{5}{4} \div \frac{7}{16}$ b. $-\frac{10}{13} \cdot \frac{5}{11}$ c. $\frac{9}{11} \div (-\frac{20}{21})$ d. $-\frac{8}{3} \div (-\frac{5}{18})$

Chapter 8 Closure   What have I learned?

Reflection and Synthesis

The activities below offer you a chance to reflect about what
you have learned during this chapter. As you work, look for
concepts that you feel very comfortable with, ideas that you
would like to learn more about, and topics you need more
help with. Look for connections between ideas as well as
connections with material you learned previously.

①   SUMMARIZING MY UNDERSTANDING

This section gives you an opportunity to show what you know about certain
math topics or ideas.

With a partner, obtain an envelope from your teacher. Follow the directions
below to demonstrate your understanding of solving equations with rate,
including those with fractional coefficients.

Part 1:   Decide which one of you is going to work a problem and which one
of you is going to listen. (You will have to do both jobs before you
are through with this lesson!) The partner working the problem
should draw a problem out of the envelope.

Part 2:   **If you are working the problem**, clearly show all of your work on
your paper, draw diagrams, and label them completely. Explain what
you are thinking to your partner as you work.

           If you are the listener, pay attention to what your partner is saying
as he or she solves the problem. When your partner is finished, you
must tell him or her whether or not you agree with the solution and
why or why not.

Part 3:   Trade jobs with your partner. The partner now working the problem
should draw a new problem out of the envelope and explain the
solution to the listener.

Two example problems are shown below. The problems are also available at
www.cpm.org/students.

Problem A	Problem F
Omar has been riding his bicycle at a speed of 15 mph for 48 miles. How long has he been riding?	34% of the students at Maple Middle School are in the seventh grade. If there are 1300 students at the school, how many students are NOT in the seventh grade?

WHAT HAVE I LEARNED?

Working the problems in this section will help you to evaluate which types of problems you feel comfortable with and which ones you need more help with. This section will appear at the end of every chapter to help you check your understanding.

Solve each problem as completely as you can. The table at the end of this closure section has answers to these problems. It also tells you where you can find additional help and practice on problems like them.

CL 8-90. Aja and Emilie were riding their skateboards. They knew that they could ride 3 miles in 20 minutes. Use your problem solving **strategies** to find out how far the girls can ride in 45 minutes.

CL 8-91. Harley was eating pizza and had already eaten six pieces before his sister, Samantha, got home. Samantha was worried that she was not going to get a fair share of the pizza and wanted to know how many pieces were in the pizza originally. Harley told her, *"I have only eaten $\frac{3}{8}$ of the pizza."* Help Samantha figure out how many pieces of pizza there were to start with.

CL 8-92. Marcus has a summer job where he makes $45 a day. Yesterday, his boss told him that he was getting a raise to $63 a day because he was such a hard worker. What is the percent increase in Marcus' salary?

CL 8-93. Find the area and circumference of a circle with a diameter of 15 cm.

CL 8-94. Simplify and solve the following equations.

a. $5x + 2 = -3x - 14$ b. $2x + 3 = 3x - 12$

c. $2x - 2 = 3x + 4 - 4x$ d. $5x + 6 - 2x = 3x - 7$

CL 8-95. Joe is downloading songs from the Internet. He can download them at a rate of eight songs every 10 minutes. Jasmine, who is also downloading songs, can download at a rate of 12 songs every 15 minutes. Who is downloading songs faster?

CL 8-96. Graph a line that goes through the points $(0, 3)$ and $(2, -1)$. What is the slope of the line?

CL 8-97. Solve the inequality $8 + x \leq 3$ and graph the solutions on a number line.

CL 8-98. For each of the problems above, do the following:

- Draw a bar or number line that represents 0 to 10.

- Color or shade in a portion of the bar that represents your level of understanding and comfort with completing that problem on your own.

If any of your bars are less than a 5, choose *one* of those problems and do one of the following tasks:

- Write two questions that you would like to ask about that problem.
- Brainstorm two things that you DO know about that type of problem.

If all of your bars are a 5 or above, choose one of those problems and do one of these tasks:

- Write two questions you might ask or hints you might give to a student who was stuck on the problem.
- Make a new problem that is similar and more challenging than that problem and solve it.

③   WHAT TOOLS CAN I USE?

You have several tools and references available to help support your learning – your teacher, your study team, your math book, and your Toolkit, to name only a few. At the end of each chapter you will have an opportunity to review your Toolkit for completeness as well as to revise or update it to better reflect your current understanding of big ideas.

The main elements of your Toolkit should be your Learning Log, Math Notes, and the vocabulary used in this chapter. Math words that are new to this chapter appear in bold in the text. Refer to the lists provided below and follow your teacher's instructions to revise your Toolkit, which will help make it a useful reference for you as you complete this chapter and as you work in future chapters.

Learning Log Entries

- Lesson 8.2.2 – Scaling Quantities
- Lesson 8.2.4 – Solving Equations with Fractional Coefficients

Math Notes

- Lesson 8.1.1 – Distance, Rate, and Time
- Lesson 8.1.2 – Equivalent Measures
- Lesson 8.2.1 – Scale Factor
- Lesson 8.2.3 – Scaling
- Lesson 8.2.5 – Percent Increase or Decrease
- Lesson 8.2.6 – Simple Interest

Mathematical Vocabulary

The following is a list of vocabulary found in this chapter. Some of the words have been seen in the previous chapter. The words in bold are the words new to this chapter. Make sure that you are familiar with the terms below and know what they mean. For the words you do not know, refer to the glossary or index. You might also want to add these words to your Toolkit for a way to reference them in the future.

distance	equivalent measure	**interest**
multiplier	**percent decrease**	**percent increase**
principal	rate	scale factor
scaling	time	

Process Words

These words describe problem solving strategies and processes that you have been involved in throughout the course of this chapter. Make sure you know what each of these words means. If you are not sure, you can talk with your teacher or other students or look through your book for problems in which you were asked to do these things.

choose a strategy	compare	connect
describe	estimate	explain your reasoning
generalize	justify	predict
reason	represent	reverse your thinking
simplify	visualize	

Answers and Support for Closure Activity #2
What Have I Learned?

Problem	Solution	Need Help?	More Practice
CL 8-90.	The girls can ride $6\frac{3}{4}$ miles in 45 minutes.	Lessons 8.1.1 and 8.1.2 Math Notes box in Lesson 8.1.1	Problems 8-1 through 8-7, 8-19, 8-20, and 8-31
CL 8-91.	There were 16 pieces in the pizza.	Lessons 8.2.3 and 8.2.4 Learning Log (problem 8-65)	Problems 8-48 through 8-53, 8-60, and 8-66
CL 8-92.	Marcus' salary increased by 40%.	Lesson 8.2.5 Math Notes box in Lesson 8.2.5	Problems 8-74 and 8-76
CL 8-93.	Area ≈ 176.7 square cm Circumference ≈ 47.1 cm	Lessons 5.3.3 and 5.3.4 Learning Log (problem 5-124) Math Notes boxes in Lessons 5.3.2 and 5.3.4	Problems 5-125, 5-127, CL 6-140, and 8-10
CL 8-94.	a. $x = -2$ b. $x = 15$ c. $x = 2$ d. no solution	Lessons 6.2.1, 6.2.2, and 6.2.3 Math Notes boxes in Lessons 6.2.1, 6.2.3, and 6.2.6 Learning Log (problem 6-98)	Problems CL 6-141, CL 7-98, and 8-8
CL 8-95.	They are downloading at the same rate.	Lessons 7.1.1, 7.1.2, 7.1.3, and 8.1.2 Math Notes boxes in Lessons 7.1.1 and 7.1.3	Problems CL 7-91 and 8-12

Problem	Solution	Need Help?	More Practice
CL 8-96.	Slope $= -2$	Lessons 7.1.4, 7.1.5, and 7.1.6 Math Notes box in Lesson 7.1.6 Learning Log (problem 7-47)	Problems 7-42, 7-43, and 8-25
CL 8-97.	$x \leq -5$![number line showing x ≤ -5 with closed point at -5 and arrow pointing left, marks at -5, -4, -3, -2, -1, 0]	Lessons 5.2.3 and 5.2.4 Math Notes box in Lesson 5.2.1 Learning Log (problem 5-76)	Problems 5-64, 5-65, 5-66, 5-72, 5-73, 5-74, 5-78, and 8-69

Puzzle Investigator Problems

PI-15. HAPPY NUMBERS

Some numbers have special qualities that earn them a title, such as "square number" or "prime number." This problem will explore another type of number, called "happy numbers."

The number 23 is a happy number. To determine if a number is a happy number, square each of its digits and add.

Repeat this process several times until you get 1, or until you get the same sum twice (see below).

$$2^2 + 3^2 = 13$$

$$1^2 + 3^2 = 10$$

$$1^2 + 0^2 = 1$$

If the final answer is 1, the original number is called a **happy number**.

The number 34 is not happy number, as demonstrated below:

Step #1	$3^2 + 4^2 = 25$
Step #2	$2^2 + 5^2 = 29$
Step #3	$2^2 + 9^2 = 85$
Step #4	$8^2 + 5^2 = \mathbf{89}$
Step #5	$8^2 + 9^2 = 145$
Step #6	$1^2 + 4^2 + 5^2 = 42$
Step #7	$4^2 + 2^2 = 20$
Step #8	$2^2 + 0^2 = 4$
Step #9	$4^2 + 0^2 = 16$
Step #10	$1^2 + 6^2 = 37$
Step #11	$3^2 + 7^2 = 58$
Step #12	$5^2 + 8^2 = \mathbf{89}$

Since 89 is repeated, the final answer will be in a never-ending loop and, therefore, will never equal 1. This means that 34 is *not* a happy number.

a. There are 17 two-digit happy numbers. Find as many as you can. Remember to keep all your work and ideas organized so you can refer back when writing up what you discovered.

b. Find 5 three-digit happy numbers.

c. Eve found out that 478 is a happy number. Based on this, what other numbers must be happy numbers? How do you know? Find at least 10 new happy numbers.

PI-16.   CANDY SALES

For a fundraiser, each math club member must
sell 30 candy bars each day for a week.
Although they all sold the same type of candy,
the members could choose their price to
compete for top sales member.

Alfredo decided to sell three candy bars for $1,
earning $10 per day, while June sold hers at
the rate of two for $1, earning her $15 per day.

One day, both Alfredo and June were on a field trip, so they asked Bomani to
sell their candy bars for them. Bomani agreed and promised he would not
change their prices. Bomani decided that instead of offering three for $1 and
two for $1, he would put them together and sell the 60 candy bars at the rate of
five for $2.

When Alfredo and June returned, Bomani handed them the money he had
earned for the day, $24. Alfredo and June were angry and demanded the dollar
they were sure Bomani stole! Bomani is now confused... what happened?

Your task: Discover what really happened to the extra dollar, and write a letter
to Alfredo and June before this scene turns really ugly.

Making Connections: Course 2

Proportions and Pythagorean Theorem

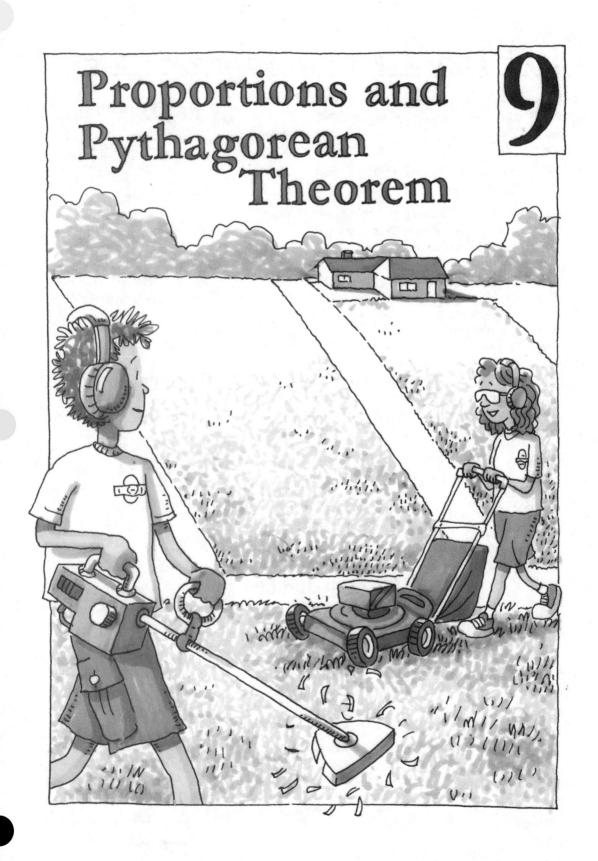

CHAPTER 9   Proportions and Pythagorean Theorem

Maps, blueprints, and scale models all have one thing in common: they are proportional to what they represent. This is a concept that you will explore in Section 9.1 for similar figures, bank accounts, and gas mileage in cars. You will study proportional relationships using tables, graphs, and the Giant One.

In Section 9.2 you will broaden your work with similar shapes to include working with their areas and perimeters. You will solve puzzles by looking at how shapes can be fit together as their area and perimeter grow and shrink and learn short cuts for finding the area and perimeter of larger and smaller similar shapes.

Guiding Questions

Think about these questions throughout this chapter:

What's the relationship?

How else can I solve it?

What is being compared?

Which shapes are similar?

In Section 9.3, you will focus on the relationships between side lengths in individual triangles. You will learn how to decide if three different lengths will be able to form a triangle. You will use the unique relationship between the sides of right triangles to solve problems involving missing side lengths. You will also learn about a new mathematical operation, square root, and how it relates to squaring a number. Finally, you will look at some special numbers called irrationals and how they are different from other numbers you have dealt with.

In this chapter, you will learn how to:

➤ Set up and solve proportional equations.

➤ Identify and use the ratio between the areas of two similar shapes.

➤ Find missing side lengths of right triangles using the Pythagorean Theorem.

➤ Find the square root of a number and identify irrational numbers.

Chapter Outline

Section 9.1   This section introduces the idea of a proportional relationship through tables, graphs and real life situations. You will learn new **strategies** for solving proportional situations.

Section 9.2   You will examine a variety of similar shapes to determine how the areas of those shapes are related.
You will use the patterns that you identify to find missing lengths and areas on shapes.

Section 9.3   You will learn how to determine if any three lengths will form a triangle, and, if they do, whether that triangle will be acute, obtuse, or right. You will find missing sides of right triangles using the Pythagorean Theorem. You will also learn about the operation square root and irrational numbers.

9.1.1 How does it grow?

Recognizing Proportional Relationships

Grocery stores often advertise special prices for fruits and vegetables that are in season. You might see a sign that says, "Special Today! Buy 2 pounds of apples for $1.29!" How would you use that information to predict how much you need to pay if you want to buy six pounds of apples? Or just 1 pound of apples? The way that the cost of apples grows (or shrinks) allows you to use a variety of different **strategies** to predict and estimate prices for different amounts (measured in pounds) of apples. In this section, you will explore different kinds of growth patterns and use those patterns to develop **strategies** for making predictions and deciding if answers are **reasonable**.

As you work in this section, ask yourself these questions to help you identify different patterns:

How are the entries in the table related?

Can I double the values?

What patterns can I see in a graph?

9-1.   COLLEGE FUND

Gustavo's grandmother put money in a college savings account for him on his birthday five years ago. The account pays simple interest, and now after five years the account is worth $500. Gustavo is planning ahead, and he predicts that if he does not deposit or withdraw any money then the account balance will be $1000 five years from now.

a.   How do you think Gustavo made his prediction?

b.   Do you agree with Gustavo's **reasoning**? Explain why or why not.

9-2.   When Gustavo got his bank statement in the mail, he was surprised to see a graph that showed that although his balance was growing at a steady rate, the bank predicted that in five years his account balance would be only $600. *"What is going on?"* he wondered. *"Why isn't my money growing the way I thought it would?"*

With your team, discuss how much Gustavo's account appears to be growing every year. Why might his account be growing in a different way than he expected? Be ready to share your ideas.

9-3. Gustavo decided to look more carefully at his balances for the last few years to see if the bank's prediction might be a mistake. He put together the table below:

Time since Original Deposit (in yrs)	2	3	4	5
Bank Balance (in dollars)	440	460	480	500

a. How has Gustavo's bank balance been growing?

b. Does Gustavo's money seem to doubling as time doubles? Explain your **reasoning**.

9-4. Once he saw the balances written in a table, Gustavo decided to take a closer look at the graph from the bank to see if he could figure out where he made the mistake in his prediction. Find the graph at right on the Lesson 9.1.1 Resource Page.

a. What additional information about Gustavo's account can you tell from the graph? For example, what was his starting balance? How much does it grow in 5 years?

b. Gustavo had assumed his money would double after 10 years. What graph would have resulted if that were true? Using a new color, add a line to the graph that represents what Gustavo was thinking.

c. How is the line for Gustavo's prediction similar to the bank's graph? How is it different?

d. Is it possible that Gustavo's account could have had $0 in it in Year 0? Why or why not?

e. Gustavo's mother looked at the graphs and his bank balance and said, *"Gustavo, you doubled the wrong amount when you made your prediction!"* What do you think his mother meant? What "doubles" in the graph? How else can you see this change?

9-5.   FOR THE BIRDS

When filling her bird feeder, Sonja noticed
that she paid $24 for four pounds of
birdseed. *"Next time, I'm going to buy
8 pounds instead so I can make it through
the spring. That should cost $48."*

a.   Does Sonja's assumption that doubling
     the amount of birdseed would double
     the price make sense? Is it
     reasonable? Why or why not? How
     much would you predict that 2 pounds
     of birdseed would cost?

b.   To check her assumption, she found a receipt for 1 pound of birdseed
     (which cost $6). She decided to make a table, which is started below.
     Copy and complete her table.

Pounds	0	1	2	3	4	5	6	8
Cost		$6			$24			

c.   How do the amounts in the table grow?

d.   Work with your team to describe two different **strategies** for finding the
     cost of 6 pounds of birdseed.

e.   Does the table confirm Sonja's doubling relationship? Give 2 examples
     from the table that show how doubling the pounds will double the cost.

9-6.   What makes the Sonja's birdseed situation different from Gustavo's college fund? Why does doubling work for one situation but not in the other? Consider this as you examine the graphs below.

a. With your team:

 • Describe how each graph is the same.

 • Describe what makes each graph different.

b. How do the differences explain why doubling works in one situation and not the other? **Generalize** why doubling works in one situation and not in another.

c. The pattern of growth in Sonja's example of buying birdseed is an example of a **proportional relationship**. In a proportional relationship, if one quantity is multiplied by a scale factor, the other is scaled by the same amount. Gustavo's bank account is *not* proportional because it grows differently; when the number of years doubled, his balance did not.

   Work with your team to list other characteristics of proportional relationships, based on Sonja's and Gustavo's examples. Be as specific as possible.

9-7.   IS IT PROPORTIONAL?

When making a prediction, it is important to be able to recognize whether a relationship is proportional or not.

Your task: Work with your team to read each new situation below. Decide whether you think the relationship described is **proportional** or **non-proportional** and **justify** your **reasoning**. Be prepared to share your decisions and **justifications** with the class.

a. Carlos wants to buy some new video games. Each game he buys costs him $36. Is the relationship between the number of games Carlos buys and the total price proportional?

b. Single tickets cost $56 while five tickets cost $250. Is the relationship between the number of tickets bought and the total price proportional?

c. Vu is four years older than his sister. Is the relationship between Vu and his sister's age proportional?

d. The triangles at right are similar. Is the relationship between the sides of one triangle and the corresponding sides of the other proportional?

e. Carl just bought a music player and plans to load 50 songs each week. Is the relationship between the number of weeks after Carl bought the music player and the number of songs on his player proportional?

f. Anna has a new video game. It takes her five hours of playing the game to master level one. After so much time, Anna better understands the game and it only takes her three hours of playing the game to master level two. Is the number of hours played and the game level proportional?

9-8.   LEARNING LOG

In your Learning Log, explain how you can tell if a relationship is proportional or not. Give several examples of a proportional relationship and at least one that is not proportional. Label this entry "Proportional Relationships" and include today's date.

9-9.   The lemonade stand at the county fair sells the lemonade at a price of two cups for $3.00. Complete the table below to find what Paula's family will pay to buy lemonade for all 8 members of the family.

# of Lemonades	Price (in dollars)
1	
2	3.00
3	
4	
5	
6	
7	
8	

9-10.   Carmen is downloading music for her piPod. It costs $1.75 for each song. Is this relationship proportional? Explain your **reasoning**.

9-11.   Graph the rule $y = \frac{3}{2}x + 2$. What is the slope? Explain what **strategies** you used to graph this rule.

9-12.   Samantha's parents are going to paint her room. Her color choices for the walls include three different shades of white, four shades of tan, two shades of blue, three shades of green, and four shades of pink. What is the probability that she will select any shade of blue or pink?

9-13.   The local sports shop has backpacks on sale for $28. The original price was $40. What is the percent of decrease for the backpack price?

9-14.   Simplify the expressions below.

a. $\frac{3}{4} - \frac{1}{3} + (-\frac{5}{24})$ b. $\frac{10}{12} \div \frac{1}{4}$ c. $3\frac{1}{2} \cdot 1\frac{3}{8}$ d. $-\frac{20}{7} \div \frac{1}{3}$

e. $-\frac{8}{25} \cdot (-\frac{15}{32})$ f. $\frac{9}{4} \div (-\frac{2}{3})$ g. $\frac{8}{21} + (-\frac{3}{7})$ h. $\frac{7}{4} \cdot (-\frac{2}{5}) \cdot \frac{3}{5}$

9.1.2 How can a graph help?

Proportional Equations

Proportional relationships can be identified in both tables and graphs. Today you will have an opportunity to take a closer look at how graphs and slope triangles for proportional relationships can help you organize your work to quickly find any missing value.

9-15.   Robert's new hybrid car has a gas tank that holds 12 gallons of gas. When the tank is full, he can drive 420 miles. Assume that his car uses gas at a steady rate.

a. Is the relationship between the number of gallons of gas used and the number of miles that can be driven proportional? For example, does it change like Sonja's birdseed prediction, or is it like Gustavo's college savings? Explain how you know.

b. Show how much gas Robert's car will use at various distances by copying and completing the table below.

Distance driven (in miles)				420
Gas used (in gallons)	0	3	6	12

c. Robert decided to graph the situation, as shown at right. Use Robert's graph to predict how far he can drive using eight gallons of gas.

d. While a graph is a useful tool for estimating, it is often difficult to find an exact answer on a graph. Ian was looking at Robert's graph and noticed two slope triangles. Both triangles have a vertex at $(0,0)$. What does x represent?

Problem continues on next page. →

9-15.   *Problem continued from previous page.*

   e.   Using the triangles, he wrote the equation $\frac{420 \text{ miles}}{12 \text{ gallons}} = \frac{x \text{ miles}}{8 \text{ gallons}}$.

        How do the ratios he wrote relate to the triangles on the graph? Why are the ratios equal?

   f.   Work with your team to use the equation to find the exact number of miles Robert can drive with eight gallons of gas. Be prepared to share your **strategy**.

   g.   Use your graph and Ian's **strategy** to find out how far Robert can go on five gallons of gas.

9-16.   Lexie claims she can send 14 text messages in 22 minutes. Her teammates Kenny and Esther are trying to predict how many text messages Lexie can send in a 55 minute lunch period if she keeps going at the same rate.

   a.   Is the relationship between the number of text messages and time in minutes proportional? Why or why not?

   b.   Kenny represented the situation using similar triangles, while Esther wrote an equation. Their work is shown below.

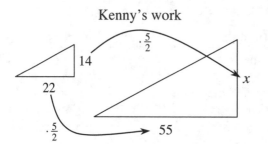

Kenny's work

Esther's work

$$\frac{14 \text{ messages}}{22 \text{ minutes}} = \frac{x \text{ messages}}{55 \text{ minutes}}$$

        Why do you think Kenny organized his information on triangles?

   c.   Why did Esther set up this equation? Does it make sense to compare these quantities?

Problem continues on next page. →

Making Connections: Course 2

9-16.   *Problem continued from previous page.*

d.   Kenny said, *"The scale factor I found can be written like a Giant One in your equation."* He wrote,

$$\frac{14 \text{ messages}}{22 \text{ minutes}} \cdot \frac{\frac{5}{2}}{\frac{5}{2}} = \frac{x \text{ messages}}{55 \text{ minutes}}$$

Does Kenny's work make sense? Simplify the expression. Is the answer the same as what you found in part (b)?

e.   Use what you know about proportional relationships to determine how many text messages Lexie could send in a different number of minutes. Show your work and your **reasoning**.

9-17.   THE YOGURT SHOP

Jell E. Bean owns the local frozen yogurt shop. At her store customers serve themselves a bowl of frozen yogurt and top it with chocolate chips, frozen raspberries, or any of the different treats available. Customers must then weigh their creation and are charged by the weight.

Jell E. Bean charges $32 for five pounds of dessert, but not many people buy that much frozen yogurt. She needs you to help her figure out how much to charge her customers. She has customers that are young children who buy only a small amount of yogurt as well as large groups that come in and pay for everyone's yogurt together.

a.   Is it **reasonable** to assume that the weight of the yogurt is proportional to its cost? How can you tell?

b.   Assuming it is proportional, make a table that lists the price for at least 10 different weights of yogurt that Jell E. Bean can enlarge to hang in her store. Be sure to include at least three weights that are not whole numbers.

c.   If Jell E. Bean decided to start charging $0.50 for each cup before her customers started filling it with yogurt and toppings, could you use the same **strategies** to find the new prices? If five pounds of yogurt still costs $32 (plus $0.50 for the cup), how much would half as much cost? How much would $\frac{1}{5}$ of a pound cost?

METHODS AND MEANINGS

Directly Proportional Relationships

A relationship is **directly proportional** if one quantity is a multiple of the other. Often in this course we will compare two quantities at the same time written as ratios and use a Giant One as the multiplier, as long as the ratio is always the same. For example, if 3 pounds of chicken costs $7, then 6 pounds of chicken costs $14. All other equivalent ratios can be found by multiplying by a Giant One.

Example: Three pounds of chicken costs $7.00. What is the cost for 12 pounds?

$$\frac{3 \text{ pounds}}{\$7} \cdot \frac{4}{4} = \frac{12 \text{ pounds}}{\$28}$$

Twelve pounds of chicken will cost $28.00. Other table values are shown and the values are plotted on the graph below.

Pounds (x)	0	3	6	9	12
Cost (y)	0	7	14	21	28

The relationship between pounds and cost is directly proportional.

Example: The county fair costs $5.00 to enter and $1.00 per ride.

Rides (x)	0	1	2	3	4
Cost (y)	5	6	7	8	9

The relationship between rides and cost is not proportional because, for example, someone who goes on four rides ($9) does not pay twice as much as someone who went on two rides ($7). There is no multiplier for the relationship.

The general form of a **direct proportion**, also called **direct variation**, is $y = kx$, where k is the constant multiplier.

9-18. Complete this proportion table and graph the results.

Pounds of Nails	2	3		6			10		x
Cost ($)			1.25	1.50	2.00			5.00	

a. What is the slope of the graph?

b. What does the slope tell you about the cost of nails?

9-19. The choir is planning a trip to the water park. The cost to use a school bus is $350. Complete the table at right, graph your result, then answer parts (a) and (b).

a. Is this a proportional relationship?

b. Is there a correlation? How do you know? If so, what is it?

Number of students on the trip	Bus cost per student ($)
10	
15	
20	
35	

9-20. Simplify and solve each equation below for x. Show your work and check your answer.

a. $24 = 3x + 3$

b. $2(x - 6) = x - 14$

c. $3(2x - 3) = 4x - 5$

d. $\frac{3}{4}x = 2x - 5$

9-21. Joaquin has agreed to lend his younger brother $45 so that he can buy a new tank for his pet lizard. Joaquin is charging his brother 2% simple interest per month. If his brother pays him back in 6 months, how much will Joaquin get back?

9-22. Tina's rectangular living room floor measures 15 feet by 18 feet.

a. How many square feet of carpet will Tina need to cover the entire floor?

b. The carpet Tina likes is sold by the square yard. How many square yards will she need?

9.1.3   How can I find the missing value?

Solving Proportions

You have examined several proportional contexts (such as the price of yogurt versus the number of pounds of yogurt) and non-proportional contexts (such as the value of a college fund over time). Today you will continue to develop **strategies** for solving proportional equations.

9-23.   J.R. reduced figure A at right so that it became the similar figure B.

a.   Write all the ratios that compare the corresponding sides of figure B to figure A. What is the relationship between these ratios? How do you know?

b.   One of the relationships between the sides can be written as $\frac{3}{4} = \frac{x}{6}$. Find two different ways to find the value of x in this equation. Is your answer **reasonable**? Be ready to share your **strategies** with the class.

9-24.   MULTIPLE STRATEGIES

J.R.'s team is trying to find multiple ways to solve $\frac{3}{4} = \frac{x}{6}$ from problem 9-23. With your team, analyze each of the **strategies** below. Some of these **strategies** might be the same as what you came up with in problem 9-23. However, others may be new. Work to understand each **strategy** so that you can use it to solve a new problem.

a.   J.R. wants to use a **Giant One** to help find the value of x. Explain how he can find a value to use as a numerator and denominator in a Giant One, then find the value of x.

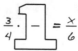

Problem continues on next page. →

Making Connections: Course 2

9-24.   *Problem continued from previous page.*

b.   Looking at J.R.'s work, Leticia said, *"I see it differently. We just need to find some number that when divided by 6 you get* $\frac{3}{4}$. *We can* **undo the division** *by multiplying each side of the proportion by 6 like this."*

$$\left(\frac{6}{1}\right)\frac{3}{4} = \frac{x}{6}\left(\frac{6}{1}\right)$$

Work with your team to explain how Leticia's idea works. Are the two ratios still equal? Why did she choose to multiply by 6? Simplify each side of the equation.

c.   Avner asked, *"But if multiplying both sides by 6 gets rid of the denominator of the x, then can we use the same* **strategy** *to get rid of the 4 in the other denominator?"* Discuss Avner's question and decide if **undoing both denominators** is a **reasonable strategy**. Does this help solve the equation?

$$\frac{3}{4} = \frac{x}{6}$$

$$\frac{4\cdot 6}{1}\left(\frac{3}{4}\right) = \left(\frac{x}{6}\right)\frac{4\cdot 6}{1}$$

$$(6)(3) = (x)(4)$$

Avner's work

9-25.   Use the **strategies** from problem 9-24 to solve the problems below.

a.   Use Leticia's method of **undoing** division to solve this proportion: $\frac{p}{22.5} = \frac{7}{5}$. When you find p, replace the value in the original proportion to confirm that the two ratios are equal.

b.   Write and solve a proportional equation for x for the similar triangles at right. Then use Avner's method of **undoing** both denominators to solve for x.

30 / 15 x / 12

c.   An apple juice container has a tiny hole in it so it is slowly leaking. If the container leaks three ounces every 19 minutes, how long will it take for the 16 ounces of juice in the container to leak out? Write a proportional equation and solve with J.R.'s **strategy** of using a Giant One.

9-26.   For each problem below, decide if the situation is proportional. If the problem is proportional, solve the problem using any **strategy you choose**. If the problem is not proportional explain why it is not proportional and then solve the problem.

a.   Steve drove 130 miles from Portland to Tacoma in 2 hours. If he continues to drive at the same speed, how long will it take him to drive 390 miles?

b.   At an amusement park you pay a $15 entrance fee and then $4 for each ride you go on. How much will it cost you to go on seven rides?

c.   Armando has collected 39 bottle caps in the past three months. At this rate, how many bottle caps will he have in five months?

d.   The grocery store sells 3 limes for 99 cents. At this rate, how much will a dozen limes cost?

e.   Margarit drove her friends to a movie. She drove for 30 minutes at 10 miles per hour in heavy traffic, then drove for 15 minutes at 40 miles per hour. How far did she travel in those 45 minutes?

9-27.   After Ramona had solved several proportional equations, she noticed a pattern. *"It looks like we just multiplied diagonally."*

$$\frac{10}{4} = \frac{x}{7}$$
$$(7)(10) = (x)(4)$$

a.   What does she mean? For each of the proportions below, apply Ramona's diagonal multiplying pattern and determine whether the result is a true mathematical equation. Will her pattern always work?

$$\frac{8}{10} = \frac{12}{15}, \quad \frac{6}{4} = \frac{9}{6}, \text{ and } \frac{15}{3} = \frac{20}{4}$$

b.   Then use her pattern to solve the equation $\frac{2}{5} = \frac{11}{x}$ for x.

M ETHODS AND MEANINGS

Solving Proportions

An equation stating that two ratios are equal is called a **proportion**. Some examples of proportions are shown at right:

$$\frac{6 \text{ mi}}{2 \text{ hr}} = \frac{9 \text{ mi}}{3 \text{ hr}} \qquad \frac{5}{7} = \frac{50}{70}$$

When two ratios are known to be equal, setting up a proportion is one strategy for solving for an unknown part of one ratio. For example, if the ratios $\frac{9}{2}$ and $\frac{x}{16}$ are equal, setting up the proportion $\frac{x}{16} = \frac{9}{2}$ allows you to solve for x.

Strategy 1: One way to solve this proportion is by using a **Giant One** to find the equivalent ratio. In this case, since the scale factor between 2 and 16 is 8, we create the Giant One below,

$$\frac{x}{16} = \frac{9}{2} \cdot \boxed{\frac{8}{8}} = \frac{9 \cdot 8}{2 \cdot 8} = \frac{72}{16} \quad \text{which shows that} \quad \frac{x}{16} = \frac{72}{16} \quad \text{so} \quad x = 72$$

Strategy 2: Use the inverse to undo. Another way to solve the proportion is to think of the ratio $\frac{x}{16}$ as, " x divided by 16." To solve for x, use the inverse operation of division, which is multiplication. Multiplying both sides of the proportional equation by 16 "undoes" the division.

$$\frac{x}{16} = \frac{9}{2}$$
$$\left(\frac{16}{1}\right)\frac{x}{16} = \frac{9}{2}\left(\frac{16}{1}\right)$$
$$x = \frac{144}{2} = 72$$

Strategy 3: Use Cross Multiplication. This is a solving strategy for proportions that is based on the process of multiplying each side of the equation by the denominators of each ratio and setting the two sides equal.

Complete Algebraic Solution	Cross Multiplication
$\frac{x}{16} = \frac{9}{2}$	$\frac{x}{16} = \frac{9}{2}$
$2 \cdot 16 \cdot \frac{x}{16} = \frac{9}{2} \cdot 2 \cdot 16$	$\frac{x}{16} \bowtie \frac{9}{2}$
$2 \cdot x = 9 \cdot 16$	$2 \cdot x = 9 \cdot 16$
$2x = 144$	$2x = 144$
$x = 72$	$x = 72$

9-28. Solve the proportions using any **strategy you choose** and show all of your steps.

a. $\frac{35}{70} = \frac{x}{100}$ b. $\frac{12}{33} = \frac{m}{11}$ c. $\frac{x}{15} = \frac{12}{75}$ d. $\frac{4}{32} = \frac{10.5}{x}$

9-29. Triangle *ABC* is similar to triangle *DEF*.

a. Find the scale factor from triangle *ABC* to triangle *DEF*.

b. Find *x*.

c. Find *y*.

9-30. Complete the table.

x	-6	3	6	0		1
y		4		2	-4	

a. Find the rule. b. What is the slope?

9-31. Find the area and circumference of a circle that has a diameter of 17 mm. Write your answers in terms of π and as a decimal approximation.

9-32. A ten-speed bicycle was originally priced at $1100. It is on sale for $500. What is the percent of decrease?

9-33. Louis recorded how many times he could jump rope without stopping. Here is his data:

50 15 102 64 29 55 100 97 48 81 61

Find the median, upper quartile, and lower quartile of his data.

9.2.1 How are the areas and perimeters related?

Area and Perimeter of Similar Shapes

As you have discovered in recent lessons, the sides of similar shapes can be compared in several different ways. In Chapter 4, you used scale factors to enlarge and reduce the size of similar figures and examined the side lengths of those figures as they changed. You also looked at perimeter and area using toothpicks and tiles. In this lesson, you will investigate whether there is a pattern to how the perimeters and areas of similar shapes grow.

9-34.   Jenna and Greg own a lawn care service. Jenna mows the lawns and charges $25 an hour. She has one customer (Mr. Dunlap) whose rectangular lawn is 18 yards by 30 yards (which takes one hour to mow). Mr. Dunlap mentions that his neighbor, Mrs. Toliver, wants to hire Jenna and that her rectangular lawn is "3 times as big" as Mr. Dunlap's. Jenna expects this job to take 3 hours.

    a.   Draw a sketch of Mr. Dunlap's lawn. What is the area of Mr. Dunlap's lawn?

    b.   According to Jenna's estimate, what is she assuming the area of Mrs. Toliver's lawn to be?

9-35.   Jenna gets the job at Mrs. Toliver's (see problem 9-34). On her first day, she is worried because after 3 hours, she has not completed even half of the job! She measures the rectangular lawn and finds out it has side lengths that are three times the length of Mr. Dunlap's.

   a.   What are the lengths of the sides of Mrs. Toliver's lawn? What is the area of her lawn?

   b.   Mr. Dunlap was describing the scale factor of the side lengths, not the area. What is the scale factor of the areas? That is, what would you multiply the area of Mr. Dunlap's lawn by to get the area of Mrs. Toliver's lawn?

   c.   Greg trims around the outside of each lawn while Jenna mows. If it usually takes him an hour to trim Mr. Dunlap's lawn, how long will it take him to trim Mrs. Toliver's lawn? Discuss the questions below with your team, and then explain your conclusion.

   •   What is the perimeter of each lawn?

   •   What is the scale factor of the two perimeters?

   •   Is the new perimeter longer than Greg expected from Mr. Dunlap's description?

9-36.   Jenna now realizes that her similarity diagram, which shows only the scale factor of the side lengths, is as unclear as Mr. Dunlap's description. She decided she should add more information, as shown in the diagram at right.

Side Length · 3 ⟶
Perimeter · ? ⟶
Area · ? ⟶

   Use your results from the previous problem to copy the figures and complete the scale factors for the perimeter and area of the larger lawn.

9-37.   Although the lawns that Jenna and Greg mowed were similar shapes, their areas and perimeters did not have the same scale factor. What exactly is the relationship of the scale factor between the sides of similar shapes and the area of those shapes? To investigate this question with your study team, get a set of pattern blocks and a copy of the Lesson 9.2.1A Resource Page from your teacher.

a.   Take out a green triangle like the one at right. Using only other green triangles, build a similar shape with new side lengths that have a scale factor of two. Record the scale factors for the side lengths, perimeter, and area of the enlargement on the diagram provided on the resource page.

b.   What if the shape is not doubled? Now use triangles to build a shape with a scale factor of 3 (so that its side lengths are three times as long as the small green triangle). Record the scale factors for the side length, perimeter, and area of the enlargement on your resource page. Repeat the process for a scale factor of 4.

c.   What if the shape is not a triangle? Take out an orange square and follow the same process by building similar figures with scale factors of 2, 3, and 4 and finding the scale factors for the side length, perimeter, and area of the enlargements. Record your work on the resource page.

d.   Do the patterns continue for other shapes? Take out a blue rhombus and follow the same process by building similar figures and finding the missing scale factors on the resource page. Record your work on the resource page.

e.   **Additional Challenge:** Does this pattern of growth work for an isosceles trapezoid when the longer base of the trapezoid pattern block is twice the length of the shorter base? Repeat the process that you have done with other shapes for a scale factor of 2 and 3. Record your work on your resource page. If you can complete the resource page for a scale factor of 4, do so. If not, build the trapezoid shape with a scale factor of 4 and record your work.

9-38.   Look carefully at the data on your scale factor resource page. How is the scale factor for side length related to the scale factor for perimeter of each enlarged shape? How is the scale factor for side length related to the scale factor for area? Be prepared to share your team's ideas with the class.

9-39.   A parallelogram with an area of 60 square units is enlarged to make a similar parallelogram with sides that are 10 times the length of the original. What is the area of the enlarged parallelogram?

9-40.   LEARNING LOG

What patterns do you see between the area of a shape and the scale factor of its side? If you know how a side of a shape is enlarged or reduced, can you use that information to make a prediction about the area? Write a Learning Log entry summarizing what you understand so far about the connection between scale factor and area in similar shapes. Title this entry, "Area Relationships in Similar Shapes," and label it with today's date.

9-41.   The two triangles at right are similar.

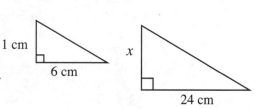

a. Find x.

b. Find the area of the smaller triangle.

c. Based on ratios of similarity, find the area of the large triangle.

d. Find the area of the larger triangle by using the formula for the area of a triangle.

e. Verify that your answers to (c) and (d) are the same.

9-42.   In the polygons at right, all corresponding angles are the same and the side lengths are as shown.

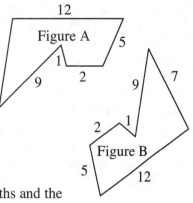

a.   Find the ratios of the corresponding sides.

b.   Are the two figures similar?

c.   What is the special name for similar figures with a scale factor of $\frac{1}{1}$?

d.   What does this tell you about the side lengths and the angles of the two shapes?

9-43.   Find the numbers that belong in the Giant One in each problem to create an equivalent fraction. Copy each problem, and show the values you used within the Giant One.

a. $\frac{7}{12} \cdot \boxed{} = \frac{56}{m}$

b. $\frac{8}{3} \cdot \boxed{} = \frac{n}{48}$

c. $\frac{20}{26} \cdot \boxed{} = \frac{k}{39}$

d. $\frac{20}{42} \cdot \boxed{} = \frac{50}{h}$

9-44.   Roger has a bag of marbles. There are 6 red, 4 blue, 3 white, and 7 green marbles in the bag. If he draws one marble and replaces it, find the following probabilities:

a.   P(red)   b.   P(not white or green)   c.   P(blue or white)

9-45.   Michaela is swimming at a rate of 25 feet in 4 minutes. At this rate, how far will she swim in 15 minutes?

9.2.2 Is the area relationship proportional?

Growth Patterns in Area

You have seen that when two figures are similar, their areas do not grow at the same rate as their sides. Is the area relationship still a proportion? Can proportions be set up to solve problems involving area of similar shapes? In today's lesson, you will investigate how to extend what you know about proportional relationships to work with the areas of similar figures.

9-46.   Ryan and Julia are working to find the area of a shape that is similar to the 2 cm by 3 cm rectangle at right. All they are told about the new shape is that it is similar and has a shorter side that is 80 cm long.

3 cm

2 cm

Julia made a sketch of the new shape, and wants to find the length of the longer side so that she can find its area. But Ryan is impatient, and he thinks he has a shortcut. *"The shapes are similar, so I think that there is a constant ratio. I am going to set up a proportion."* Here is Ryan's equation:

$$\frac{\text{side length}}{\text{area}} = \frac{2 \text{ cm}}{6 \text{ cm}^2} = \frac{80 \text{ cm}}{x \text{ cm}^2}$$

When Julia finished her calculations, she looked at Ryan's work and his answer. *"That's really different from what I found, Ryan,"* she said. *"I'm not sure that we can use a proportion here."* What is Julia talking about?

a. Solve Ryan's equation to find his answer for area. Follow Julia's process to find the missing side, then calculate the area she found for the enlarged shape.

b. Which answer is more **reasonable**? Why? Work with your team to **justify** your conclusion.

9-47. In Lesson 9.2.1, you noticed that the area and perimeter of shapes did not grow at the same rate. Which relationships between similar shapes are proportional, and which are not? Work with your team to investigate.

a. On graph paper, draw rectangles similar to the 2 cm by 3 cm rectangle in problem 9-46. Use scale factors of 2, 3, 4, 5, and 6. Record your data in a table like the one below.

scale factor (side)	Original (1)	2	3	4	5	6
Length (cm)	3	6				
Width (cm)	2	4				
Perimeter (cm)	10					
Area (cm²)	6					

b. Is the ratio between the length and width of similar rectangles proportional? How can you tell?

c. Is the relationship between a rectangle's area and length proportional? **Justify** your conclusion.

d. If a new similar shape has a scale factor of 10 for its length and width, how could you predict its area *without* calculating the new shape's length and width? Work with your study team to describe a **general** process.

9-48. Jenna thinks she understands how scale factor relates to perimeter and area, but she has now been asked to mow lawns that are smaller than Mr. Dunlap's 18 yard by 30 yard lawn. She is trying to give a price quote for the smaller lawns and wonders if she can use the same patterns she found for scale factor when the similar lawns were bigger.

a. Work with your team to draw diagrams for lawns so that the scale factors for the side lengths are $\frac{1}{2}$, $\frac{1}{3}$, and $\frac{1}{6}$. Use graph paper so you can accurately find the perimeter and area of the new lawns. Then complete similarity diagrams for each scale factor.

b. Explain to Jenna how she can use the patterns she has found for scale factors to figure out how much to charge for mowing any size lawn.

9-49.   Use the patterns you identified between the scale factor for sides of similar shapes and their areas to find the missing scale factors and areas below.

a.   If the area of rectangle A is 14 cm^2, what is the area of rectangle B?

b.   If the area of triangle C is 125 in^2, what is the area of triangle D?

9-50.   **Additional Challenge:** Use what you know about ratios between similar figures to draw similarity diagrams and answer the following questions:

a.   If you start with a 4 by 4 square and enlarge each side by a factor of $\frac{5}{4}$, calculate the perimeter and area using the scale factors.

b.   Sketch the 4 by 4 square and its $\frac{5}{4}$ enlargement on graph paper. Was your answer from part (a) correct? Explain in complete sentences.

c.   Begin with a 6 by 9 rectangle and create a new smaller rectangle using a scale factor of $\frac{1}{3}$. Calculate perimeter and area of the new rectangle.

d.   A 3 by 5 rectangle is enlarged by a scale factor of $\frac{3}{1}$. Calculate the perimeter and area of the enlargement.

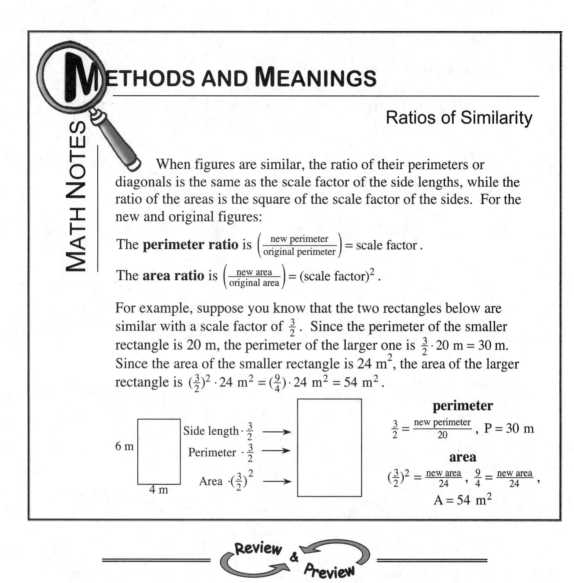

METHODS AND MEANINGS

Ratios of Similarity

When figures are similar, the ratio of their perimeters or diagonals is the same as the scale factor of the side lengths, while the ratio of the areas is the square of the scale factor of the sides. For the new and original figures:

The **perimeter ratio** is $\left(\frac{\text{new perimeter}}{\text{original perimeter}}\right) = $ scale factor.

The **area ratio** is $\left(\frac{\text{new area}}{\text{original area}}\right) = (\text{scale factor})^2$.

For example, suppose you know that the two rectangles below are similar with a scale factor of $\frac{3}{2}$. Since the perimeter of the smaller rectangle is 20 m, the perimeter of the larger one is $\frac{3}{2} \cdot 20$ m $= 30$ m. Since the area of the smaller rectangle is 24 m^2, the area of the larger rectangle is $(\frac{3}{2})^2 \cdot 24$ m$^2 = (\frac{9}{4}) \cdot 24$ m$^2 = 54$ m^2.

6 m

4 m

Side length $\cdot \frac{3}{2}$ ⟶

Perimeter $\cdot \frac{3}{2}$ ⟶

Area $\cdot (\frac{3}{2})^2$ ⟶

perimeter

$\frac{3}{2} = \frac{\text{new perimeter}}{20}$, $P = 30$ m

area

$(\frac{3}{2})^2 = \frac{\text{new area}}{24}$, $\frac{9}{4} = \frac{\text{new area}}{24}$,

$A = 54$ m^2

Review & Preview

9-51. The area of a rectangle is 42 cm^2. If the length and width each grow four times longer, what will the new area be?

9-52. $\triangle ABC$ and $\triangle DEF$ are similar.

a. Find x.

b. Find y.

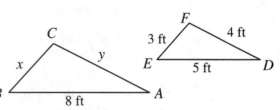

c. Find the ratio of the perimeters of the two triangles.

d. Can you predict the ratio of the areas of the two triangles? If so, state it. If not, write the information you would need or the question you would need to answer first.

Problem continues on next page. →

9-52.   *Problem continued from previous page.*

e.   Triangle *RST* is congruent to triangle *DEF*.
Based on this, what are the side lengths of
triangle *RST*? What is the measure of angle *E*?

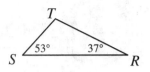

9-53.   Find the perimeter and area of each figure.

a.

b.
$\frac{3}{8}$ inch

$\frac{7}{8}$ inch

9-54.   If each triangle below is drawn accurately, identify whether it is an obtuse,
acute, or right triangle. Name the angle or angles that helped you to decide.

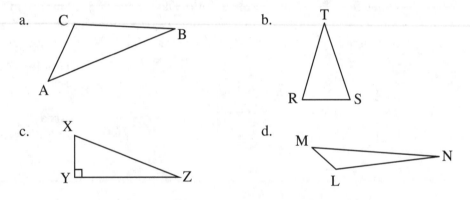

a.

b.

c.

d.

9-55.   A candy store's specialty is taffy. Customers can fill a bag with taffy and the
price is based on how much the candy weighs. The store charges $2 for 10
ounces of taffy.

a.   Copy the table below and fill in the missing values. Add three more entries.

Amount of taffy (ounces)	2	5	10	12	15	20
Price ($)			$2			$4

b.   Graph the values in the table. Let *x* represent the number of ounces and
y represent the price in dollars.

c.   Is this situation proportional? Explain your **reasoning**.

d.   What is the slope of the line you graphed? What information does the slope
tell you?

9.2.3 How can I use the area ratio?

Applying the Ratio of Areas

The ratios between similar shapes allow you to solve a variety of problems. Identifying the ratios that are equivalent can be challenging. It is often helpful to be able to **visualize** shapes in different ways and to develop multiple ways of seeing and representing relationships. As you work today, ask these questions in your team to focus discussion:

What is the relationship?

How can we solve the problem?

Is the answer **reasonable**?

9-56. The scale factor of two similar figures is $\frac{5}{3}$. Based on this information, answer each of the following questions.

a. If the perimeter of the smaller figure is 15 cm, what is the perimeter of the larger figure?

b. If the area of the larger figure is 50 cm², what is the area of the smaller figure?

9-57. The two parallelograms at right are similar.

a. Find the missing length x.

b. What is the ratio of the areas of these shapes?

c. Find the area of each shape to check your ratio, or explain why you cannot.

9-58. Jonas has built a scale model of a basketball
court for his NBA player action figures. His
model is built in the ratio $\frac{6 \text{ ft.}}{1 \text{ cm}}$.

a. If the real basketball court is 94 feet long,
how long is his scale model?

b. The hoop on Jonas' model is $1\frac{2}{3}$ cm above
the court floor. If he has constructed his
model correctly, how high does this make
the real-life hoop?

c. A real backboard is 72 inches wide. Jonas has made a model that is 8 cm
wide. Did he scale his model correctly?

d. The area of an NBA court is 4700 square feet. What should the area of
Jonas' model be?

9-59. Tatiana set up these equations for the
similar trapezoids at right:

$$\frac{10}{16} = \frac{y}{5} \qquad \frac{x}{10} = \frac{16}{12}$$

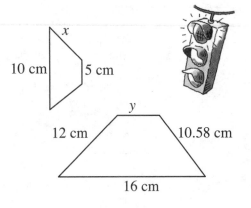

a. Are her equations correct?
Explain completely.

b. Make any necessary corrections
to her equations, then find the
lengths of the missing sides.

9-60. If one shape has area of 10 square units, and another similar shape has area of
250 square units, how can you find the scale factor between the sides?

9-61. Find each missing area.

a. One linear foot is equal to 12 inches. How many square inches cover the
same area as one square foot?

b. One inch is approximately equal to 2.54 centimeters. How many square
centimeters are in 15 square inches?

c. There are 3 feet in one yard. How many square feet cover the same area as
4 square yards?

9-62.   Ms. Murray and her class are looking at a series of similar triangles, and they are wondering if comparing the base of each triangle to its area is proportional. Find the base of the last two triangles and the area of all four triangles. Graph the base length compared to the area for each triangle. Does the graph show a proportional relationship? Why or why not?

9-63.   LEARNING LOG

Reread your Learning Log entry titled, "Area Relationships in Similar Shapes" (from Lesson 9.2.1). What new information can you add? Explain how the ratio of the sides of similar shapes is related to the ratio of their areas. Give an example of how can you use the area of a shape to predict the area of another, similar shape if you know the scale factor for the sides. Add today's date to your entry.

9-64.   The perimeter of one shape is 5.5 times larger than the perimeter of a similar shape.

   a.   How many times larger are the sides of the large shape than the corresponding sides of the smaller shape?

   b.   How many times larger is the area?

9-65.   If each triangle below is drawn accurately, identify whether it is most likely an obtuse, acute, or right triangle. Label the angle or angles that helped you to decide.

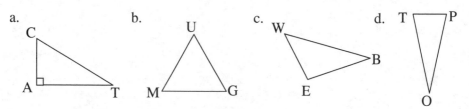

9-66.   Calculate the percent change in each problem below.

   a.   Robert wanted to buy a computer game that cost $25 last week. This week
        when he went back to buy the game, the price was $35. What was the
        percent of increase in the price?

   b.   Susan bought a jacket on sale. The original price of $35 was marked down
        to $25. What was the percent discount because of the sale?

   c.   Why were your answers to parts (a) and (b) different?

9-67.   Simplify each expression.

   a. $\frac{12}{5} \div \frac{7}{10}$ b. $\frac{9}{4} \div \left(-\frac{1}{3}\right)$ c. $-\frac{3}{5} \div \left(-\frac{1}{6}\right)$

9-68.   Hank is planning his
         vegetable garden. He has
         created the scale drawing at
         right. He is planning for the
         actual area for the tomatoes
         to be 12 feet by 9 feet. All
         angles are right angles.

   a.   How many feet in the garden does each inch on the drawing represent?

   b.   What are the length and width of the herb garden on the drawing in inches?

   c.   What are the length and width of the real herb garden in feet?

   d.   What is the area of the real herb garden (in square feet)?

   e.   Remember that there are 12 inches in one foot. If Hank measures the real
        herb garden in square inches instead of square feet, what will its area be?

9.3.1   What kind of triangle can I make?

Side Lengths and Triangles

Triangles are made of three sides. But can any three lengths make a triangle? Is it possible to predict what kind of triangle – obtuse, acute, or right – three side lengths will make? Today, you will investigate these questions with your team.

9-69.   IS IT A TRIANGLE?

When do three lengths form a triangle? Are there special patterns in lengths that always make obtuse triangles or combinations of lengths that make right or acute triangles? To investigate these questions, you and your study team will build triangles and look for patterns that will allow you to predict what kind of triangle three lengths will make.

Your task: Obtain the Lesson 9.3.1A, B, and C Resource Pages. Cut out each square on the Lesson 9.3.1A Resource Page (shown at right). Using different combinations of three squares, decide if a triangle can be made by connecting the corners of the squares. If you can make a triangle, what kind of triangle is it? (The angle on the Lesson 9.3.1B Resource Page can help you determine if an angle is a right (90°) angle.) Record the side lengths and areas for each combination of squares you try on the Lesson 9.3.1C Resource Page. If you can make a triangle, complete the other columns of the chart. If you cannot make a triangle, write "No Triangle" across the other columns. The headings for the columns on that page appear below.

Is it a Triangle?

How many different triangles can you make using these squares?

$5^2 = 25$ $6^2 = 36$

$13^2 = 169$

$10^2 = 100$

$4^2 = 16$

$3^2 = 9$ $8^2 = 64$ $12^2 = 144$

Side Length			Area of Small Square	Area of Medium Square	Area of Large Square	Small Area + Medium Area	Equal (=) Greater than (>) Less than (<)	Large Area	Acute △ Obtuse △ Right △
Sm	Med	Lg							

Discussion Points

How can we organize our data?

What other combinations can we make?

What do we expect will happen?

9-70.   Look at your data for the combinations that did *not* form triangles.

- What do you notice about how the three side lengths compare to each other?

- How are the sets that did not form triangles different from the sets of side lengths that *did* form triangles? Be as specific as you can.

When your team has reached a conclusion, copy and complete the two statements below on your paper.

Three side lengths WILL NOT make a triangle if...

Three side lengths WILL make a triangle if...

9-71.   Now look at the data that you collected for the acute, obtuse, and right triangles. What patterns do you see between the sum of the areas of the two smaller squares and the area of the larger square that formed the triangles in each row? Copy and complete the sentence starters below to summarize the patterns that you see.

If three squares have sides that make an acute triangle, *then the area of the two small squares...*

If three squares have sides that make an obtuse triangle, *then the area of the two small squares...*

If three squares have sides that make a right triangle, *then the area of the two small squares...*

9-72.   Use the patterns you found to predict whether each set of lengths below will form a triangle. If a set will form a triangle, state whether the triangle will be acute, obtuse, or right. **Justify** your conclusion.

a.   5 cm, 6 cm, and 7 cm

b.   2 cm, 11 cm, 15 cm

c.   10 cm, 15 cm, 20 cm

d.   10 cm, 24 cm, 26 cm

e.   1 cm, 3 cm, 9 cm

f.   2 cm, 10 cm, 11 cm

9-73.   **Additional Challenge:** Lewis wants to build an obtuse triangle. He has already decided to use a square with an area of 81 square units and a square with an area of 25 square units.

   a.   What area of square could he use to form the third side of his triangle? Explain your **reasoning**.

   b.   If he makes an acute triangle instead, what size square should he use? Explain your **reasoning**.

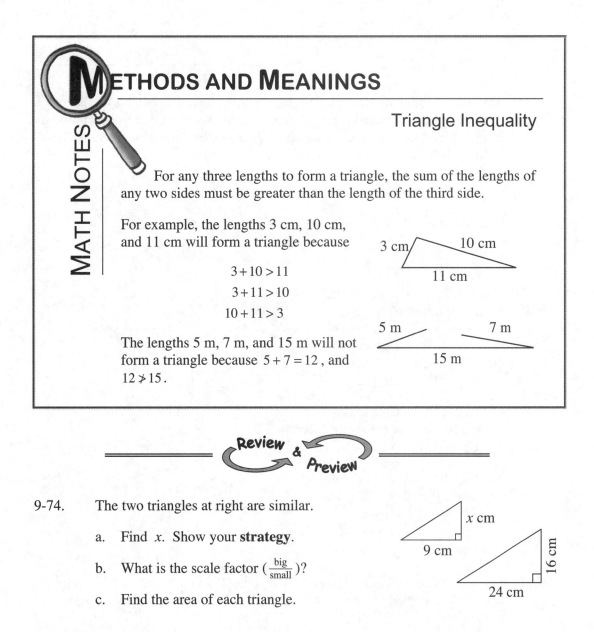

METHODS AND MEANINGS

MATH NOTES

Triangle Inequality

For any three lengths to form a triangle, the sum of the lengths of any two sides must be greater than the length of the third side.

For example, the lengths 3 cm, 10 cm, and 11 cm will form a triangle because

3 cm / 10 cm / 11 cm

$$3 + 10 > 11$$
$$3 + 11 > 10$$
$$10 + 11 > 3$$

The lengths 5 m, 7 m, and 15 m will not form a triangle because $5 + 7 = 12$, and $12 \not> 15$.

5 m / 7 m / 15 m

Review & Preview

9-74.   The two triangles at right are similar.

   a.   Find x. Show your **strategy**.

   b.   What is the scale factor ($\frac{\text{big}}{\text{small}}$)?

   c.   Find the area of each triangle.

x cm

9 cm

16 cm

24 cm

9-75.   Sasha saved $850 from her summer job last summer. She put it in an account that earns simple interest each month. After 9 months, her account is worth $1003. What percent interest did she earn each month?

9-76.   Anthony has added a trend line to the scatterplot at right. Do you agree with where he put the line? Explain your **reasoning**.

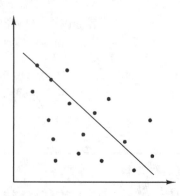

9-77.   A rental car company allows a customer to select any car available on the lot. Currently there are three blue sedans, two tan trucks, two black trucks, four red convertibles, four blue minivans, two black SUVs, and three tan hybrids. What is the probability a customer will select a black vehicle?

9-78.   Find the area and circumference of a circle with a radius of 7 cm.

9-79.   Elyse, Paul and J'Marcus were looking at the graph at right. Based on the graph, Elyse wrote the rule $y = 3x + 22$. Paul wrote the rule $y = 22x + 3$. J'Marcus wrote the rule $y = 22 + 3x$.

   a.   Are the three equations equivalent, or are they different? Explain your conclusion.

   b.   Which equation (or equations) match the line on the graph? **Justify** your answer.

9-80.   Jenna is working with three squares with areas of 16 cm², 9 cm², and 36 cm². She thinks they will make an obtuse triangle. Do you agree? Explain your **reasoning**.

9-81.   Find the missing side lengths of each rectangle (a and c) or square (b and d).

a.

x cm

100 cm | A = 500 cm²

b.

y cm

A = 64 cm² | 8 cm

c.

5 cm

r cm | A=82 cm²

d.

A = 25 cm² | w cm

5 cm

9-82.   Copy and complete the following table.

x	5			4			−2	3
y	−17	−5			−2	4	−11

a.   What is the rule?

b.   What is the slope?

9-83.   Simplify each expression.

a. $\frac{5}{12}+(-\frac{7}{8})-(-\frac{1}{6})$

b. $-\frac{11}{15}-\frac{4}{5}-(-\frac{57}{60})$

c. $4\frac{1}{12}+(-1\frac{5}{6})$

d. $-\frac{7}{11}\cdot\frac{8}{9}$

e. $\frac{1}{3}\cdot\frac{1}{2}+\frac{5}{6}$

f. $-\frac{4}{6}\cdot(-\frac{9}{2})$

9-84.   Use the graph below to answer the following questions.

a.   What is this graph describing? Write an appropriate title for the graph.

b.   How far from home is the person when the graph starts?

c.   How fast is the person traveling? Explain how you can use the graph to determine the rate of travel.

d.   Write an equation to represent the line on the graph.

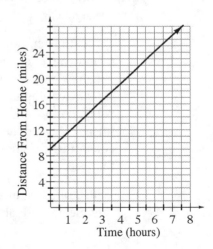

9.3.2 What is special about a right triangle?

Pythagorean Theorem

In Lesson 9.3.1, you saw that in order for three lengths to form a triangle they must be related to each other in a special way. Today, you will investigate a special relationship between the side lengths of right triangles. This relationship will allow you to find the length of a missing side.

9-85.   Use your patterns from Lesson 9.3.1 to decide if the squares listed below will form a right triangle.

   a.   Squares with side lengths 6, 8, and 10 meters

   b.   Squares with areas 64 in², 100 in², 144 in²

   c.   Two squares with side length 5 feet and a square with area 50 square feet

   d.   Explain how you know whether three squares will join at their corners to form a right triangle.

9-86.   THE PYTHAGOREAN RELATIONSHIP

   Based on your work so far, if you know the area of three squares you can tell if they will connect at their corners to form a right triangle. But what if you know that a triangle has a right angle? Will the squares of the side lengths be related in this way? Work with your team to look more closely at side lengths of some right triangles.

   a.   On centimeter graph paper, form a right angle by drawing one 5 cm length and one 12 cm length as shown at right. (If you do not have centimeter graph paper then use any graph paper to draw and measure these lengths with a ruler.) Then create a right triangle by connecting the ends of the two lengths with a third side.

   b.   With a ruler, measure the longest side of the triangle in centimeters and label the side length.

Problem continues on next page. →

Making Connections: Course 2

9-86.   *Problem continued from previous page.*

c.   **Visualize** a square connected to each side of the right triangle. Sketch a picture like the one at right on your paper. What is the area of each square? Is the area of the square connected to the longest side equal the sum of the areas of the other two squares?

d.   Check this pattern with a new example.

- Draw a new right angle on the centimeter paper using 9 cm and 12 cm lengths.

- Connect the endpoints to create a triangle and measure the third side.

- Create a sketch for this triangle like the one you created in part (c) and find the areas of the squares.

Is the area of the square connected to the longest side equal to the sum of the other two areas?

e.   The two shorter sides of a right triangle are called the **legs**, and the longest side is called the **hypotenuse**.

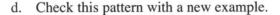

Use words to describe the relationship between the lengths of the legs and the length of the hypotenuse.

9-87. The relationship you described in part (e) of problem 9-86 is called the **Pythagorean Theorem**. It states that in a right triangle, the length of one leg squared plus the length of the other leg squared is equal to the length of the hypotenuse squared, and can be written as an equation like this:

$$(\text{leg A})^2 + (\text{leg B})^2 = (\text{hypotenuse})^2$$

Use the Pythagorean Theorem to write an equation for each diagram below. Find each missing area.

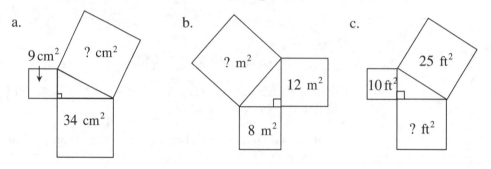

9-88. Your earlier work with squares that formed right triangles used the **converse of the Pythagorean Theorem**. That is, you found that if the sum of the squares of the two shortest sides in a triangle equals the square of the length of the longest side, then the triangle is a right triangle. Use this idea to determine whether the lengths listed below form a right triangle. Explain your **reasoning**.

a. 15 feet, 36 feet, and 39 feet

b. 20 in., 21 in., and 29 in.

c. 8 yards, 9 yards, and 12 yards

d. 4 meters, 7 meters, and 8 meters

9-89. Find the area of the square in each picture below.

9-90. How long is the missing side of each triangle in parts (b) and (c) of problem 9-89? Be prepared to explain your **reasoning**.

METHODS AND MEANINGS

MATH NOTES

Right Triangles and the Pythagorean Theorem

A **right triangle** is a triangle in which the two shorter sides form a right (90°) angle. The shorter sides are called **legs**. The third and longest side, called the **hypotenuse**, is opposite the right angle.

The **Pythagorean Theorem** states that for any right triangle, the sum of the squares of the lengths of the legs is equal to the square of the length of the hypotenuse.

Leg 1   Hypotenuse

Leg 2

$$(\text{leg } 1)^2 + (\text{leg } 2)^2 = (\text{hypotenuse})^2$$

Example:

x

3 in.

4 in.

$$3^2 + 4^2 = x^2$$
$$9 + 16 = x^2$$
$$25 = x^2$$
$$5 = x$$

The **converse of the Pythagorean Theorem** states that if the sum of the squares of the lengths of the two shorter sides of a triangle equals the square of the length of the longest side, then the triangle is a right triangle. For example:

Do the lengths 6, 9, and 11 form a right triangle?

$$6^2 + 9^2 \overset{?}{=} 11^2$$
$$36 + 81 \overset{?}{=} 121$$

$117 \neq 121$ No, these lengths do not form a right triangle.

Do the lengths 9, 40, and 41 form a right triangle?

$$9^2 + 40^2 \overset{?}{=} 41^2$$
$$81 + 1600 \overset{?}{=} 1681$$

$1681 = 1681$ Yes, these lengths form a right triangle.

9-91.   If you have 24 square tiles, how many different rectangles can you make? Each rectangle must use all of the tiles. Sketch each rectangle on graph paper and label its length and width. Can you make a square with 24 tiles?

9-92.   Lydia has four straws of different lengths, and she is trying to form a right triangle. The lengths are 8, 9, 15, and 17 units. Which three lengths should she use? **Justify** your answer.

9-93.   What kind of triangle will the edges of these squares form? What will the side lengths be?

36 u^2 400 u^2 625 u^2

9-94.   Find the missing dimension on each rectangle or square.

a.   8 ft $A=100 \text{ ft}^2$

b.   12 mm $A= 144 \text{ mm}^2$

c.   10 cm $A= 144 \text{ cm}^2$

d.   7 in. $A= 49 \text{ in.}^2$

e.   6 km $A=144 \text{ km}^2$

9-95.   Eric set up this ratio for two similar triangles:

$$\frac{x}{12} = \frac{5}{9}$$

He solved the problem and found $x \approx 6.67$. What was his mistake?

5

12

9

x

9-96.   Write an equation to represent this situation and answer the question. You may choose to use the 5-D Process to help you organize your thinking.

Ella is trying to determine the side lengths of a triangle. She knows that the longest side is three times longer than the shortest side. The medium side is ten more than twice the shortest side. If the perimeter is 142 cm, how long is each side?

9.3.3 How can I find the side length?

Understanding Square Root

You have developed a way to decide if a triangle is a right triangle by looking at the squares of the side lengths of the triangle. If you already know a triangle is a right triangle, how can the Pythagorean Theorem help you determine the length of a leg or the hypotenuse? Today you and your team will develop new ways to find missing lengths of right triangles.

9-97. Nikita wants to use the area of the squares in the figure at right to help him find the lengths of the sides of a right triangle.

 a. Find the missing area.

 b. What are the lengths of the legs of the right triangle in Nikita's diagram? How do you know?

 c. About how long is the hypotenuse? Are you able to find the length exactly? Explain your **reasoning**.

9-98. The numbers 36, 64, 4, 16, 100, 144, 121, and 225 are all examples of **perfect squares**.

 a. If each of these numbers represents the number of square units in a square, what is the side length of each square?

 b. Why do you think these numbers are called perfect squares?

9-99. To find the side length of a square with a particular area, we use a process called the **square root**. The square root symbol looks like $\sqrt{}$, and is also called a **radical sign**.

To find the side length of a square with an area of 81 square units, for example, we would write $\sqrt{81}$ (read, "the square root of 81"). Since $9 \cdot 9 = 81$, then $\sqrt{81} = 9$.

Copy each square root expression below. If the expression is the side length of a square, what does it tell you about the area of the square? Rewrite each square root as an equivalent expression without the radical sign. Explain your method for finding the square root of these numbers.

 a. $\sqrt{49}$ b. $\sqrt{121}$ c. $\sqrt{9}$ d. $\sqrt{169}$

9-100.　Look back at problem 9-91, when you tried to make a perfect square with 24 tiles and could not. Why was it impossible?

a.　Estimate the length of a side of a square with an area of 24 square units. What two whole numbers is the length between?

b.　Is $\sqrt{24}$ closer to one of the whole numbers or to the other? If you did not already do so, make your estimate to the nearest tenth.

c.　Multiply your estimate by itself. How close to 24 is your answer? If you revised your estimate, how would you change it?

9-101.　Between which two whole numbers is each of the following square roots? To which whole number do you think it is closer? Estimate the value of the square root to the nearest tenth (0.1). You may find it helpful to create a list of the whole numbers from one to 17 and their squares to use with this kind of problem.

a.　$\sqrt{40}$　　　　　　b.　$\sqrt{95}$　　　　　　c.　$\sqrt{3}$

d.　$\sqrt{59}$　　　　　　e.　$\sqrt{200}$　　　　　f.　$\sqrt{154}$

g.　Describe your method for estimating the approximate value of a square root when the number is not a perfect square. Check each estimate for parts (a) through (f) on a calculator.

9-102.　ESTIMATING WITH A GRAPH

In Chapters 6, 7, and 8, you examined the graphs of various relationships. What would the relationship between the side length of a square and the area of a square look like on a graph?

a.　On the Lesson 9.3.3 Resource Page, complete the table for the side lengths and areas. Graph the points. Does it make sense to connect them? If so, connect them with a smooth curve.

b.　Describe the relationship between the side length of a square and the area of the square. How is it the same or different than other relationships you have graphed?

c.　How can you use the graph to estimate the side length for a square with an area of 24 square units? Does this estimate match your estimate in problem 9-100?

d.　Use your graph to estimate these square roots:

　　i.　$\sqrt{10}$　　　ii.　$\sqrt{15}$　　　　iii.　$\sqrt{5}$　　　　iv.　$\sqrt{33}$

9-103.   In Chapter 1, you worked with decimals that repeated and terminated. All of these numbers are called **rational** because they can be written as a ratio, like $\frac{2}{3}$ and $\frac{5}{1} = 5$. Because $\sqrt{9} = 3$, $\sqrt{9}$ is also a rational number.

However, there are some numbers that, when written as a decimal, do not repeat or terminate. $\sqrt{2}$ is one example of a number like this. These numbers are called **irrational**, and they cannot be written as a ratio of any two integers (in other words, as a fraction).

$\sqrt{2} = 1.41421356237...$

Use your calculator to find the square root of the following numbers. Decide whether the decimals are rational (those that have decimals that terminate or repeat) or irrational.

a. $\sqrt{6.25}$ b. $\sqrt{100}$ c. $\sqrt{7}$

9-104.   **Additional Challenge:** Nikita wonders, "*What can we say about the square root of a negative number?*" Discuss this question with your team. For example, can you find $\sqrt{-16}$? Write an explanation of your thinking. Be ready to share your ideas with the class.

9-105.   LEARNING LOG

How can you estimate a square root? Write directions for a fifth grader to follow, explaining how to estimate a square root to the nearest tenth. Include examples of perfect squares and non-perfect squares. Title this entry in your Learning Log, "Estimating Square Roots," and label it with today's date.

METHODS AND MEANINGS

Squaring and Square Root

When a number or variable is multiplied by itself, it is said to be **squared**. **Squaring** a number is like finding the area of the square with that number or variable as its side length. For example,

$6 \cdot 6 = 6^2 = 36$ and

36 cm²

6 cm

6 cm

$a \cdot a = a^2$ and

a^2

a

a

The **square root** of a number or variable is the positive factor that, when multiplied by itself, results in the given number. Use a **radical sign**, $\sqrt{}$, to show this operation. If you know the area of a square, then the square root of the numerical value of the area is the side length of that square.

For example, $\sqrt{49}$ is read as, "the square root of 49," and means, "Find the positive number that multiplied by itself equals 49." $\sqrt{49} = 7$, since $7 \cdot 7 = 49$.

By definition, -7 is not the square root of 49 even though $(-7) \cdot (-7) = 49$, since we only consider positive numbers to be square roots. No real square region could have a negative side length.

Review & Preview

9-106.   Find the missing length or area.

a.

x

| x | 225 cm² |

b.

11 cm

11 cm

c.

5 m

| 100 m² |

w

d.

y

| y | 150 ft² |

9-107.   A triangle is enlarged by a scale factor of $\frac{10}{3}$.

    a.   If the perimeter of the enlargement is 36 m, find the perimeter of the original triangle.

    b.   If the area of the enlarged triangle is 25 square meters, what is the area of the original triangle?

9-108.   Cisco was looking at a table of values from a silent board game of $y = x^2$. She said, "This table contains $(0,0)$ so I think it shows a proportional relationship." Is Cisco correct? Why or why not?

9-109.   The hypotenuse and one leg of a right triangle are 65 and 60 meters. What is the length of the third side?

9-110.   Solve these equations for x. Check your answers.

    a. $2(x+4.5)=32$ b. $6+2.5x=21$ c. $\frac{x}{9}=\frac{5}{16}$

9-111.   A box contains 15 yellow, 15 orange, and 15 green tennis balls. If Izzy draws a tennis ball at random out of the box, what is the probability that he drew either a green or an orange tennis ball? Show your work and express your answer as a percent.

9-112.   Find the area and circumference of a circle with a diameter of 14.4 inches. Round your answer to the nearest hundredth.

9-113.   One of the triangles at right is a reduction of the other. Find each of the missing parts listed below.

    a.   Find the length of side BC.

    b.   Find the length of side AB.

    c.   Find the ratio of the areas of the two triangles.

9-114. Determine the positive value that makes each equation true. If the answer is not a whole number, write it as a square root, then approximate it as a decimal rounded to the nearest tenth.

a. If $x^2 = 36$, $x = ?$

b. If $x^2 = 65$, $x = ?$

c. If $x^2 = 84$, $x = ?$

d. If $x^2 = 13$, $x = ?$

9-115. Copy the following table on your paper.

x	4	$\frac{1}{2}$	-2		-1	7
y	-11		1	-3	-1	

a. Complete the table.   b. Write the rule.   c. What is the slope?

9.3.4 How can I find missing parts?

Applications of the Pythagorean Theorem

In this section you have studied different properties of triangles and have used the Pythagorean Theorem to describe the special relationship between the sides of a right triangle. In this lesson, you will use these ideas to solve a variety of different problems.

9-116. Ann is measuring some fabric pieces for a quilt. Use the Pythagorean Theorem and your calculator to help her find each of the missing lengths below. Decide whether each answer is rational or irrational. If it is rational, explain whether the decimal repeats or terminates.

a.

32 in.

24 in.

b.

10 m

20 m

c.

7.6 cm

9.5 cm

9-117. Coach Kelly's third period P.E. class is playing baseball. The distance between each base on the baseball diamond is 90 feet. Lisa, at third base, throws the ball to Dano, at first base. How far did she throw the ball? State whether or not your answer is rational or irrational.

9-118.   As the city planner of Right City, you are responsible to report information to help the Board of Supervisors make decisions about the budgets for the fire and police departments. The board has asked for a report with answers to the following questions. Each grid unit in the figure at right represents 1 mile.

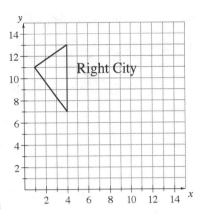

a. For fire safety, bushes will be cleared along the perimeter of the city. What is the length of the perimeter? Please include all of your calculations in your report.

b. Some people say that Right City got its name from its shape. Is the shape of the city a right triangle? Show how you can tell.

9-119.   Clem and Clyde have a farm with three different crops: a square field of corn, a rectangular field of artichokes, and a right triangle grove of walnut trees (as shown at right). A fence totally surrounds the farm. Find the total area of their land in square miles and tell them how much fencing they need to enclose the outside of their farm.

9-120.   Scott and Mark are rock climbing. Scott is at the top of a 75-foot cliff, when he throws a 96-foot rope down to Mark, who is on the ground below. If the rope is stretched tightly from Mark's feet to Scott's feet, how far from the base of the cliff (directly below Scott) is Mark standing? Draw a diagram and label it. Then, find the missing length. Is the length irrational?

9-121.   Nicole has three long logs. She wants to place them in a triangle around a campfire to allow people to sit around the fire. The logs have lengths 19, 11, and 21 feet.

a. Can she form a triangle with these lengths? If so, what type of triangle (acute, obtuse, or right) will the logs form? **Justify** your answers.

b. Nicole realized she wrote the numbers down incorrectly. Her logs are actually 9, 11, and 21 feet. Will she still be able to surround her campfire with a triangular seating area? If so, will the shape be a right triangle? **Justify**.

9-122. LEARNING LOG

The Pythagorean Theorem describes the special
relationship that exists between the side lengths of a
right triangle. In your Learning Log, describe how the
Pythagorean Theorem can be used to find a missing side
length on a right triangle. Make up examples where the
hypotenuse length is missing or a leg length. Be sure to
include pictures, and to describe how you would find
each missing length. Title this entry, "Pythagorean
Theorem," and label it with today's date.

METHODS AND MEANINGS

Side Length Patterns in Triangles

The Triangle Inequality (Lesson 9.3.1 Math Note) establishes
the required relationships for three lengths to form a triangle. You can
also use these lengths to determine the type of triangle they form —
acute, obtuse, or right — by comparing the squares of the lengths of
the sides as follows:

Acute triangle: The sum of the
squares of the lengths of the two
shorter sides is greater than the
square of the length of the longest
side.

$x^2 + y^2 > z^2$

Obtuse triangle: The sum of the
squares of the lengths of the two
shorter sides is less than the square
of the length of the longest side.

$p^2 + q^2 < r^2$

Right triangle: The sum of the
squares of the lengths of the two
shorter sides is equal to the square of
the length of the longest side.

$a^2 + b^2 = c^2$

Making Connections: Course 2

9-123.   The figure shown at right is made up
         of a right triangle and a rectangle.

   a.   Copy the shape on your paper. Then
        draw a line to help divide the figure
        into two separate shapes.

   b.   Use the dimensions given to find the
        area of the triangle, the rectangle, and
        the whole figure. Be sure to show all of
        your subproblems.

9-124.   On a coordinate grid, draw a triangle with vertices at $(2,6)$, $(2,2)$, and $(5,6)$.

   a.   Find the lengths of each side of the triangle. What is the perimeter?

   b.   What type of triangle is formed by these points? **Justify** your answer.

9-125.   Graph the rule $y = -2x + 5$.

   a.   What is the slope of the line?

   b.   Where does the line cross the y-axis?

9-126.   Stephanie is earning simple interest of 3.5% on her money each month. She
         currently has $1325 in her account. What will her balance be in 5 months?

9-127.   Ann lives on the shoreline of a large lake. A market is located 24 km south and
         32 km west of her home on the other side of the lake. If she takes a boat across
         the lake directly toward the market, how far is her home from the market?

Chapter 9 Closure   What have I learned?

Reflection and Synthesis

The activities below offer you a chance to reflect about what you have learned during this chapter. As you work, look for concepts that you feel comfortable with, ideas that you would like to learn more about, and topics with which you need more help. Look for understanding of the ideas in this chapter as well as connections with material you learned previously.

①   SUMMARIZING MY UNDERSTANDING

This section gives you an opportunity to show what you know about certain math topics or ideas.

Jasmine and Jason are spending the summer with their Uncle Simon. He lives in an old castle that has many interesting doors, not all of them rectangles. One day, while looking through the books in the castle library, Jasmine found an unusual piece of paper in a book.

"Look, Jason! This looks like some kind of a treasure map," she exclaimed. Jason looked at the paper and read, *"A valuable secret is hidden inside. But beware – danger lurks behind the other doors. Only those who can follow the clues will succeed in the search."*

He also saw that it had a series of clues and pictures of triangular doors. Read the clues below and, with your team, help Jasmine and Jason find the secret door and the treasure.

- My sides are not congruent.

- My angles are not congruent.

- I am similar to another door.

- One of my sides is $\sqrt{41}$ units long.

a.   Look at the doors on the Closure Resource Page A, available at www.cpm.org/students.

b.   Using what you have learned in this chapter, decide which door is the secret door.

c.   **Justify** your answer.

Problem continues on next page. →

Making Connections: Course 2

①   *Problem continued from previous page.*

d.   List the triangles which were not the secret door and **justify** why each one did not fit the clues.

When you have solved the problem and found the treasure, answer the following questions:

- What skills learned in this chapter did I use to solve this problem?
- What knowledge from earlier chapters helped solve the problem?

②   WHAT HAVE I LEARNED?

This section will help you determine which kinds of problems you feel comfortable with and those with which you need more help, based on the kinds of problems you have seen so far. Even if your teacher does not assign this section, it is a good idea to try these problems and find out for yourself what you know and what you need to work on.

To help you determine how well you understand the concepts in this chapter, solve each problem as completely as you can. The table at the end of this closure section has answers to these problems. It also directs you to additional help and other similar practice problems.

CL 9-128. Solve the proportion $\frac{22}{7} = \frac{5}{x}$ in two different ways. Show your work.

CL 9-129. The triangles at right are similar.

     a.   Find x.

     b.   Find y.

     c.   Find the ratio of the perimeters of the two triangles.

     d.   Find the ratio of the areas of the two triangles.

CL 9-130. The hypotenuse and one leg of a right triangle are 85 and 51 feet long. What is the length of the third side?

CL 9-131. The rent for Sonja's Haircuts shop has just been raised, so Sonja decided to increase the cost of a haircut from $8.50 to $10. What is the percent increase for a haircut?

CL 9-132. At a family reunion, each family member recorded their age and their height.

a. What kind of correlation does the scatter plot have?

b. Copy the scatterplot and draw the trend line.

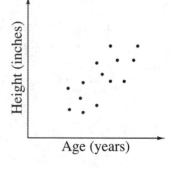

CL 9-133. At the farmer's market Laura bought three pounds of heirloom tomatoes. If the tomatoes are priced at $8 per five pounds, what did Laura pay for her tomatoes?

CL 9-134. Find the area and circumference of a circle with a radius of 6.5 cm.

CL 9-135. Juana has three red belts, four black belts, two purple belts, and five navy belts in her drawer. It is still dark and her sister is sleeping so she does not want to turn on the light. What is the probability that she will select a red or a black belt?

CL 9-136. For each of the problems above, do the following:

- Draw a bar or number line that represents 0 to 10.

- Color or shade in a portion of the bar that represents your level of understanding and comfort with completing that problem on your own.

If any of your bars are less than a 5, choose *one* of those problems and do one of the following tasks:

- Write two questions that you would like to ask about that problem.
- Brainstorm two things that you DO know about that type of problem.

If all of your bars are a 5 or above, choose one of those problems and do one of these tasks:

- Write two questions you might ask or hints you might give to a student who was stuck on the problem.
- Make a new problem that is similar and more challenging than that problem and solve it.

③   WHAT TOOLS CAN I USE?

You have created or have available to you several tools and references that help support your learning – your teacher, your study team, your math book and your Toolkit to name a few. At the end of each chapter you will have an opportunity to review your Toolkit for completeness as well as to revise or update your Toolkit to better reflect your current understanding of big ideas.

Listed below are the main elements of your Toolkit, Learning Log Entries, Methods and Meanings Boxes, and vocabulary used in this chapter. The words that appear in bold are new to this chapter. Use these lists and follow your teacher's instructions to ensure that your Toolkit is a useful tool as well as a complete reference for you as you complete this chapter and prepare to begin the next one.

Learning Log Entries
- Lesson 9.1.1 – Proportional Relationships
- Lesson 9.2.1 – Area Relationships in Similar Shapes
- Lesson 9.3.3 – Estimating Square Roots
- Lesson 9.3.4 – Pythagorean Theorem

Math Notes
- Lesson 9.1.2 – Directly Proportional Relationships
- Lesson 9.1.3 – Solving Proportions
- Lesson 9.2.2 – Ratios of Similarity
- Lesson 9.3.1 – Triangle Inequality
- Lesson 9.3.2 – Right Triangles and the Pythagorean Theorem
- Lesson 9.3.3 – Squaring and Square Root
- Lesson 9.3.4 – Side Length Patterns in Triangles

Mathematical Vocabulary

The following is a list of vocabulary found in this chapter. Some of the words have been seen in the previous chapter. The words in bold are the words new to this chapter. Make sure that you are familiar with the terms below and know what they mean. For the words you do not know, refer to the glossary or index. You might also want to add these words to your Toolkit for a way to reference them in the future.

hypotenuse	inverse	**irrational**
legs	**non-proportional**	**perfect squares**
proportional	**proportional relationship**	**proportions**
Pythagorean Theorem	**radical sign**	**rational**
square root		

Process Words

The list of words below are problem solving strategies and processes that you have been involved in throughout the course of this chapter. Make sure you know what it means to use each of the following strategies. If you are not sure, look through your book for problems when you were asked to think in the following ways.

brainstorm	choose a strategy	describe
explain your reasoning	generalize	justify
predict	reason	reverse your thinking
test your prediction	visualize	

Answers and Support for Closure Activity #2
What Have I Learned?

Problem	Solution	Need Help?	More Practice
CL 9-128.	$x = \frac{35}{22} \approx 1.59$	Lesson 9.1.3 Math Notes box in Lesson 9.1.3	Problems 9-23, 9-27, and 9-28
CL 9-129.	a. $\frac{63}{4}$ b. $\frac{49}{4}$ c. $\frac{35}{20} = \frac{7}{4}$ d. $\left(\frac{7}{4}\right)^2 = \frac{49}{16}$	Lessons 9.1.3, and 9.2.1 Math Notes box in Lesson 9.2.2 Learning Log (problem 9-40)	Problems 9-23, 9-25, 9-29, 9-41, 9-52, 9-74, and 9-113
CL 9-130.	68 feet	Lessons 9.3.2, 9.3.3, and 9.3.4 Math Notes boxes in Lessons 9.3.2 and 9.3.3 Learning Log (problem 9-122)	Problems 9-87, 9-89, 9-109, and 9-120
CL 9-131.	17.6%	Lesson 8.2.5 Math Notes box in Lesson 8.2.5	Problems CL 8-92, 9-13, 9-32, and 9-66
CL 9-132.	a. positive correlation b. 	Lessons 6.1.2 and 6.1.3 Math Notes box in Lesson 6.1.4 Learning Logs (problems 6-26 and 6-47)	Problems CL 6-140, CL 7-95, and 9-76

Problem	Solution	Need Help?	More Practice
CL 9-133.	$4.80	Lessons 9.1.1, 9.1.2, and 9.1.3 Math Notes boxes in Lessons 9.1.2 and 9.1.3 Learning Log (problem 9-8)	Problems 9-5, 9-9, 9-26, 9-45, and 9-55
CL 9-134.	$A \approx 132.7 \text{ cm}^2$ $C \approx 40.8 \text{ cm}$	Lessons 5.3.3 and 5.3.4 Math Notes box in Lesson 5.3.4 Learning Log (problem 5-124)	Problems CL 6-143, CL 8-93, 9-31, 9-78, and 9-112
CL 9-135.	$P = \frac{7}{14}$ or $\frac{1}{2}$ or 50%	Lessons 1.2.1 and 1.2.2 Math Notes boxes in Lessons 1.2.1 and 1.2.2	Problems CL 2-162, 9-12, 9-44, 9-77, and 9-111

Puzzle Investigator Problems

PI-17.   ROMAN NUMERALS

Perhaps you learned to count by counting on your fingers! The fact that we have 10 fingers might explain why we count in the base 10 system. This means that as we count, we group objects in sets of 10 (and sets of 100, which are each 10 sets of 10). We also write our numbers in a way to quickly represent the number of sets of 10. For example, when we want to count 21 objects, the digit 2 represents the number of 10s and the digit 1 represents 1.

However, throughout history, there were other number systems, as well as other ways of writing numbers. Romans counted in base 10, but used a different symbol system. The letter I is used for the digit "1," V is used for "5," X is used for "10," and L is used for "50." Then other numbers up to 98 are created by placing combinations of these letters together.

Study the examples at right to figure out the Roman Number system of writing.

a. Based on these examples, describe the process for writing a Roman Numeral. For example, why does "XL" represent 40 while "L" represents 50?

b. Based on your patterns, how would Romans write the number 87? 55? 98?

c. What is the smallest number you can create with one of each letter? What is the largest?

Sample Roman Numerals

I	=	1	XI	=	11
II	=	2	XVI	=	16
III	=	3	XVIII	=	18
IV	=	4	XIX	=	19
V	=	5	XXIII	=	23
VI	=	6	XXIX	=	29
VII	=	7	XL	=	40
VIII	=	8	XLIX	=	49
IX	=	9	LXIV	=	64
X	=	10	LXXI	=	71

d. Katrina thinks that adding Roman Numerals is similar to collecting like terms, so that XIX + XL = LXXXI. Explain to her why this is not correct and give her another counterexample. Does her **strategy** ever work? If so, what are the conditions that will enable her to use this **strategy**?

PI-18.   TO TELL THE TRUTH

Alicia, Ben, Cassie, and Daryl shared some birthday cake before going into the living room to work on their homework. During the rest of the afternoon, each one of them left the room by themselves for a few minutes.

When they finished their homework, they went into the kitchen and discovered that the rest of the cake was missing. Below are their statements:

Alicia: *"Ben ate it!"*

Cassie: *"I didn't eat it!"*

Ben: *"Daryl must have eaten it."*

Daryl: *"Ben is lying."*

a.   If only one of these statements is a lie, who ate the rest of the cake? Explain how you know which statement is false.

b.   If only one of the above statements is the truth, who ate the rest of the cake? Explain how you know which statement is true.

c.   While sorting out this mess, Ben's dad said, "What I am saying is not true." Is this statement true or false? Explain.

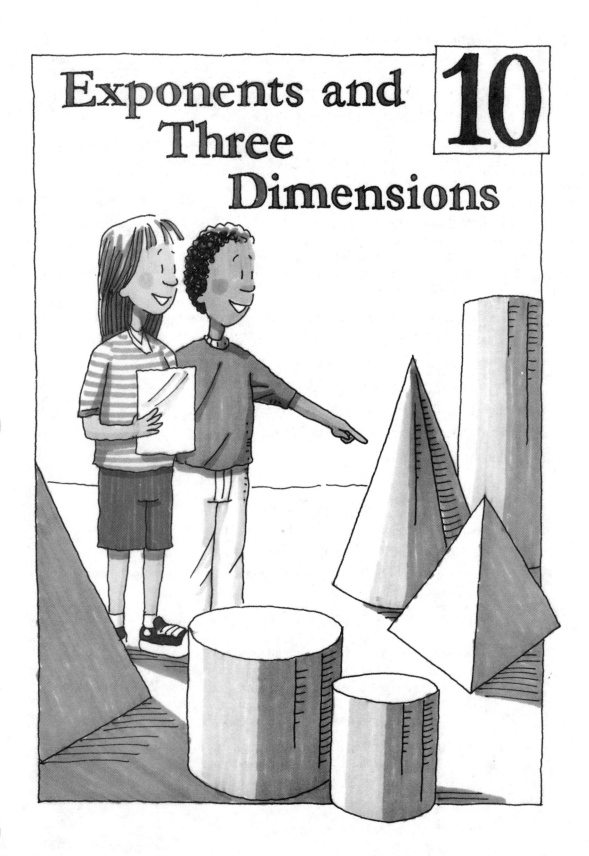

Exponents and Three Dimensions

10

CHAPTER 10   Exponents and Three Dimensions

In previous chapters you have investigated relationships that have a constant rate and can be represented as lines on a graph. Other relationships do not change at the same rate all of the time. For example, the height of the tide on a beach increases and decreases over the course of a day, and the number of cells in a sample gets larger very quickly as each cell divides and makes a new cell. In Section 10.1, you will work with percentages and interest to investigate one kind of non-linear growth called exponential growth. You will look for patterns to identify the characteristics of this kind of growth in tables, graphs, and expressions.

In Section 10.2, you will explore how to measure the surface area and volume of three-dimensional solids by designing and building cereal boxes. You will practice **visualizing** flattened shapes, called nets, to think about how their parts fit together to make different three-dimensional solids. Finally, you will experiment with the surface area and volume of shapes that cannot be sliced into equal layers.

Guiding Questions

Think about these questions throughout this chapter:

How is it changing?

What patterns can I see?

How much will it hold?

Am I measuring in one, two or three dimensions?

How are they related?

In this chapter, you will learn how to:

➢ Calculate compound interest.

➢ Determine whether a relationship grows linearly or exponentially.

➢ Rewrite expressions using exponents and scientific notation.

➢ Find the surface area and volume of rectangular prisms.

➢ Find the surface area and volume of non-rectangular shapes including pyramids, cylinders, and cones.

Chapter Outline

	Section 10.1	You will learn about compound interest, and use patterns of growth to write expressions. You will analyze the patterns in tables, graphs, and expressions to compare linear and exponential growth. You will also learn new ways to rewrite numbers and expressions.
	Section 10.2	You will compare how surface area and volume are related by building three-dimensional rectangular prisms. Then you will **visualize** shapes using nets. Finally you will learn to find both the surface area and volume of cylinders, pyramids, and cones.

10.1.1 Is the graph linear?

···

Patterns of Growth in Tables and Graphs

Have you ever noticed that the sun rises earlier and sets later in the summer than it does in the winter? If you live north of the equator, you may have noticed that in December you often wake up for school while it is still dark, but if you wake up at the same time of day in May the sun is shining. The number of hours of sunlight in any one place changes during the year (unless you live directly at the equator). This is because the earth's tilt changes in comparison to the sun. The number of hours of daylight is approximately equal to the number of hours of darkness at just two times of year – the fall equinox and the spring equinox.

If you compared the average number of hours of daylight to the time of year on a graph, you would be able to see a pattern in how the number of hours of daylight changes. Today you will explore situations, tables and graphs that change in different ways and build **strategies** for **visualizing** different patterns of growth. As you work with your team, ask each other these questions:

How does this grow?

What happens when one measurement changes?

How can we see the pattern of growth in the table?

10-1.   With your team, discuss each of the comparisons described below. Consider how the measurements are related and **visualize** what each relationship would look like on a graph. Sketch your prediction after you discuss your ideas with your team.

a.   The month of the year compared to the average daily hours of sunlight.

b.   The number of months money has been invested compared to the total balance for a bank account earning simple interest.

c.   The cost of an item that has had its price repeatedly increased by 50%.

d.   The length of the base of a rectangle that has an area of 24 square centimeters compared to its height.

10-2. Now that you have predicted what different graphs will look like, investigate how some of the measures are related. To start, consider this situation:

Oscar puts $1000 of principal in a bank account that earns 2% simple interest each month. He wants to track how his money is growing over time.

a. On the Lesson 10.1.1A Resource Page, complete the table to show the interest Omar has earned after 1, 2, 3, 4, and 5 months. How do you find his new balance each month?

Months	Total Interest Earned	Bank Balance
0	$0	$1000
1		

b. Make a graph comparing months and interest on the resource page.

c. What patterns do you notice in the table and the graph? How can you see each pattern in the other representations (situation, table, graph)?

d. Use the patterns you have found to predict how long it will take before Oscar has $1800 in the bank. **Justify** your prediction.

e. Compare your graph from part (b) to the sketch you made in part (b) of problem 10-1. Did you predict that the graph would be a straight line? Explain why your prediction was correct, or any changes you would make and why.

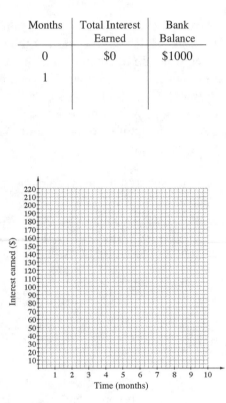

10-3.   PROFIT, PROFIT, PROFIT

Anita bought a special baseball card for $8.00. Later, she decided to sell it but she wanted to make a profit. She added 50% to the price she paid and sold the card to Brandon. When he decided to sell it, he also wanted to make a profit, so he added 50% to the price he paid for the card and sold it to Casey. Casey increased the price by 50% and sold the card to Eli, who increased the price another 50% when he sold it to Fernanda.

a.   On the Lesson 10.1.1B Resource Page, make a table and graph of the new price after 1, 2, 3, 4, and 5 exchanges. How do you find the new price at each exchange?

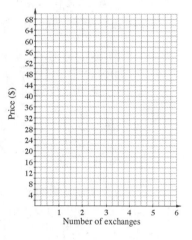

Exchanges	Increase in Price	New Price
0	$0	$8
1		

b.   What patterns do you notice in the table and the graph? Is the graph a straight line? How can you **justify** your conclusion based on the table or the graph?

c.   How does the graph you made compare to your sketch from part (c) of problem 10-1? Did you predict that the graph would curve?

d.   How much did Fernanda pay for the baseball card?

10-4.   In problems 10-2 and 10-3, one graph made a straight line while the other curved.

a.   How was the situation that created a straight line changing (growing)?

b.   Growth that creates a straight line shows constant change, and is called **linear growth**. What made the graph in problem 10-3 curve? How did the growth show in the table and the graph?

10-5.   Guillermo was studying the two different situations below. He knows that one
is represented by a line on a graph but that the other is represented by a curve.

The Basketball Tournament: The first
round of a basketball tournament starts with
16 teams that each play one game. The eight
winning teams move on to Round 2 and the
other teams are done competing. The
tournament continues in this way until Round
4, the finals, where the last two teams play to
determine the champion.

The Basketball Tournament	
Round	Number of teams left
1	16
2	8
3	4
4	2

Finishing Homework: You have 16
problems to finish at home tonight. You can
finish 4 problems in 10 minutes.

Help Guillermo by explaining how you see
the situations above changing over time. For
each situation:

Finishing Homework	
Time spent working	Problems left to complete
0	16
10	12
20	8
30	4

a.   Copy the table and describe to
Guillermo how you see the values
in the table changing.

b.   Explain whether the change is constant from one row to the next.

10-6.   Guillermo graphed the points for each table and sketched a trend line for each
graph to show the pattern in the points. He forgot to label his axes. Decide
which graph matches the basketball data and which graph matches the
homework data. Explain how you know that they match.

Graph A

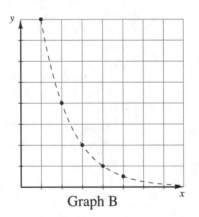

Graph B

Making Connections: Course 2

10-7.   Cassandra is calculating how much
          interest she will earn on investments that
          are earning simple interest using the
          formula at right. She knows that simple
          interest is paid only on the original amount
          that was deposited (the principal). For one
          amount of money that was invested for
          three years, she wrote the equation below.

Simple Interest Formula
$I = Prt$ where
P = Principal
I = Interest
r = Rate
t = Time

$$I = 500(0.025)(3) = \$37.50$$

Use what you know about simple interest to answer the questions below. Refer
to the Math Notes box in Lesson 8.2.6 if you need additional information.

a.   In Cassandra's equation, identify the principal, interest, rate, and time.

b.   Use this formula to calculate how much interest you would earn if you
     deposit $200 for 5 years at an annual (yearly) simple interest rate of 4%.

10-8.   Mighty Max started the wrestling season weighing 135 pounds. By the time the
          season ended, he weighed 128 pounds. What was the percent decrease in his
          weight?

10-9.   Which is a better deal? Sabrina wants
          to buy a new digital camera. The one
          she wants is currently on sale for $300.
          She could borrow the money at a
          monthly interest rate of 4% simple
          interest and pay it off after 6 months.
          Her other option is to work for 6
          months and then pay cash, but the
          camera will no longer be on sale and
          will cost $350.

Which option will cost her the least money? Include calculations to **justify**
your advice.

10-10.	Scooter and Kayla are building a chicken coop in their back yard. The coop will be in the shape of a right triangle. One of the sides will be the wall of the garage. They have 11 feet of fencing, and one leg will be 4 feet long.

    a.	If the garage forms the hypotenuse of the triangle, how long will the other leg be? How long will the hypotenuse be?

    b.	If the garage wall is one leg of the triangle, how long will the hypotenuse be? How long will the leg along the garage be?

    c.	What is the area of each chicken coop in parts (a) and (b)?

10-11.	The two pentagons at right are similar.

    a.	What is the scale factor between their side lengths?

    b.	What is the scale factor between their areas?

    c.	If the original shape has an area of 60 square centimeters, what is the area of the new shape?

10.1.2 How can I describe the growth?

Compound Interest

So far in this course you have studied simple interest, which only pays interest on the amount invested. It might be used for informal loan arrangements made between parents and children. However, banks and other financial institutions calculate interest in a different way. They commonly use **compound interest**.

In the last lesson you explored how simple interest increases a bank balance and how that growth can be seen in a table and a graph. You also saw that in another situation, where prices grow by 50% each time they increase, the amount added is not constant. In this lesson you will learn about **compound interest** and how to create an expression to describe this non-linear growth. Continue to ask these focus questions in your team:

What patterns do we see?

How can we show the connection?

10-12. Ms. Hartley won $20,000 in the lottery! She decided to spend half of it right away, and invest the other half of the money for her retirement.

The interest rate on the account Ms. Hartley chose is 5%. She calculated that after 10 years, based on simple interest her account balance should be $15,000. But the banker told her that after 10 years the account balance would be $16,289.

A financial adviser explained to her that the bank is paying her **compound interest**. That means that the bank is calculating the interest each year on the total of the principal and any interest she has earned so far, rather than just the $10,000. If Ms. Hartley leaves the money in the account for 30 years, her $10,000 will grow to more than $40,000.

To help Ms. Hartley see the difference between simple interest and compound interest, her adviser made the following tables for her.

Simple Interest		Compound Interest	
Years of Teaching	Account Balance	Years of Teaching	Account Balance
0	$10,000	0	$10,000
5	$12,500	5	$12,763
10	$15,000	10	$16,289
15	$17,500	15	$20,789
20	$20,000	20	$26,533
25	$22,500	25	$33,864
30	$25,000	30	$43,219

a. Explain how you see the interest growing in the simple interest chart.

b. Explain how the interest grows in the compound interest chart.

c. After 30 years, how does the simple interest balance compare to the balance in the compound interest table?

10-13.   Compound interest is calculated on all of the money in an account at specific points in time. Each time interest is calculated it is based on both the principal amount and any interest that was earned before. This is similar to how the price of the baseball card grew in problem 10-3. In that situation each price increase was based on what the seller paid, not on what the card originally cost.

Mariana's grandfather invested $500 for her college tuition in a savings account when she was born. The account pays 5% compound interest every year. How could you figure out how much money was in Mariana's account at the end of one year? How much will be there on her 8th birthday?

a. On the Lesson 10.1.2 Resource Page, complete the middle column of the table to show the account balance each year after the money was deposited. How do you find the new balance each year?

Time (years)	Balance ($)	
0	500	·1.05
1	525	·1.05
2	551.25	
3		
4		
5		
6		

b. Use the information in this column to fill in the "Total Interest Earned" column in the table (on the resource page) to show the total interest earned after any number of years. How can you calculate the total interest earned?

c. Make a graph of the years and total interest earned on the resource page. Work with your team to show the growth in both the table and the graph.

   • What patterns do you see on the graph and in the table?

   • How does the interest increase?

10-14. Mariana is curious how much money will be in her account when she is 18 and graduates from high school. She went back to the table she had created. As she looked at the numbers in the first two columns (years and balance), she noticed a pattern that she thought she could rewrite into a shortcut. Study the table and her work:

Time (years)	Balance ($)	
0	500	
1	525	$= 500 \cdot 1.05$
2	551.25	$= (500 \cdot 1.05) \cdot 1.05$
3	578.81	$= (500 \cdot 1.05 \cdot 1.05) \cdot 1.05$
4		

a. What changes in Mariana's calculations as she works down the table to fill in entries? What patterns do you see in her work?

b. In her calculation for 2 years, what does $(500 \cdot 1.05)$ represent? What is $(500 \cdot 1.05)$ equal to?

c. How could you rewrite Mariana's balance at the end of any year in terms of the principal, $500? **Generalize** the pattern you see in the table in words.

d. Based on this pattern, describe how you would find Mariana's balance after 18 years *without* first finding her balance at 17 years. Then, use your calculator to find out her balance in year 18.

10-15. The pattern you described in words in part (c) of problem 10-14 can be rewritten in symbols using an exponent. For example, $4 \cdot 4 \cdot 4 \cdot 4 \cdot 4$ can be rewritten using an exponent like this:

$$4 \cdot 4 \cdot 4 \cdot 4 \cdot 4 = 4^5$$

Here, 4 is the **base** and 5 is the **exponent** (sometimes called a power). 4^5 is read, *"Four raised to the fifth power"* or *"Four multiplied by itself 5 times."*

a. Write the numbers you multiplied in part (d) of problem 10-14 as an expression using an exponent.

b. Write an expression to represent this situation:

A comic book is purchased for $6. It is resold 7 times, and each time it is resold the seller charges 15% more than she paid for it.

10-16.   Simplify each expression.

   a. 5^3 b. 3^5 c. $\left(\frac{2}{3}\right)^4$ d. $(0.8)^3$

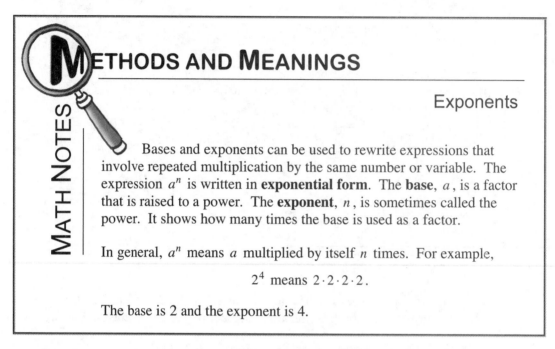

METHODS AND MEANINGS

Exponents

Bases and exponents can be used to rewrite expressions that involve repeated multiplication by the same number or variable. The expression a^n is written in **exponential form**. The **base**, a, is a factor that is raised to a power. The **exponent**, n, is sometimes called the power. It shows how many times the base is used as a factor.

In general, a^n means a multiplied by itself n times. For example,

$$2^4 \text{ means } 2 \cdot 2 \cdot 2 \cdot 2.$$

The base is 2 and the exponent is 4.

Review & Preview

10-17.   Rachel has been given $1000 to put into a savings account. She earns 2% simple interest every month. Rachel hopes to buy a car in two years. Help Rachel determine whether she will have enough money if the car will cost $1500.

10-18.   Jack noticed there was a sale on his favorite model of All-Terrain Vehicle (ATV). The salesperson said the company was cutting the price for that weekend, so Jack got an 8% discount.

   a.   If the usual price of the ATV was $4298, estimate how much the discount will be. Explain your **reasoning**.

   b.   Calculate the amount Jack did pay with the 8% discount.

   c.   If the store sold three of the ATVs that weekend, how much money was saved by the three customers combined?

10-19.   Copy and complete the table at right for powers of 10.

a. Use the pattern in the completed table to decide how many zeros 10^7 will have. How many zeros will 10^{23} have?

b. How would you tell someone to write 10^{50}? Do not actually write the number; just write a sentence telling someone how s/he would write it.

Powers of 10	Standard Form
10^0	
10^1	10
10^2	100
10^3	
10^4	
10^5	

10-20.   Multiply each pair of numbers below.

a. $68 \cdot 100$ b. $0.68 \cdot 100$ c. $6.8 \cdot 1000$

d. Describe in words what is happening to the decimal point in each problem.

10-21.   Rewrite each decimal as a fraction or fraction as a decimal.

a. 0.007   b. 0.103   c. 1.21

d. $\frac{505}{1000}$ e. $\frac{505}{100}$ f. $\frac{2}{100000}$

10-22.   There are 18 chocolate chip cookies, 12 oatmeal cookies, and 10 raisin cookies in a cookie jar. If Miguel takes a cookie from the jar without looking, what is the probability that he does *not* get a chocolate chip cookie? Show your work to support your answer.

10.1.3 What patterns can I see?

Linear and Exponential Growth

Patterns in tables, graphs, and expressions give clues about the kind of growth that is being represented. Today, you will work with your team to identify whether a table, graph, or situation represents simple interest or compound interest based on the kind of growth that is shown. You will also compare the different kinds of interest in situations to see which one is a better deal. By the end of this lesson, you should be able to answer these questions:

> What are the patterns in the tables, graphs, and
> expressions for each kind of interest?

> What are the differences between the two kinds of interest?

> How does the pattern relate to how the amounts are growing?

10-23. John needs to borrow $250. Moneybags Municipal Bank will charge him 8% simple interest each week to borrow the money. Scrooge Savings will charge him 6% compound interest each week. With your team, help John decide which loan is the better choice.

a. Make a table for each bank showing the amount John owes after each week. Graph both tables on the same set of axes.

b. Which bank will charge him more if he pays the loan back in 12 weeks? Should he choose the same bank if he plans to pay back the loan in just 4 weeks?

c. Simple interest is an example of **linear growth**, and compound interest is an example of **exponential growth**. Talk with your team about how you could explain the difference between the two kinds of growth to someone else.

10-24.   The table at right represents the balance in Devin's bank account for the last five months. Has Devin been earning simple interest or compound interest? How do you know?

Time (months)	Balance ($)
0	257.50
1	263.25
2	269.00
3	274.75
4	280.50
5	286.25

10-25.   Imari borrowed money from her uncle to buy a new bicycle. She made the graph at right to show how much interest she will need to pay him if she pays back the loan at different points in time.

Time (months)

a.   About how much interest will Imari owe him if she pays him back in 3 months? When will she owe him $40 in interest?

b.   Is her uncle charging her simple or compound interest? **Justify** your answer. How would the graph be different if he was charging her the other type of interest (simple or compound)?

10-26.   Tom has the option of borrowing $250 from his grandmother, who will charge him simple interest, or the bank, which will charge him compound interest at the same percentage rate. He plans to pay off the loan in 8 months. He wrote the two equations below to figure out how much he would owe for both of these options:

$$250(1.02)^8 \qquad\qquad 250 + 8(5.00)$$

a.   What percent interest will he be charged? Where can you see the rate (percent) in each expression?

b.   Which expression represents the amount he would owe his grandmother? Which one represents what he would owe the bank? **Justify** your conclusion.

c.   Evaluate each expression. From whom should he borrow the money?

10-27.   **Additional Challenge:** Four years ago, Spencer borrowed $50 from his cousin, who charged him a simple interest rate each year. If he pays him back $62 today, what annual interest rate did his cousin charge? Could you figure this out if he had been charged compound interest instead?

10-28.   LEARNING LOG

How can you describe the differences between simple and compound interest? In your Learning Log, write down what each kind of interest looks like in a table, on a graph, and in an expression. Be sure to answer the questions given at the beginning of the lesson (reprinted below). Title this entry, "Simple and Compound Interest" and include today's date.

What are the patterns in the tables, graphs, and expressions for each kind of interest?

What are the differences between the two kinds of interest?

How does this relate to how the amounts are growing?

MATH NOTES

METHODS AND MEANINGS

Compound Interest

Compound interest is interest paid on both the original principal (amount of money at the start) and the interest earned previously.

The formula for compound interest is: $A = P(1+r)^n$

where A = total amount including previous interest earned,
P = principal,
r = interest rate for each compounding period, and
n = number of time periods

Example: Theresa has a student loan that charges a 1.5% monthly compound interest rate. If she currently owes $1425.00 and does not make a payment for a year, how much will she owe at the end of the year (12 months)?

$$A = P(1+r)^n \implies A = 1425(1+0.015)^{12}$$

$$\implies 1425(1.015)^{12} = 1425 \cdot 1.1956 = \$1703.73$$

Theresa will owe $1703.73 after 12 months (1 year).

10-29. Read the Math Notes box about compound interest in this lesson, then answer the questions below.

a. What does the $(1+r)$ represent in the formula? Why are the two quantities added together?

b. If Melanie invests \$2500 at a 3% interest rate compounded annually, how much will she have at the end of four years?

10-30. Simplify each exponential expression.

a. 2^4 b. 3^6 c. 25^3

d. 4^2 e. 9^3 f. 5^6

g. What patterns do you see between the expressions in parts (a) through (f) whose simplified forms are equal?

10-31. Copy and complete the chart at right.

10-32. Divide each pair of numbers below.

a. $75 \div 10$

b. $75 \div 100$

c. $75 \div 1000$

d. Describe in words what happens to the decimal point in each problem.

Exponent Form	Factored Form	Standard Form
2^3	$2 \cdot 2 \cdot 2$	8
3^3		
	$4 \cdot 4 \cdot 4$	
		125
6^3		
7^3		
	$8 \cdot 8 \cdot 8$	
9^3		

10-33. Write and solve a proportion for the following problem.

In a recent survey for the student council, Dominique found that 150 students out of a total of 800 students on campus did *not* like soda. If half of the student body was going to attend a dance, how many students could she expect would want soda?

10-34. The art club has made a scale drawing of the new mural they will paint on the wall of the school. The area of the actual mural is 36 times larger than the area of the drawing. What is the scale factor between the side length of the drawing and the side length of the mural?

10.1.4 How can I rewrite it?

Exponents and Scientific Notation

Earlier in this chapter you worked with expressions for interest problems. You could rewrite them in simpler ways using multiplication in place of repeated addition, and use exponents in place of repeated multiplication. Rewriting expressions in different forms can be a powerful tool for simplifying expressions and for seeing patterns. In this lesson, you will develop new ways of rewriting expressions using exponents.

10-35.   Is 3^5 the same as $3 \cdot 5$? Explain.

10-36.   Exponents allow you to rewrite some multiplication problems in a simpler form. Can exponent expressions also be simplified? Complete the table below on the Lesson 10.1.4 Resource Page, or copy and complete it on your own paper.

Original Form	Factored Form	Simplified Form
$5^2 \cdot 5^5$	$(5 \cdot 5) \cdot (5 \cdot 5 \cdot 5 \cdot 5 \cdot 5)$	5^7
$2^2 \cdot 2^4$		
$3^7 \cdot 3^2$		
$x^3 \cdot x^5$		
$x^3 y^2 \cdot xy^2$		
$7^2 \cdot x^3 \cdot 7 \cdot x^2$		
$2 \cdot x^4 \cdot 3 \cdot xy^2$		

a.   Work with your team to compare the bases and exponents of the original form to the base and exponent of the simplified form. Write a statement to describe the relationships you see.

b.   **Visualize** how you would expand $20^{12} \cdot 20^{51}$ in your mind. What would this expression be in a simplified form? Describe your **reasoning**.

c.   One study team rewrote the expression $10^3 \cdot 5^4$ as 50^7. Is their simplification correct? Explain your **reasoning**.

10-37.　When you multiply, the order of the factors does not matter. That means that you will get the same answer if you multiply $3 \cdot 2 \cdot 3$ and if you multiply $2 \cdot 3 \cdot 3$. This is the **Commutative Property of Multiplication**.

　　a.　Check that $2 \cdot 10$ is equal to $10 \cdot 2$. Is it also true that $2 \div 10$ is equal to $10 \div 2$?

　　b.　Write the expression $5^2 \cdot x^4 \cdot 5x$ in factored form. Explain how the Commutative Property helps you to simplify the expression to equal $5^3 \cdot x^5$.

10-38.　Multiplying a number by 10 changes the number in a special way. Simplify each expression below without using a calculator. As you work, pay attention to how the number changes when you multiply it by powers of 10.

　　a.　$9.23 \cdot 10$　　　　　　　　b.　$9.23 \cdot 10^2$

　　c.　$9.23 \cdot 10^3$　　　　　　　　d.　$9.23 \cdot 10^4$

10-39.　Talk with your team about any patterns you see in your answers in problem 10-38. Based on those patterns, what do you think $9.23 \cdot 10^7$ would be? Why?

　　a.　Use the patterns you have found to predict the product for each expression without calculating it.

　　　　i.　78.659×10^2　　　　　　　　ii.　346.38×10^5

　　b.　With your team, write a statement describing **in general** how you can quickly multiply by powers of 10. You may want to include information about where the decimal point moves after multiplying the number by a power of 10 or why you have to add zeros. Work with your team to write a clear explanation for why this pattern works.

10-40.   When astronomers describe distances in space, often the numbers are so large that they are difficult to write. For example, the diameter of the sun is approximately one million, three hundred ninety thousand kilometers, or 1,390,000 km. To make these numbers easier to write, astronomers use **scientific notation**. Using scientific notation, the diameter of the sun is:

$$1.39 \times 10^6 \text{ km}$$

a.   Rewrite 10^6 as a single number without an exponent. What happens when you multiply 1.39 by this number?

b.   In scientific notation, the mass of the sun is approximately 1.99×10^{30} kg. What does this number mean? Discuss with your team how to rewrite this number without scientific notation, then write it.

10-41.   Scientific notation requires that one factor is a power of 10, and the other factor is a number greater than or equal to 1 but less than 10. For example, 2.56×10^5 is written in scientific notation, but 25.6×10^4 is not. Scientific notation also uses the symbol "×" for multiplication instead of "·" or parentheses. None of the numbers below are correctly written in scientific notation. Explain why each one does not meet the criteria for scientific notation, then write it using correct scientific notation.

a. 25.6×10^4 b. $5.46 \cdot 100$ c. 0.93×10^8

10-42.   Scientific notation makes large numbers easier to write, but it also provides you with quick information about the size of the numbers. For example, Pluto and Haumea are both dwarf planets. Pluto has a mass of 1.305×10^{22} kilograms and Haumea has a mass of 4.006×10^{21} kilograms.

Without rewriting the mass of each planet, can you tell which of these dwarf planets is larger? Explain your **reasoning**.

10-43.   **Reverse** your thinking. Write each number below in scientific notation.

a.   370,000,000   b.   48,710,000,000

METHODS AND MEANINGS

Commutative and Associative Properties of Multiplication

When two numbers or variables are combined together using multiplication, the order in which they are multiplied does not matter. This fact is known as the **Commutative Property of Multiplication**, so $5 \cdot 10 = 10 \cdot 5$. This result may be generalized using variables as:

$$a \cdot b = b \cdot a$$

Note that division does not satisfy the Commutative Property of Multiplication since $10 \div 5 \neq 5 \div 10$.

When three factors are multiplied together, we usually multiply the first two of them together and then multiply that product by the third factor. However, we could also multiply the last two together and then multiply the first with that product. The **Associative Property of Multiplication** tells us that the order in which three or more numbers are multiplied together does not matter. The answer to the problem $(5 \cdot (-6)) \cdot 10$ is equal to $5 \cdot (-6 \cdot 10)$. This is generalized using variables as:

$$(a \cdot b) \cdot c = a \cdot (b \cdot c)$$

Note that division is not associative since $(10 \div 2) \div 5 \neq 10 \div (2 \div 5)$
$$5 \div 5 \neq 10 \div 0.4$$

Review & Preview

10-44.   Which number is greater, 3.56×10^4 or 1.9×10^6. Explain how you know.

10-45.   Rewrite each of the expressions below in a simpler form using exponents.

a. $4 \cdot 4 \cdot 5 \cdot 5 \cdot 5$ b. $3 \cdot 3 \cdot 3 \cdot 3 \cdot 3 \cdot y \cdot y$ c. $(6x)(6x)(6x)(6x)$

10-46. Maria and Jorge were trying to simplify the expression $1\frac{2}{5} \cdot (-\frac{3}{4}) \cdot (-\frac{4}{3})$. Maria started by rewriting $1\frac{2}{5}$ as $\frac{7}{5}$. Her work is below.

$$1\frac{2}{5} \cdot (-\frac{3}{4}) \cdot (-\frac{4}{3})$$

$$\frac{7}{5} \cdot (-\frac{3}{4}) \cdot (-\frac{4}{3})$$

$$(-\frac{21}{20}) \cdot (-\frac{4}{3})$$

$$\frac{84}{60} = 1\frac{24}{60} = 1\frac{2}{5}$$

Jorge had a different idea. He multiplied $(-\frac{3}{4}) \cdot (-\frac{4}{3})$ first.

a. Simplify the expression $1\frac{2}{5} \cdot (-\frac{3}{4}) \cdot (-\frac{4}{3})$ using Jorge's method. Is your answer equal to Maria's?

b. Why might Jorge have decided to multiply $(-\frac{3}{4}) \cdot (-\frac{4}{3})$ first?

c. In a multiplication problem, the factors can be grouped together in different ways. This is called the **Associative Property of Multiplication**. Read the Math Notes box for this lesson, then show that $(\frac{3}{4} \cdot \frac{2}{5}) \cdot (-2) = \frac{3}{4} \cdot \left(\frac{2}{5} \cdot (-2)\right)$.

d. Simplify each expression. First, decide if you want to group some factors together.

   i. $(-9) \cdot (\frac{1}{9}) \cdot (\frac{3}{8})$ ii. $-\frac{5}{12} \cdot \frac{3}{7} \cdot \frac{4}{9}$ iii. $-8.1 \cdot 5 \cdot 2$

10-47. Calculate the following products.

Factors	Product
6.5901×10^2	
0.6893×10^7	
5.86×10^4	
0.092×10^3	

10-48. Simplify each expression.

   a. 6^5 b. $\left(\frac{2}{3}\right)^3$ c. $(2+3)^4$ d. $2(-\frac{1}{2}+\frac{3}{4})^3$

10-49. Determine the compound interest earned on $220 invested at 3.25% compounded annually for 6 years.

10.1.5 How can I write it in simpler form?

Exponent Rules

In the previous lesson you expanded expressions written with exponents into factored form and then rewrote them in simpler form (problem 10-36). You also looked at ways to rewrite very large numbers in order to compare them easily.

In this lesson you will continue to develop ways to rewrite expressions using exponents. Use the questions below to focus discussion in your study team:

> What part of the expression is being raised to a power?

> What are the factors?

> How can we rewrite the expression to have fewer terms?

10-50. Rewrite each expression below in a simpler form.

a. $10^2 \cdot x^3 \cdot 10 \cdot y$ b. $20^3 \cdot 20^8$ c. $x^2 y^2 z^2 \cdot x^3 z^5$

10-51. Erin wants to rewrite the expression $5^2 x^2 \cdot 5^4 x^3$ in simpler form. She started by expanding the expression like this:

$$5 \cdot 5 + x \cdot x + 5 \cdot 5 \cdot 5 \cdot 5 + x \cdot x \cdot x$$
$$25 + x^2 + 625 + x^3$$

Do you agree with her work so far? Work with your team to complete the problem or, if you do not agree, to write Erin a note explaining how to correct her work.

10-52.   When a number is raised to a power, and then raised to a power again, the result follows a consistent pattern. Copy the table below or find it on the Lesson 10.1.5 Resource Page. Complete the table by expanding each expression into factored form and then rewriting it with new exponents.

Original Form	Factored Form	Simplified Form
$(5^2)^5$	$(5 \cdot 5)(5 \cdot 5)(5 \cdot 5)(5 \cdot 5)(5 \cdot 5)$	5^{10}
$(2^2)^4$		
$(3^7)^2$		
$(x^3)^5$		
$(x^3 y^2)^2$		

a.   Work with your team to describe the pattern between the exponents in the original form and the exponent(s) in the simplified form.

b.   **Visualize** $(20^3)^8$ written in factored form. What is multiplied, that is, what is the base? How many times is it multiplied? Use the expression you **visualized** to help you rewrite the expression in simplified form. Describe in detail how you figured out what exponent to use in the simplified form.

10-53.   In problem 10-50 you simplified the expression $20^3 \cdot 20^8$. Compare the factored form you wrote for that expression to the expression you **visualized** in part (b) of problem 10-52. How are the two expressions different?

10-54. Heidi is trying to rewrite the two expressions below.

$$(2x)^3 \qquad 2x^3$$

"Are these two ways of writing the same thing? Or do they mean something different?" Heidi wonders.

a. Rewrite $(2x)^3$ by expanding and then simplifying. What part is being raised to the third power? What is the result?

b. Heidi thinks $2x^3$ is the same as $2 \cdot x^3$. Do you agree? If so, how would you expand the expression?

c. Are $(2x)^3$ and $2x^3$ equivalent? Explain why or why not.

10-55. Alex was trying to simplify the exponent expression $\frac{5^7}{5^3}$, and started by writing out the factored form. Once he saw the factors he recognized a Giant One in his work.

a. Copy Alex's expression on your paper and write out the factored form. Where did he see a Giant One?

b. Work with your study team to use the Giant One to simplify and rewrite the expression. What is the result?

10-56. Expand each expression below into factored form, then rewrite it in simplified form.

a. $\dfrac{2^4}{2^2}$
    b. $\dfrac{3^4}{3^5}$
    c. $\dfrac{y^7}{y^4}$
    d. $\dfrac{x^3 y^2}{x y^2}$

10-57. Two of the problems below are correct, and four contain errors. Expand each original expression to verify that it is correct. If it is not, identify the mistake and simplify to find the correct answer.

a. $x^3 y^2 x^4 \overset{?}{=} x^7 y^2$
    b. $2^3 \cdot 2^4 \overset{?}{=} 2^{12}$

c. $\dfrac{7^2 \cdot 8^3}{7^3 \cdot 8^2} \overset{?}{=} \dfrac{8}{7}$
    d. $3^5 \cdot 3^2 \overset{?}{=} 9^7$

e. $\dfrac{6^2}{6^5} \overset{?}{=} 6^3$
    f. $\dfrac{z^3}{z^3} \overset{?}{=} 0$

10-58.   **LEARNING LOG**

You have worked with your team to describe ways to
rewrite and simplify exponent expressions involving
multiplication and division. In your Learning Log, give
examples of each kind of expression. Describe in words
how to rewrite each one. Include factored and simplified
expressions to go with your descriptions. Title this entry,
"Simplifying Exponent Expressions," and label it with
today's date.

10-59.   Rewrite each expression in a simpler form using the patterns you have found for
rewriting expressions with exponents. If it is reasonable, write out the factored
form to help you.

a. $2^3 \cdot 2^4$
b. $\dfrac{2^8}{2^5}$
c. $(5x^2)^3$
d. $(4x)^2(5x^2)$

10-60.   **Additional Challenge:** Alice was simplifying the
expressions at right when she noticed a pattern.
Each exponent under the radical (square root) sign
was two times the exponent of the final answer.
She wanted to know more about why this was
happening.

$$\sqrt{3^4} = \sqrt{81} = 9 = 3^2$$
$$\sqrt{6^2} = \sqrt{36} = 6 = 6^1$$
$$\sqrt{5^4} = \sqrt{625} = 25 = 5^2$$
$$\sqrt{2^6} = \sqrt{64} = 8 = 2^3$$

a.   Confirm Alice's pattern by simplifying the expression $\sqrt{5^6}$ on your
calculator. Can you rewrite your answer as five raised to a power?

b.   What does the operation "square root" do to an expression? What operation
does it "**undo**"?

c.   Investigate this pattern using the expression $\sqrt{4^6}$.

 • Expand the expression.

 • Rewrite 4^6 as an expression raised to the second power.

 • Use the square root to "**undo**" the squaring.

 • Write your final answer, and check it on your calculator.

d.   Use that thinking to rewrite each expression below.

 i. $\sqrt{7^4}$
 ii. $\sqrt{9^8}$
 iii. $\sqrt{3^{14}}$

Making Connections: Course 2

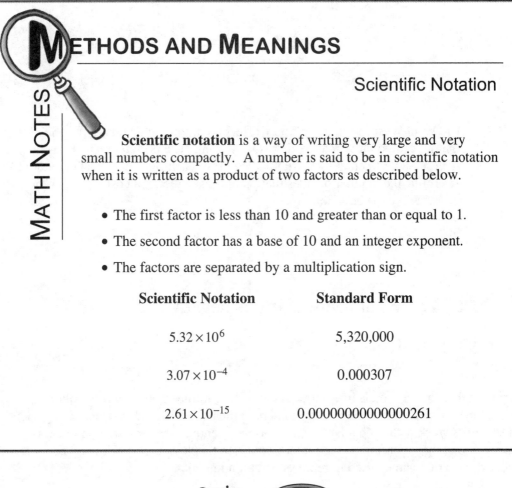

METHODS AND MEANINGS

Scientific Notation

MATH NOTES

Scientific notation is a way of writing very large and very small numbers compactly. A number is said to be in scientific notation when it is written as a product of two factors as described below.

- The first factor is less than 10 and greater than or equal to 1.
- The second factor has a base of 10 and an integer exponent.
- The factors are separated by a multiplication sign.

Scientific Notation	Standard Form
5.32×10^6	5,320,000
3.07×10^{-4}	0.000307
2.61×10^{-15}	0.00000000000000261

Review & Preview

10-61.   Simplify each expression.

a. $\dfrac{3^2 \cdot 5^3 \cdot 8}{3 \cdot 5^3 \cdot 8}$ b. $(3x)^4$ c. $3^3 \cdot 3^5 \cdot (\tfrac{1}{3})^2$ d. $\dfrac{7^4 \cdot 9^2}{9^3 \cdot 7^2}$

10-62.   Gail bought a new baseball cap for $7.50, which was $\frac{1}{3}$ off the original price. What was the original price?

10-63.   Find the missing side on this right triangle.

x cm

8 cm

17 cm

10-64.　Simplify each expression.

a.　$\frac{9}{15} \div \frac{4}{3}$　　　b.　$-\frac{19}{20} + \frac{4}{5}$　　　c.　$-\frac{8}{9} \div (-\frac{2}{5})$　　d.　$3\frac{1}{2} \div 1\frac{1}{7}$

e.　$-\frac{3}{4} - (-\frac{11}{16})$　f.　$\frac{2}{9} \cdot \frac{14}{15} \cdot (-\frac{9}{10})$　g.　$-10\frac{4}{5} + (-\frac{3}{8})$　h.　$\frac{12}{5} \div (-\frac{1}{10})$

10-65.　The Wild West Frontier Park now offers an unlimited day pass. For $29.00, visitors can go on as many rides as they want. The original plan charged visitors $8.75 to enter the park plus $2.25 for each ride. Write an equation to determine the number of rides that would make the total cost equal for the two plans. Solve the equation.

10.1.6 What happens if it is negative?

Negative Exponents

Earlier in this chapter you learned how to write large numbers in scientific notation. Those large numbers are used by astronomers to measure the great distances in space. Not all scientists work with such a large scale. Some scientists use very small numbers to describe what they measure under a microscope. In this lesson you will learn about how scientific notation can be used to represent small numbers.

10-66.　Salvador was studying microscopic pond animals in science class. He read that amoebas were 0.3 millimeters to 0.6 millimeters in length. He saw that euglenas are as small as $8.0 \cdot 10^{-2}$ millimeters, but he did not know how big or small a measurement that was. He decided to try to figure out what a negative exponent could mean.

a.　Copy and complete Salvador's calculations at right. Use the pattern of dividing by 10 to fill in the missing values.

b.　How is 10^2 related to 10^{-2} ?

c.　What type of numbers did the negative exponents create? Did negative exponents create negative numbers?

$$10^3 = 1000$$
$$10^2 = 100$$　$\div 10$
$$10^1 = 10$$　$\div 10$
$$10^0 =$$　$\div 10$
$$10^{-1} =$$
$$10^{-2} =$$
$$10^{-3} =$$

10-67. Ngoc was curious about what Salvador was doing and began exploring patterns himself. He completed the calculations at right.

$2^5 = 32$

$2^4 = 16$

$2^3 = 8$

...

...

$2^{-1} = \frac{1}{2}$

$2^{-2} =$

$2^{-3} =$

   a. Copy and complete his calculations. Be sure to include all of the integer exponents from 5 to −3.

   b. Look for patterns in his list. How are the values to the right of the equal sign changing? Is there a constant multiplier between each value?

10-68. In problems 10-66 and 10-67 you saw that 10^0 and 2^0 both simplify to the same value. What is it? Do you think that any number to the zero power would have the same answer? Explain.

10-69. Both Ngoc and Salvador are looking for ways to calculate values with negative exponents without extending a pattern. Looking at the expression 5^{-2}, they each started to simplify differently.

Salvador thinks that 5^2 is 25, so 5^{-2} must be $\frac{1}{25}$. Ngoc thinks 5^{-2} is $\frac{1}{5} \cdot \frac{1}{5}$. Which student is correct?

10-70. **Reverse** your thinking. If negative exponents can create fractions, then can fractions be written as expressions including negative exponents? Simplify the expressions below. Write your answer in two different forms: as a fraction and as an expression with a negative exponent.

   a. $\dfrac{6^3}{6^5}$ b. $\dfrac{3^2}{3^6}$ c. $\dfrac{m^5}{m^6}$ d. $\dfrac{b^2}{b^5}$

10-71. Salvador's first questions about negative exponents came from science class where he had learned that euglenas measured 8.0×10^{-2} millimeters. Use your understanding of negative exponents to rewrite 8.0×10^{-2} in standard form.

10-72.   The list below contains a star, a river and a type of bacteria. Which one is
          which? Use your understanding of scientific notation to put the three items
          listed below in order from largest to smallest. Which of these items is very
          small? Explain how you know.

    a.   Yangtze measures 6.3×10^5 meters

    b.   Staphylococcus measures 6×10^{-7} meters

    c.   Eta Carinae measures 7.1×10^{17} meters

10-73.   Which of the numbers below are written in scientific notation? For each that is
          not, rewrite it correctly.

    a. 4.51×10^{-2} b. 0.789×10^5 c. 31.5×10^2 d. 3.008×10^{-8}

10-74.   Rewrite each expression in a simpler form. **Visualize** the factored form to help
          you, or write it out if it is reasonable to do so.

    a. $2^3 \cdot 2^4$ b. $\dfrac{2^8}{2^5}$ c. $(5x^2)^3$ d. $(4x)^2(5x^2)$

10-75.   **Additional Challenge:** Lamar has a list of 600 words to learn for the upcoming
          spelling bee. His goal is to learn half of the words left on his list each day.

    a.   How many words will Lamar have to learn the first day? How many will
         he have left to learn after 3 days?

    b.   How many words will he need to learn on day 8? With your team, write
         two different expressions to show how you found your answer.

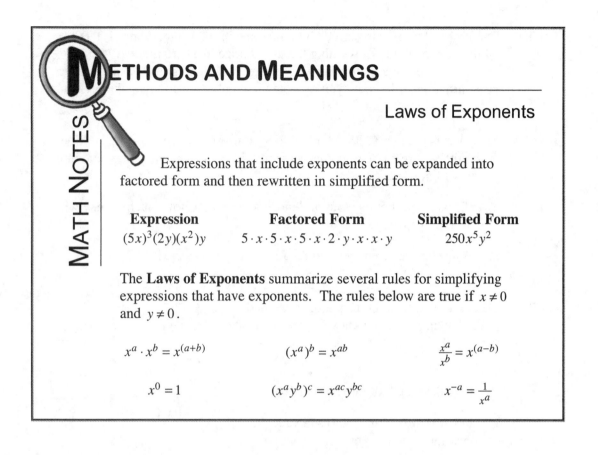

METHODS AND MEANINGS

Laws of Exponents

Expressions that include exponents can be expanded into factored form and then rewritten in simplified form.

Expression	Factored Form	Simplified Form
$(5x)^3(2y)(x^2)y$	$5 \cdot x \cdot 5 \cdot x \cdot 5 \cdot x \cdot 2 \cdot y \cdot x \cdot x \cdot y$	$250x^5y^2$

The **Laws of Exponents** summarize several rules for simplifying expressions that have exponents. The rules below are true if $x \neq 0$ and $y \neq 0$.

$$x^a \cdot x^b = x^{(a+b)} \qquad (x^a)^b = x^{ab} \qquad \frac{x^a}{x^b} = x^{(a-b)}$$

$$x^0 = 1 \qquad (x^a y^b)^c = x^{ac}y^{bc} \qquad x^{-a} = \frac{1}{x^a}$$

Review & Preview

10-76. Decide which numbers below are correctly written in scientific notation. If they are not, rewrite them.

a. 92.5×10^{-2} b. 6.875×10^2 c. 2.8×10 d. 0.83×100^2

10-77. In the table at right, write each power of 10 as a decimal and as a fraction.

a. Describe how the decimals and fractions change as you progress down the table.

b. How would you tell someone how to write 10^{-12} as a fraction? You do not have to write the actual fraction.

Power of 10	Decimal Form	Fraction Form
1		
10^{-1}	0.1	$\frac{1}{10}$
10^{-2}		$\frac{1}{100}$
10^{-3}		
10^{-4}		
10^{-5}		

10-78.   The probability of being struck by lightening in the United States is 0.000032%, while the probability of winning the grand prize in a certain lottery is 6.278×10^{-7} percent. Which event is more likely to happen? Explain your **reasoning**, including how you rewrote the numbers to compare them.

10-79.   Mary wants to have $8500 to travel to South America when she is 21. She currently has $6439 in a savings account earning 4% annual compound interest. Mary is 13 now.

   a.   If Mary does not take out or deposit any money, how much money will Mary have when she is 15?

   b.   Will Mary have enough money for her trip when she is 21?

10-80.   Daniel needed to paint his patio, so he made a scale drawing of it. He knows the width of the patio is 10 feet, but the scale drawing is in inches.

   a.   Find the length of the patio in feet.

   b.   Find the area of the patio so Daniel knows how much paint to buy.

   c.   One can of paint covers 125 square feet. How many cans of paint will Daniel need to buy?

10.2.1   Does surface area affect volume?

Surface Area and Volume

In your work with two-dimensional (flat) shapes you have described their dimensions, their perimeters, and their areas. For three-dimensional shapes — shapes that have length, width, *and* depth — you can measure the lengths of their edges and calculate the areas of their faces (sides). Three-dimensional shapes can also be described by their volume, that is, how much space they enclose. Today you will work with rectangle-based prisms. As you work, keep these questions in mind:

How many cubes would it take to fill it?

How many squares would it take to cover the outside of it?

Making Connections: Course 2

10-81.   PERFECT PACKAGING

Cereal boxes come in different shapes and sizes. Some are tall and skinny, others are shorter or deeper. The Bravo Breakfast cereal company is considering changing the size of its box, and the staff need some data to help them make the best choice.

The company currently packages its Morning Math Crunch cereal in a box that is 2" deep by 4" wide by 8" tall, as pictured at right. This shape is called a **right rectangular prism** because the top and bottom faces are rectangles that are congruent and parallel to each other. These are called the **bases**. The other faces (sides of the box) are also rectangles that are perpendicular to the bases. Use a set of cubes to build a model of this box. Assume that the edge of one cube represents 1" of length on the real cereal box.

a.   Describe the box as completely as you can.

- What shapes do you see when you look at the faces of the box?

- What lengths or other measurements can you describe?

- Sketch each shape on your paper, and label it completely.

b.   The cardboard sides of the box are called its **faces**. How much cardboard is needed to create all of the faces of the box? Work with your team to develop a method for calculating this amount. Discuss the kind of units to use. Be ready to explain your method to the class.

c.   The square units that it takes to cover the outside of an object, like the amount of cardboard you found in part (b), is called the object's **surface area**. The **volume** of a shape is the measure of how much it will hold. Volume is measured in cubic units.

How many cubes did you use to make this model of the cereal box? How many cubic inches of cereal will the box hold?

10-82. The waste management division at Bravo Breakfast is worried that the box for Morning Math Crunch uses too much cardboard. They want to make a box that holds the same amount of cereal but uses less cardboard.

a. What measurement of the box is the waste management division interested in **minimizing** (making as small as possible)? What measurement does the company want to keep the same? What could change?

b. With your team, use the cubes to build different rectangular prisms that will hold 64 cubic inches of cereal. Each box must be a rectangular prism with exactly six faces. For each prism you create:

- Sketch the prism.

- Label the dimensions on your sketch.

- Find the surface area.

How many different prisms can you make?

c. Do all of the prisms you built have the same volume? How do you know?

d. Which box will use the smallest amount of cardboard?

10-83. Use cubes to build each prism below. Find the surface area and volume of each shape.

a.

b.

c. Use at least 15 cubes to build a prism of your own design. Sketch the prism and find its surface area and volume.

d. Write step-by-step directions explaining to another student how to find the surface area of a prism. You may want to use one of the prisms above as an example. Give **reasons** for each step.

MΕΤΗΟDS AND MEANINGS

MATH NOTES

Polygons, Prisms, and Pyramids

A **polygon** is a two-dimensional closed figure made of straight-line segments connected end to end. The segments may not cross. The point where two sides meet is called a **vertex** (plural: vertices). Polygons are named by the number of sides they have. Polygons with three through 10 sides are named and illustrated below:

Triangle:

Hexagon:

Nonagon:

Quadrilateral:

Septagon:

Decagon:

Pentagon:

Octagon:

Three-dimensional figures are those that have length, width, and height. If a three-dimensional figure is completely bounded by polygons and their interiors, it is a **polyhedron**. The polygons are called **faces**, and an **edge** is where two faces meet. A cube and a pyramid are each an example of a polyhedron.

face

edges

A **prism** is a special kind of polyhedron that has two congruent, parallel faces called **bases**. The other faces (called **lateral faces**) are parallelograms (or rectangles). No holes are permitted in the solid.

A prism is named for the shape of its base. For example:

triangular prism

pentagonal prism

A **pyramid** is a three-dimensional figure with a base that is a polygon. The lateral faces are formed by connecting each vertex of the base to a single point (the vertex of the pyramid) that is above or below the surface that contains the base.

10-84.   Read the Math Notes box in this lesson. Use the information to determine
          whether each shape below is a polygon.

a. b.   c.   d.

10-85.   Find the volume and surface area of each shape below. Assume that the edge of
          each cube measures 1".

a.   b.   c.

10-86.   Copy the graph at right on graph paper.
          Draw a line through the two points.

          a.   What is the slope of the line?

          b.   What is the rule for all points on the line?

10-87.   Simplify each of the following expressions.

          a. $8^2 + 7^2$ b. $7^2 \cdot 7 \cdot 7$ c. $(\frac{1}{2})^2 + (\frac{2}{3})^2$

          d. $(2^2 + 6)^2$ e. $-4 \cdot 3^2 - 2$ f. $x - x$

          g. $3 \cdot 3 \div 3$ h. $4x + x - 2x$ i. $-2 \cdot 4 \div 4$

10-88.   Juan found that 20 new pencils weigh 12 ounces.
          How much will 50 new pencils weigh? Show your
          reasoning.

10-89. A principal made the histogram at right to analyze how many years teachers had been teaching at her school.

a. How many teachers work at her school?

b. If the principal randomly chose one teacher to represent the school at a conference, what is the probability that the teacher would have been teaching at the school for more than 10 years? Write the probability in two different ways.

c. What is the probability that a teacher on the staff has been there for fewer than 5 years?

10.2.2 How can I visualize it?

Visualizing Three-Dimensional Shapes

Can you picture what something will look like, even before you see it built? Are you able to look at leftovers after a meal and decide what size container you will need in order to hold them, or do you often choose a container that is too big or too small? Being able to **visualize** what something will look like in a different form or shape is a useful skill that can be developed with practice. Today you will work with your team to **visualize** different three-dimensional shapes.

10-90. Your teacher will show you a cardboard box. What will this box look like when it is unfolded and flattened out? Look carefully at the box and discuss possibilities with your team. Draw a picture or write a description of the unfolded box.

10-91. Picture in your mind each figure below as a three-dimensional object. What would each shape look like if it were unfolded so that each face was flat on the table? A flat picture that can be folded up to form a three-dimensional solid is called a **net**. Work with your team to draw a net for each of the shapes below. Listen carefully to your teammates' ideas, because there is more than one way to unfold each shape.

a.

b.

10-92. Mark and Thomas are looking at the two nets shown below. They have decided that each one will form a pyramid, but they disagree about whether the pyramids will be identical or not. Look carefully at the two nets, and decide whether you agree that they will each form a pyramid. Then, explain what the boys should compare about the two nets to decide if the shapes will be identical when they are built.

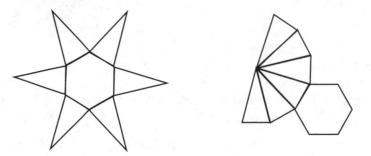

10-93.   SHAPE VISUALIZATION CHALLENGE

How much can you tell about a shape from its net? In this challenge, each member of your study team will receive a different net for a three-dimensional solid. Together, you must describe each shape completely *without building it*. Use the questions below to help you make a complete description.

Will the shape be a pyramid or a prism?

What shape is the base?

Will the shape be tall or short?

Will the shape be narrow or wide?

How many different faces will it have?

When you are satisfied that you have described as much as you can, call your teacher over to check that your description is complete. If it is, cut out the net and fold it into the shape to check your work.

Net A   Net B   Net C   Net D

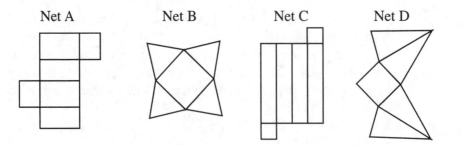

Making Connections: Course 2

10-94.   When the nets in problem 10-93 are cut and folded to create solids, which solid has the greatest surface area? Write down a prediction along with your **justification**. Then test your prediction by measuring the dimensions of your shape in centimeters, calculating the surface area and sharing your data with your team. Was your prediction correct?

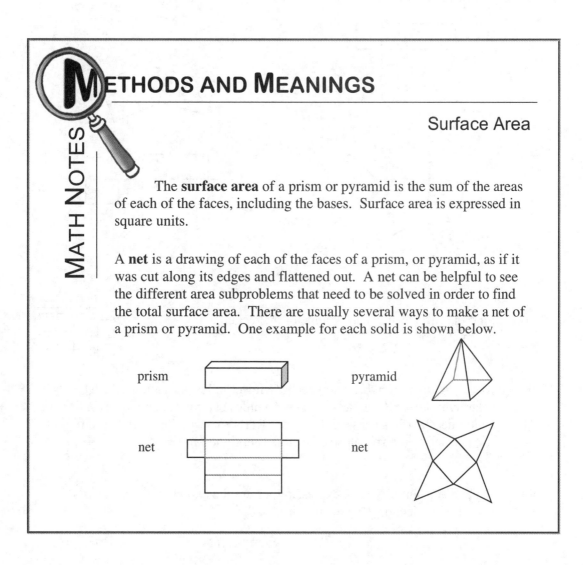

METHODS AND MEANINGS

Surface Area

The **surface area** of a prism or pyramid is the sum of the areas of each of the faces, including the bases. Surface area is expressed in square units.

A **net** is a drawing of each of the faces of a prism, or pyramid, as if it was cut along its edges and flattened out. A net can be helpful to see the different area subproblems that need to be solved in order to find the total surface area. There are usually several ways to make a net of a prism or pyramid. One example for each solid is shown below.

prism

net

pyramid

net

10-95.   Which net(s) below will fold up to make a complete prism? If a net will not form a prism, explain what is wrong.

a.

b.

c.

d.

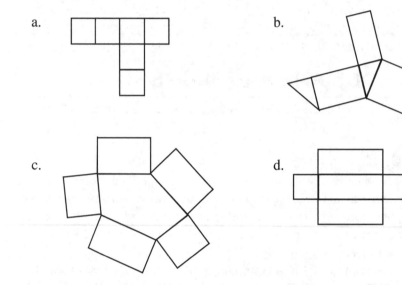

10-96.   Find the surface area and volume of the rectangular prism at right.

10-97.   Karla's traditional hybrid car gets 35% fewer miles per gallon than Jeenie's solar hybrid car. If Jeenie's car gets 60 miles per gallon, how many miles per gallon does Karla's car get? Calculate Karla's car's mileage in two different ways, using two different scale factors (multipliers).

10-98.   Expand and simplify each expression, or use the exponent patterns you identified in Section 10.1 to simplify.

a. $\dfrac{x^4}{x^3}$ b. $(x^3)^4$ c. $(2y^2)^2$ d. $(x^2)^4$

e. x^2x^{-3} f. $(xy^2)^2$ g. $(x^2y^2)^4$ h. $(2x)^3$

10-99.   Josue called his father to say that he was almost home. He had traveled 61.5 miles, which was $\frac{3}{4}$ of the way home. Write and solve an equation to calculate the total distance he will travel to get home.

10.2.3 How much will fill it?

Volume of a Prism

You have had a lot of practice with finding the area of flat, two-dimensional shapes. Today you will begin using those skills to help you understand shapes with a third dimension. As you work on the problem, consider the following questions:

How can I see the shape in layers?

How can I slice the shape so that the layers are identical?

10-100.   BIRTHDAY SWEETS

Laverne is making a birthday dessert for her cousin Leslie. She wants to incorporate Leslie's favorite ingredients, cookies and chocolate mousse. She will make the dessert in a special L-shaped pan that is 9.5 cm deep.

First, Laverne is going to make a cookie crust as the bottom layer. The crust will be 1 cm thick so that it is nice and crunchy. She is going to add chocolate mousse on top of the crust until the mousse is 7 cm thick. Finally, she will add a 1.5 cm layer of whipped cream on the mousse and top it with chocolate sprinkles.

top view

36 cm

22 cm

12 cm

24 cm

1.5 cm whipped cream

7 cm chocolate mousse

1 cm cookie crust

a.   What area will the dessert cover (in square centimeters) on the pan?

b.   Laverne needs to know what quantity of cookies to buy to make the crust layer of the dessert. Does the measurement she needs describe length, area, or volume? Discuss this with your team, and then write down your explanation.

c.   One cookie will crush into about 5 cubic centimeters of cookie crumbs. Show Laverne how to find out how many cookies she will need to make the crust layer. Be sure to explain your **reasoning**. How many cookies should she buy?

10-101. Laverne wants the mousse on top of the crust to be seven cm thick. Use your answer from part (c) of problem 10-100 to help you figure out how many cubic centimeters of mousse Laverne will need. Explain your **reasoning**.

10-102. Laverne has 1200 cubic centimeters of whipped cream ready to spread on top of the mousse. Erika looked at Laverne's notes about how much cream she would need and exclaimed, *"You have too much! You will overflow the pan!"*

How could Erika know that Laverne has too much whipped cream? Be prepared to share your ideas with the class.

10-103. Laverne needs to be sure that her finished dessert will be enough to serve everyone.

   a. What is the total volume of dessert that Laverne is planning to make? Be ready to share your study team's **strategy** with the class.

   b. If one serving is 285 cm³, how many people will the dessert serve?

10-104. For the prism at right, find the volume of a one cm high layer. Then, find the total volume of the prism. Every face is a rectangle.

10-105. When finding the volume of the shape below, Audrey found the volume of the shaded layer first. Her work is shown below:

$$5 + 20 = 25, \text{ so } 25 \cdot 8 = 200 \text{ ft}^3$$

Then she said, *"The shape is 22 feet high, so there are 22 one-foot-high layers."* She then multiplied and got this answer:

$$22 \cdot 200 = 4400 \text{ ft}^3$$

   a. What was Audrey's mistake?

   b. What is the actual volume of the shape? Explain how you found it.

METHODS AND MEANINGS

Measurement in Different Dimensions

Measurements of **length** are measurements in **one dimension**. They are labeled as cm, ft, km, etc.

1 centimeter

Measurements of **area** are measurements in **two dimensions**. They are labeled as cm², ft², m², etc.

$1 \text{ cm} \times 1\text{cm} = 1 \text{ cm}^2$

Measurements of **volume** are measurements **in three dimensions**. They are labeled as cm³, ft³, m³, etc.

$1 \text{ cm} \times 1 \text{ cm} \times 1 \text{ cm} = 1 \text{ cm}^3$

MATH NOTES

Review & Preview

10-106.   Find the surface area and volume of the prism shown at right.

10-107.   Find the area of each circle below.

a.   radius = 8 cm

b.
60 cm

10-108.   Write each number in scientific notation.

a.   5467.8   b.   0.0032   c.   8,007,020

10-109. Find the missing length on this right triangle.

30 mm

7 mm

10-110. Graph the rule $y = -3x + 2$.

    a. What is the slope?   b. What is the y-intercept?

10-111. Simplify each of the following expressions.

    a. $3\frac{1}{5} \cdot \frac{7}{4}$ b. $5^3 \cdot (-\frac{4}{5})$ c. $2^4 \cdot \frac{5}{8}$ d. $-\frac{1}{2} \cdot 3^2$

    e. $-\frac{5}{6} + (\frac{1}{2})^2$ f. $(-\frac{4}{5})^2 - \frac{3}{50}$ g. $(\frac{3}{10})^2 - (-\frac{2}{5})^2$ h. $8^2(-\frac{7}{8}) - \frac{1}{2}$

10.2.4 How much will it hold?

. . . .

Volume of Non-Rectangular Prisms

In this lesson you will investigate different **strategies** for finding the volume of non-rectangular prisms. The problems require you to describe how you **visualize** each shape. As you work with your team, ask each other these questions to focus your discussion:

> How can the shape be broken down into simpler shapes?

> Can we break the shape into equal layers or slices?

10-112.   THE SHELL BOX

Laurel keeps her seashell collection in a small box that is shaped like a rectangular prism with a base of 4" x 3" and height of 5" (see diagram at right). She wants to make a bigger box for her shells, and she has found a pattern that she likes. The pattern has two sides that are pentagons and the finished box will look like a miniature house (see picture at right). Use the net on the Lesson 10.2.4 Resource Page to construct a paper model of Laurel's new box.

a.   Calculate the volume of Laurel's original small box. What method did you use?

b.   Laurel was trying to figure out the volume of the new box.

One of her friends said, *"Why don't you find the volume of one layer and then figure out how many layers there would be?"*

Another friend said, *"What if you separated the pentagon into two parts, so that you have a rectangular prism and a prism with a triangle base? Then you could find the volume of the two parts separately and put them back together."*

Talk about each of these **strategies** with your team. Could Laurel use these ideas to find the volume of her new box?

c.   Work with your team to calculate the volume of Laurel's new box. Show your thinking clearly and be prepared to share your method with the class.

10-113. Locate the two nets for prisms you cut out in Lesson 10.2.2. Decide which face is the base on each shape and which edge is the height. Then:

- Mark each base with one color.

- Mark each height with another color.

- Write down which color signifies the bases and which signifies the heights.

- Find the volume of each prism.

10-114. Find the volume of the prism at right using any method you choose. Be prepared to explain your **reasoning**.

10-115. Bryan was looking at the prism in problem 10-114 with his team. He wondered how they could slice the prism into layers horizontally that would all be the same size.

a. If the team slices the shape so that the bottom layer has the 10 m by 38 m rectangle as its base, will each layer be equal in size?

b. How could the team turn or tip the shape so that if the shape is sitting on a table and is cut horizontally, each layer will be the same size and shape? Which face will rest on the table?

c. When does it make sense to tip the shape in order to see the layers? Discuss this question with your team and summarize your conclusion on your paper.

10-116. LEARNING LOG

The method for finding the volume of a prism is commonly described as "finding the area of the base, then multiplying by the height." Discuss with your study team how this **strategy** works. How does the area of the base help to find the volume? Does it matter which face is the base? Why do you multiply by the height? Record your conclusions in your Learning Log. Title the entry, "Volume of a Prism," and label it with today's date.

MᴇTHODS AND Mᴇᴀɴɪɴɢs

MATH NOTES

Volume of a Prism

The **volume** of a prism can be calculated by dividing the prism into layers that are each one unit high. To calculate the total volume, multiply the volume of one layer by the number of layers it takes to fill the shape. Since the volume of one layer is the area of the base (B) multiplied by 1 (the height of that layer), we can use the formula below to compute the volume of a prism.

If h = height of the prism, V = (area of base) · (height)

$V = Bh$

Example:

Area of base = (2 in.)(3 in.) = 6 in.^{2}

(Area of base)(height) = (6 in.^{2})(4 in.) = 24 in.^{3}

Volume = 24 in.^{3}

4 in.

2 in.   3 in.

Review & Preview

10-117. Is each shape below a prism? If so, identify the shape that is the base. If not, explain why not.

a.   b.   c.   d.

10-118. Find the volume of a 1-unit-high layer of each prism below. Then find the total volume and the surface area of each figure.

a. A rectangular prism

10 m

10 m

50 m

b. A triangle-based prism

12.7 cm

8 cm

9 cm   9 cm

10-119. Sketch a circle with a radius of 4 cm. Find the area and circumference of the circle.

10-120. If the area of this triangle is 132 cm², what is the height?

16 cm

10-121. Leonard has purchased packages of grid paper for $2.25. If he wants to make a 40% profit on each package he sells to his classmates, by how much should he increase the price? What will the new price be?

10-122. Simplify each expression.

   a. $(3x)^4 x^3$

   b. $\dfrac{2^4 \cdot 3}{2^3 \cdot 3^2}$

   c. $4^{-3} \cdot 4^2$

10.2.5 What if the base is not a polygon?

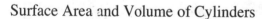

Surface Area and Volume of Cylinders

Soup cans and rolls of paper towels are each examples of **cylinders**. Cylinders are like prisms in many ways, except that, unlike prisms that have polygons as bases, cylinders have circles as bases. In this lesson you will compare the surface area and volume of prisms and cylinders.

10-123.   COMPARING THE GYM BAGS

The CPM Sports Company is planning a new product
line of gym bags. They have decided that the outside
of the bag (without the ends) will be made with a
rectangular piece of cloth that is 40 inches by 52
inches. They are trying to decide whether the end
pieces will be squares or circles. They will decide by
comparing the surface area and volume of each bag
and considering their advantages and disadvantages.
Your team will provide data for their decision.

40 inches

40 inches

Use a standard piece of paper that measures 8.5" on
one edge and 11" on the other to create a model of
each gym bag. To model the square-based prism:

- Fold the paper in half so that the 8.5" edges
  match up, then unfold.

- Fold each 8.5" edge in to the center crease, then
  unfold.

- Tape the 8.5" edges together to form the **lateral
  face** of a square-based prism. The open squares
  at either end are the bases.

40 inches

Use a new piece of paper to model the cylinder:

- Roll the paper so that one 8.5" edge matches up
  with the other.

- Tape the edges together to form the **lateral face**
  of a cylinder. The open circles formed at each
  end are the bases.

40 inches

Your task: Using the models for reference, find the surface area and volume of
each gym bag. How much fabric will it take to make each bag? How much will
each bag hold? Remember that the shorter length on the paper (8.5") models
the 40" dimension of the cloth, and the longer length (11") models the 52"
dimension of the cloth. The model you have created is *not* to scale.

Discussion Points

What dimensions will we need to find?

How can we organize our work?

What shape is each surface?

How are prisms and cylinders alike? How are they different?

10-124. Focus first on the square-based prism. Sketch
the prism on your paper, and then use the
dimensions given for the cloth to answer the
questions below.

    a.   What is the perimeter of the square base?
How long is each side of the square base?

    b.   What is the surface area of the prism?

    c.   Calculate the volume of the prism.

10-125. Sketch the cylinder on your paper.

    a.   Label all of the lengths that you know on your sketch. What shape is the
lateral face (the face formed by the original piece of cloth)? Find the area
of the lateral face and the area of each base. If you do not have enough
information to find the area, list the measurements that you need.

    b.   Melissa is looking at the base of the cylinder, and realizes that the only
measurement she knows is the circumference of the circle. She thinks she
can use the circumference to find out other measurements. What is the
circumference of this circle? What other lengths can Melissa find using this
measurement?

    c.   Find the area of each base of the cylinder and then calculate the total
surface area.

10-126. To find the volume of the cylinder, Melissa started by comparing it to a prism.
*"To find the volume of a prism, I slice it into equal layers. I wonder if the same
method will work for a cylinder?"* she asks. Work with your team to answer
Melissa's question. How could a cylinder be sliced into layers? What shape
would each layer be? Find the volume of the cylinder.

—————   *Further Guidance*   —————
section ends here.

10-127. How does the amount of fabric required to make the cylindrical bag compare to
the amount of fabric required to make the square-based prism bag? How much
will each bag hold? Based on this information, which bag style do you think the
CPM sports company should make? Explain your **reasoning**.

10-128. Find the surface area and volume of this cylinder. Show your work clearly.

diameter = 10 cm

10 cm

10-129. LEARNING LOG

With your team, look carefully at how you found the surface area of the cylindrical bag. What measurements did you use to find the area of the base of a cylinder? What measurements did you use to find the lateral area? What measurement is important for both calculations? After your team has discussed these questions, record your ideas in your Learning Log. Title this entry, "Surface Area and Volume of a Cylinder," and label it with today's date.

10-130. **Additional Challenge:** Louise calculated the volume of the prism at right to be 702 m³. She is trying to find the surface area, but needs help.

12 m

9 m   13 m

a. Sketch the shape on your paper and label any lengths that you know. How can you find the lengths of the unlabeled edges?

b. What are the length and width of each rectangle?

c. What is the total surface area of the shape?

METHODS AND MEANINGS

Volume of a Cylinder

The **volume of a cylinder** can be calculated in exactly the same way as the volume of a prism. That is, the volume can be calculated by dividing the cylinder into layers that are each one unit high. To calculate the total volume, multiply the volume of one layer by the number of layers it takes to fill the shape.

The volume of a cylinder can also be calculated by multiplying the area of the base (B) by the height (h).

Volume = (area of base)(height)

$$V = Bh = (r^2\pi)(h)$$

12 cm

15 cm

For example, for the cylinder at right,

Area of the base: $B = (12)^2\pi = 144\pi$

Volume: $V = 144\pi(15) = 2160\pi \approx 6785.84$ cm^3

10-131.   Find the area of the base of each cylinder below, and then calculate the volume of each cylinder. Show your steps.

a. $r = 5$cm

10 cm

b. $r = 3.4$

9 cm

10-132.   What is the volume of a hexagonal-based prism with a height of 12 in. and a base area of 62 in.²? Would the volume be different if the base were a pentagon with an area of 62 in.²? Explain.

10-133.   Find the length of the side labeled x in each of the right triangles pictured below.

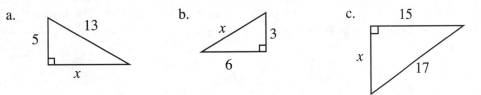

a.

13

5

x

b.

x

3

6

c.

15

x

17

10-134.   Solve these equations for x.

a. $(x + 3.5)2 = 16$

b. $23 + 5x = 7 + 2.5x$

c. $3x + 4.4 = -(6.6 + x)$

10-135.   Two employees of Frontier Fence Company can install 100 feet of fence in three days. At the same rate, how many employees are needed to install 150 feet of fence in one day?

10-136.   Simplify each expression.

a. $\dfrac{3^5}{3^{10}}$

b. $10x^4(10x)^{-2}$

c. $(\frac{1}{4})^3 \cdot (4)^2$

d. $\dfrac{(xy)^3}{xy^3}$

10.2.6 What if the layers are not the same?

Volume of Cones and Pyramids

Cones and **pyramids** are three-dimensional objects that have only one base, and come to a point opposite their base. A **cone** has a circular base, while a **pyramid** has a base that is a polygon and lateral faces that are triangles. Today you will be investigating how to use what you know about cylinders and prisms to find the volume of a cone and a pyramid. Questions to keep in mind as you work are:

What is the shape of the base?

How does the shape compare to a cylinder or a prism?

10-137. **HOW MUCH SHOULD IT COST?**

You have a choice of purchasing a small or a large serving of popcorn at the movies. A small popcorn comes in a cone and costs $1.50, and a large popcorn comes in a cylinder that costs $3.50. Both containers have the same height and bases with the same circular area. Based on their prices, discuss with your team which container of popcorn you think is a better deal. Be prepared to share your **reasons** with the class.

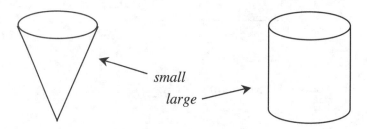

10-138. Your teacher will lead you through a demonstration about the volume of cones.

a. How are the radius and height of each cone related to the radius and height of each corresponding cylinder?

b. Sketch each cone and cylinder on your paper, and estimate which cone will have a greater volume.

c. How many cones full of rice were needed to fill each corresponding cylinder?

d. Based on the demonstration, describe how the volume of a cone compares to the volume of a cylinder when their heights and base areas are equal.

10-139.   Based on the relationship you found in
           problem 10-138, if a cone of popcorn
           costs $1.50 what would a fair price be
           for the cylinder of popcorn? At the
           advertised prices (problem 10-137),
           which popcorn is the better deal?

10-140.   A different movie theater sells popcorn in the containers shown below. This
           time the small container is a pyramid priced at $2.50. The large container is a
           prism with the same height and base as the pyramid and is priced at $5.50. At
           this theater, which popcorn do you think is a better deal? Be prepared to give
           reasons for your prediction.

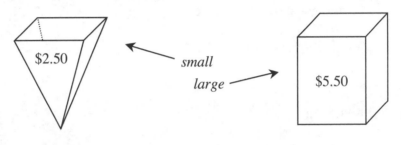

10-141.   Your teacher will now lead you through another demonstration to help you
           decide if you need to adjust your thinking about the relationship between the
           volume of a pyramid and a prism that have the same base and the same height.
           After you have seen the demonstration with the pyramid and the prism, which
           container of popcorn is a better deal? **Justify** your answer.

10-142.   Ann and Dan were trying to find the volume of the
           cone at right. Ann thinks that the cone is 8 inches tall
           and Dan thinks that the cone is 10 inches tall. Write
           them a note explaining who is correct.

10-143. Ann, Dan, and Jan calculated the volume of some shapes and got different answers. Look at their work shown below and make a sketch of the shape that each set of calculations might represent. Why do Dan and Jan's calculations have the same result even though they look different?

Dan's work: $V = \frac{(4^2\pi)(9)}{3} = 150.8 \text{ cm}^3$

Ann's work: $V = (4^2\pi)(9) = 452.4 \text{ cm}^3$

Jan's work: $V = \frac{1}{3}(4^2\pi)(9) = 150.8 \text{ cm}^3$

10-144. Find the volume of the pyramid at right. The hexagonal base has an area of 128 cm².

10-145. LEARNING LOG

If you know the volume of any prism, how can you find the volume of a pyramid that has the same base area and height as the prism? If you know the volume of any cylinder, how can you find the volume of a cone that has the same base area and height as the cylinder? Answer these questions in your Learning Log. Label this entry with today's date, and title it "Volume of Cones and Pyramids."

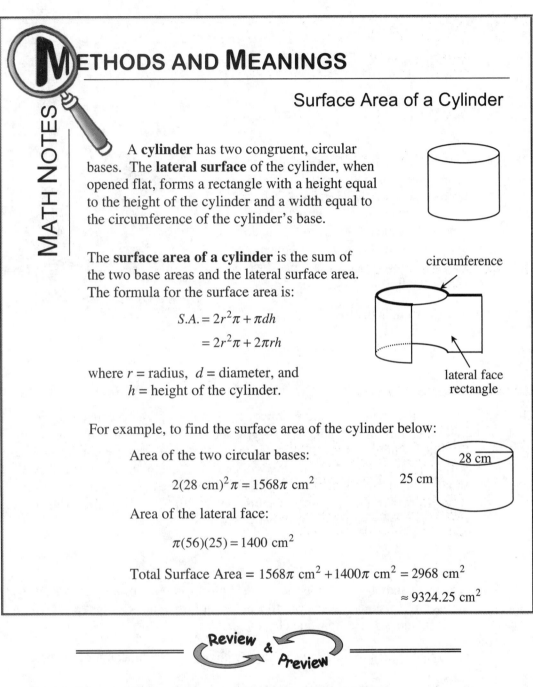

METHODS AND MEANINGS

Surface Area of a Cylinder

A **cylinder** has two congruent, circular bases. The **lateral surface** of the cylinder, when opened flat, forms a rectangle with a height equal to the height of the cylinder and a width equal to the circumference of the cylinder's base.

The **surface area of a cylinder** is the sum of the two base areas and the lateral surface area. The formula for the surface area is:

$$S.A. = 2r^2\pi + \pi dh$$
$$= 2r^2\pi + 2\pi rh$$

where r = radius, d = diameter, and h = height of the cylinder.

For example, to find the surface area of the cylinder below:

Area of the two circular bases:

$$2(28 \text{ cm})^2 \pi = 1568\pi \text{ cm}^2$$

Area of the lateral face:

$$\pi(56)(25) = 1400 \text{ cm}^2$$

Total Surface Area = $1568\pi \text{ cm}^2 + 1400\pi \text{ cm}^2 = 2968 \text{ cm}^2$

$$\approx 9324.25 \text{ cm}^2$$

Review & Preview

10-146.   Find the volume of the cone shown in problem 10-142.

10-147.   The pyramid at right has a volume of 312 cubic feet. If the prism next to it has the same base area and height, what is its volume? Explain how you know.

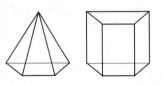

10-148. Complete the table.

x	−5	1	3	0	8	−2	−1
y	7			2		4	

    a.   Find the rule.

    b.   What is the slope?

10-149. Jack has a tree in his backyard that he wants to cut down to ground level. He needs to know how tall the tree is because when he cuts it, it will fall towards his fence. Jack measured the tree's shadow and it is 20 feet long. At the same time, Jack's shadow was 12 feet long. Jack is five feet tall.

    a.   How tall is the tree?

    b.   Will the tree hit the fence if the fence is nine feet away?

10-150. The Shones' family orchard produces 130 pounds of fruit per tree using traditional farming techniques. They would like to change to biodynamic farming techniques that will increase their crop by 20%. Changing techniques will cost money, but the fruit crop will be larger. Help them decide if they should change by calculating how much they will be able to grow two different ways, using two different scale factors (one multiplier will be greater than one). How many more pounds of fruit per tree will they get?

10-151. A box of candy holds 36 pieces. Sixteen pieces in the box are caramels, three pieces are marshmallow chews, five pieces are fruit centers, eight pieces are nut clusters, and the rest are white chocolate.

    a.   What is the probability of randomly choosing a caramel out of the box?

    b.   What is the probability that you will not choose a fruit center or a nut cluster?

    c.   In a different box, there is a $\frac{1}{6}$ chance that you will choose a fruit center. From which box is it more likely that you will choose a fruit center?

Chapter 10 Closure   What have I learned?

Reflection and Synthesis

The activities below offer you a chance to reflect about what you have learned during this chapter. As you work, look for concepts that you feel very comfortable with, ideas that you would like to learn more about, and topics you need more help with. Look for connections between ideas as well as connections with material you learned previously.

① SUMMARIZING MY UNDERSTANDING

This section gives you an opportunity to show what you know about certain math topics or ideas.

THE INTEREST GAME

Today you are going to play a game with your teacher. Your team task is to have more money in your account than any other team at the end of the game. You will start with an account balance of $1000. You will record your work and your balances throughout the game on Closure Resource Page A. Your team will also need an envelope containing interest rate cards.

To start the game, your teacher will select a card that gives you a time. Record the starting balance and time in the first section on your resource page. Then, as a team, pull a card from the envelope and compute the interest on your account based on the card and the time given to you by your teacher. When you have finished with a card, you will leave it on the desk. Transfer your new account balance to the starting amount in a new section on the resource page. Your teacher will then give you a new time and you will draw another card from your envelope. Your teacher will tell you how many cards to select during the course of the game. While playing the game, ask your teammates the following questions.

- How do we determine compound interest?

- How do we find simple interest?

- How is the interest growing? How can we see this in the interest expression?

Problem continues on next page. →

①   *Problem continued from previous page.*

When playing the Interest Game, you were trying to get the most amount of money in your team account.

     a.   What was your final amount?

     b.   Did you do more compound interest or simple interest problems?

     c.   What do you think made the most difference in the amount of money you made, the interest rate or the kind of interest earned (simple or compound)?

②   **WHAT HAVE I LEARNED?**

Working the problems in this section will help you to evaluate which types of problems you feel comfortable with and which ones you need more help with. This section will appear at the end of every chapter to help you check your understanding.

Solve each problem as completely as you can. The table at the end of this closure section has answers to these problems. It also tells you where you can find additional help and practice on problems like them.

CL 10-152.   Find the surface area and volume of each solid below.

     a.   All angles are right angles.   b.   Right prism with base area = 48 cm²

CL 10-153.   Rewrite each expression in a simpler form. If it is reasonable, write out the factored form to help you.

     a. $3^2 \cdot 3^5$ b. $\dfrac{4^5}{4^3}$ c. $(3x^2)^4$ d. $(3x^3)(7x^5)$

CL 10-154.   Daniel has $1200 in the bank. He is earning 3.5% compound interest each month. How much money will he have in the bank in one year?

CL 10-155.   Find the surface area and volume of a prism with a square base with sides of eight inches and a height of 12 inches.

CL 10-156.   Jamie bought a music player on sale for $65. The original price was $80. What percent discount did she receive?

CL 10-157.   Copy and complete the table.

x	−1	4	2	0	−4	−2
y	7		−2			10

a.   What is the rule for the table?

b.   What is the slope of the line through the points?

CL 10-158.   Find the area and circumference of a circle with a radius of 6.25 cm.

CL 10-159.   Shawn's science class has a ratio of 4:5, girls to boys.

a.   What is the ratio of boys to girls?

b.   What is the ratio of boys to total students?

c.   What percent of the class is boys?

d.   What fraction of the class is girls?

CL 10-160.   Sara walks ten blocks north from her house, turns a corner, and walks five blocks west. She wants to know how far she is from her house, that is, the direct distance from where she is standing (not how far she walked). How far is it?

CL 10-161.   For each of the problems above, do the following:

- Draw a bar or number line that represents 0 to 10.

- Color or shade in a portion of the bar that represents your level of understanding and comfort with completing that problem on your own.

If any of your bars are less than a 5, choose *one* of those problems and do one of the following tasks:

- Write two questions that you would like to ask about that problem.

- Brainstorm two things that you DO know about that type of problem.

If all of your bars are a 5 or above, choose one of those problems and do one of these tasks:

- Write two questions you might ask or hints you might give to a student who was stuck on the problem.

- Make a new problem that is similar and more challenging than that problem and solve it.

③   WHAT TOOLS CAN I USE?

You have several tools and references available to help support your learning – your teacher, your study team, your math book, and your Toolkit, to name only a few. At the end of each chapter you will have an opportunity to review your Toolkit for completeness as well as to revise or update it to better reflect your current understanding of big ideas.

The main elements of your Toolkit should be your Learning Log, Math Notes, and the vocabulary used in this chapter. Math words that are new to this chapter appear in bold in the text. Refer to the lists provided below and follow your teacher's instructions to revise your Toolkit, which will help make it a useful reference for you as you complete this chapter and as you work in future chapters.

Learning Log Entries

- Lesson 10.1.3 – Simple and Compound Interest
- Lesson 10.1.5 – Simplifying Exponent Expressions
- Lesson 10.2.4 – Volume of a Prism
- Lesson 10.2.5 – Surface Area and Volume of a Cylinder
- Lesson 10.2.6 – Volume of Cones and Pyramids

Math Notes

- Lesson 10.1.2 – Exponents
- Lesson 10.1.3 – Compound Interest
- Lesson 10.1.4 – Commutative and Associative Properties of Multiplication
- Lesson 10.1.5 – Scientific Notation
- Lesson 10.1.6 – Laws of Exponents
- Lesson 10.2.1 – Polygons, Prisms, and Pyramids
- Lesson 10.2.2 – Surface Area
- Lesson 10.2.3 – Measurement in Different Dimensions
- Lesson 10.2.4 – Volume of a Prism
- Lesson 10.2.5 – Volume of a Cylinder
- Lesson 10.2.6 – Surface Area of a Cylinder

Mathematical Vocabulary

The following is a list of vocabulary found in this chapter. Some of the words have been seen in a previous chapter. The words in bold are the words new to this chapter. Make sure that you are familiar with the terms below and know what they mean. For the words you do not know, refer to the glossary or index. You might also want to add these words to your Toolkit for a way to reference them in the future.

area	base	base of a polygon
compound interest	**cone**	**cylinder**
edge	**exponent**	**faces**
interest rate	lateral faces	length
linear growth	**net**	one dimension
polygon	**power**	principal
prism	**pyramid**	right rectangular prism
scientific notation	simple interest	**surface area**
three dimensions	two dimensions	volume

Process Words

These words describe problem solving strategies and processes that you have been involved in throughout the course of this chapter. Make sure you know what each of these words means. If you are not sure, you can talk with your teacher or other students or look through your book for problems in which you were asked to do these things.

brainstorm	calculate	choose a strategy
compare	describe	explain your reasoning
generalize	justify	measure
predict	reason	reverse your thinking
simplify	test your prediction	visualize

Answers and Support for Closure Activity #2
What Have I Learned?

Problem	Solution	Need Help?	More Practice
CL 10-152.	a. SA = 1512 ft^2 V = 2744 ft^3 b. SA = 572 cm^2 V = 672 m^3	Lessons 10.2.1, 10.2.2, 10.2.3, and 10.2.4 Math Notes boxes in Lessons 10.2.2 and 10.2.4 Learning Log (problem 10-116)	Problems 10-85, 10-96, 10-104, 10-106, 10-114, 10-118, and 10-132
CL 10-153.	a. 3^7 b. 4^2 c. 81x^8 d. 21x^8	Lessons 10.1.2, 10.1.4, and 10.1.5 Math Notes boxes in Lessons 10.1.2 and 10.1.6 Learning Log (problem 10-58)	Problems 10-15, 10-36, 10-45, 10-50, 10-51, 10-52, 10-57, 10-59, 10-61, 10-74, and 10-98
CL 10-154.	$1242	Lessons 10.1.2 and 10.1.3 Math Notes box in Lesson 10.1.3 Learning Log (problem 10-28)	Problems 10-12 through 10-14, 10-26, 10-29, 10-49, and 10-79
CL 10-155.	Surface area = 512 in^2 Volume = 768 in^3	Lessons 10.2.1, 10.2.2, and 10.2.3 Math Notes boxes in Lessons 10.2.2 and 10.2.4 Learning Log (problem 10-116)	Problems 10-85, 10-96, 10-104, 10-106, 10-114, 10-118, and 10-132
CL 10-156.	About 19%	Lesson 8.2.5 Math Notes box in Lesson 8.2.5	Problems CL 8-92, CL 9-134, and 10-8

Problem	Solution	Need Help?	More Practice
CL 10-157.	$\begin{array}{c\|c\|c\|c\|c\|c\|c} x & -1 & 4 & 2 & 0 & -4 & -2 \\ \hline y & 7 & -8 & -2 & 4 & 16 & 10 \end{array}$ $y = -3x + 4$ slope $= -3$	Lessons 6.1.6, 7.1.4, and 7.1.5 Math Notes box in Lesson 7.1.6 Learning Log (problem 7-47)	Problems CL 7-94, 10-86, 10-110, and 10-148
CL 10-158.	$A \approx 122.7$ cm^2 $C \approx 39.27$ cm	Lessons 5.3.3 and 5.3.4 Math Notes box in Lesson 5.3.4 Learning Log (problem 5-124)	Problems CL 6-143, CL 8-93, CL 9-134, and 10-119
CL 10-159.	a. 5:4 b, 5:9 c. about 56% d. $\frac{4}{9}$	Lesson 7.1.1 Math Notes box in Lesson 7.1.1	Problems 7-11, and 8-18
CL 10-160.	Distance $= \sqrt{125} \approx 11.18$, or about 11 blocks	Lessons 9.3.2, 9.3.3, and 9.3.4 Math Notes boxes in Lessons 9.3.2 and 9.3.3 Learning Logs (problems 9-105 and 9-122)	Problems CL 9-130, 10-10, 10-63, and 10-133

Puzzle Investigator Problems

PI-19.   GEOMETRIC GIFTWRAP

Rowena is wrapping presents for the
Geometry club party. The gifts are
geometric blocks of various shapes, and
she is cutting the wrapping paper in "nets"
that can be folded to perfectly cover each
object, without any overlap or uncovered
parts. Two of the many nets that she can
use to cover a cube are shown at right.

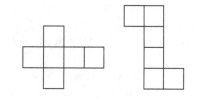

a.   Study the two nets above and try to **visualize** how they could each be
      folded to cover a cube completely. Then find three new arrangements of
      6 squares that will fold to cover a cube. Assume that if a design can be
      turned or flipped to look like another then they are the same.

b.   After wrapping a cube box, Rowena decided to reinforce the edges with
      tape. If she places tape on all edge lengths (leaving no part of the edge
      without tape), how much tape is needed? Assume the cube has side lengths
      of 5 inches.

c.   Below are some gifts Rowena still needs to wrap. Help her by creating a
      net that would wrap each box. Draw your designs accurately on graph
      paper and use arrows and/or colors to help show which squares of the paper
      would lie on top of which faces of the box. Assume each small block
      below is a unit cube and that no cubes are floating or otherwise hidden.

i.   *ii.*   *iii.*

PI-20.   MAKING DECISIONS

Carlos wanted to get a part-time job to have extra money for the holidays. After reading the advertisement at right, he applied. His interview went well, and he was offered the job. He had to choose between the following two pay scales:

Pay Scale # 1

He would earn $10 per hour.

Pay Scale # 2

On day # 1, he would earn a total of 1¢.
On day # 2, he would make a total of 2¢.
On day # 3, he would make a total of 4¢.

Each day, his salary rate would double from the day before.

a.   Before starting the problem, guess which pay scale Carlos chose. Explain why you think this.

b.   If the store is closed on Thanksgiving (November 27th), and Carlos works every day that the store is open through December 24th, make a table that shows how much he makes each day using both pay scales.

c.   If you had a job offer like this one, which pay scale would you choose? Why?

Making Connections: Course 2

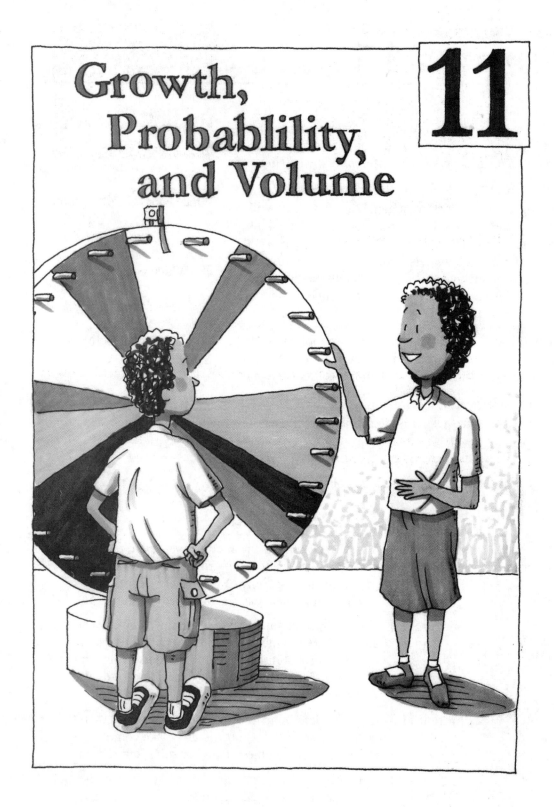

Growth, Probablility, and Volume

11

CHAPTER 11 Growth, Probability, and Volume

What kind of equation makes a graph that is not a line? In the first section of this chapter, you and your team will investigate non-linear graphs and identify patterns of growth for these graphs in different representations.

In Section 11.2, your team will return to probability and investigate whether different games are fair. You will calculate the probability of more than one event taking place, such as drawing a two out of a deck of cards and then a queen. You will also learn new ways to organize the possible outcomes to help you determine different probabilities, and explore situations where one outcome is more likely than another.

Finally, you will work with your team to look more closely at the volume of prisms. You will build cubes and investigate how the volumes of similar solids are related.

In this chapter, you will learn how to:

➢ Identify patterns of growth for non-linear equations in graphs and tables.
➢ Determine which of two events will be more likely.
➢ Calculate probability of compound (multiple) events.
➢ Use the scale factor to find the volume of a similar solid.

Guiding Questions

Think about these questions throughout this chapter:

What shape will the graph be?

How does it grow?

Which is more likely?

Is it fair?

How many cubes fit inside?

Chapter Outline

Section 11.1 You will graph non-linear equations called parabolas, and investigate patterns of growth in tables and graphs of non-linear equations. You will also learn about a new function that creates a V-shaped graph.

Section 11.2 You will investigate probability using a deck of cards and a random number generator. You will learn to represent probabilities of multiple events using a tree diagram, a list, and an outcome chart. You will also revisit the fairness of events.

Section 11.3 You will determine how many one-inch cubes will fit inside larger cubes. You will also make conjectures about how the volumes of similar solids are related.

Section 11.4 This section offers several problems to connect the math ideas you have worked with during this course and guides you to reflect about your learning.

11.1.1 How does it grow?

Non-Linear Growth

In this course, you have looked at several situations that model linear growth. Other curves can also be described mathematically. When engineers design satellite dishes or headlights for cars, it is critical that the curves they design are smooth and evenly shaped. If the curve is not correct, satellite dishes will not receive a clear signal and a car's headlights will not focus light on the road so the driver can see. In this section, you are going to explore several situations that are not linear. As you work with patterns, think about how these new patterns are growing.

11-1.   CHANGING BASES

In previous lessons you determined that simple interest grows at a constant (linear) rate, that is, by adding the same amount each time the x-value increases. Compound interest grows by multiplying by the same amount (exponential) each time the x-value increases. Work with your team to analyze the patterns created by the equation $y = x^2$.

a.   What is changing in this equation? What stays the same? Predict what the graph will look like and explain your **reasoning**.

b.   Create and complete a table like the one at right for the rule $y = x^2$. What patterns can you identify in the table? Use arrows, labels, and color to show them.

x	y
−5	
−4	
−3	
⋮	
3	
4	
5	

c.   Based on these patterns (and without graphing), do you predict that this equation is linear (makes a line)? Why or why not?

d.   Graph the equation. Use arrows, labels, and color to show how each of the patterns you found in the table shows in the graph. If you see new patterns, add them to the graph and then find them in the table.

11-2.   A.J. noticed some interesting patterns in her table from problem 11-1.

> *"Even if the x-value I use is negative, my y-value comes out positive."*

> *"Each y-value seems to show up in my table twice – one time with a positive x-value and one time with a negative x-value."*

With your team, discuss these patterns. What happens in the equation that causes the pattern? How does it affect the shape of the graph? Analyze any other patterns you found in problem 11-1 as well. Be as specific as you can. Be prepared to share your **reasoning** with the class.

11-3.   Colin noticed that when he folded his graph down the center of the U-shape, both sides matched up perfectly. This characteristic is called **symmetry**. Colin wondered if other graphs with similar equations would make this same U-shape (called a **parabola**) and have the same symmetry patterns. He created the three graphs below:

What do these graphs appear to have in common with the equation $y = x^2$? What is different about each graph?

11-4.   Do all equations that have a variable as a base raised to a power show these same patterns? Investigate the equation $y = x^3$ with your team.

Your task: On the Lesson 11.1.1 Resource Page, make a new table and graph for the equation. Work with your team to find as many patterns in the table, rule, and graph as you can. Be ready to share your patterns with the class.

Discussion Points

How do the values in the table grow? How does it show on the graph?

What happens when x is negative? What if x is positive, or equals zero?

Is there symmetry in the graph or table? Why or why not?

11-5.   With your team, examine the patterns you found in the graphs of $y = x^2$ and $y = x^3$. How are the two kinds of growth similar? How are they different? Summarize your conclusions in a short paragraph.

Review & Preview

11-6.   Anna kept track of the height of her fast-growing corn. Her records are shown in the table below.

Day	0	2	4	6	8	x
Height (cm)	2	7.5	13	18.5	24	

   a.   What is the growth rate of Anna's corn? Is this number always the same?

   b.   If you graph the points in this table, will they form a line or a curve? Explain how you know.

   c.   How would the growth rate show in the graph?

   d.   If Anna harvests the corn when it reaches 3 meters, when will she harvest it?

11-7.   Howie and Steve are making cookies for themselves and some friends. The recipe they are using will make 48 cookies, but they only want to make 16 cookies. They have no trouble reducing the amounts of flour and sugar, but the original recipe calls for $1\frac{3}{4}$ cups of butter. Help Howie and Steve determine how much butter they will need.

11-8.   Find the area of the figure. Copy the figure on your paper, and show your work for each of the different pieces you use to find the total area.

11-9.   Find the volume of each shape below.

a.   Rectangle-based prism

b.   Rectangle-based pyramid

11-10.   Use the laws of exponents to simplify the following expressions.

a. $(x^2)(x^5)$

b. $\dfrac{y^7}{y^4}$

c. $x^3 \cdot x^4$

11-11.   Write the following numbers in scientific notation.

a.   370,000,000

b.   0.0000000000076

11.1.2 How can growth be described?

Absolute Value

In Lesson 11.1.1 you used equations to generate tables and graphs, and then analyzed the patterns that you found. Today, you and your team will **reverse** this process; you will analyze graphs to see what they can tell you about new kinds of equations.

11-12.   AN UNUSUAL GRAPH

Lauren was flipping through her sister's algebra book when she noticed an unusual graph. She copied it into her notebook to show her study team. The graph she drew is shown at right.

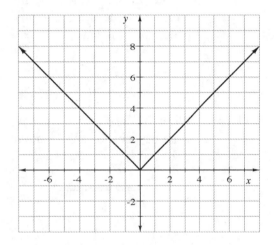

Lauren wondered what the equation for such an unusual graph could be. *"It's not a parabola, but it's not a line either! It doesn't look like compound interest. What do you think?"* Lauren asked her team. *"Clearly there are lots of patterns..."*

Your task: Obtain a copy of the graph on the Lesson 11.1.2 Resource Page. Work with your team to identify patterns in the graph and use them to describe the math operations that would create these patterns. Use the questions below to help you get started.

Discussion Points

How does the graph grow?

How is the new graph similar to a parabola or a line? How is it different?

What would a table of values tell us?

11-13. Lars focused on the graph to see what he could learn. *"This graph is kind of like a line, and kind of like a parabola,"* he said. What do you think Lars means? What does the graph have in common with a line? With a parabola? How is it different? Be specific.

x	y
−4	4
−3	3
−2	2
−1	1
0	0
1	1
2	2
3	3
4	4

11-14. *"I see patterns better with numbers than pictures,"* Mackenzie said. She used information from the graph to create the table at right. Copy the table and find as many patterns as you can.

11-15. Based on the patterns you have found, describe in words what happens to each input value as it becomes an output.

—————   *Further Guidance*   —————
            section ends here.

11-16. Lauren went back to her sister to ask what she knew about the graph. She learned that the V-shape showed that this was an **absolute value** graph, and the equation for it is $y = |x|$. *"From the patterns I've found, I know that this seems to take any inputs and turn them into positive outputs,"* Lauren said. Her sister explained that when you find the **absolute value** of a number, you actually find the distance between that number and zero on a number line. She used this example:

If $x = -7$, then the distance between −7 and 0 on the number line is 7 units, so $|-7| = 7$. The distance from +7 to zero is the same number of units, so $|7| = 7$. Because we are counting a number of units, the absolute value is always positive.

Find each absolute value below:

a. $|-20|$ b. $|25|$ c. $|-8 + 4|$ d. $2 \cdot |-500|$

11-17. Create a table to represent the equation $y = |-2x|$.

    a. What shape do you predict the graph will be? Explain your **reasoning**.

    b. Can y ever have a negative value in this expression? Why or why not?

11-18. Lars was curious about other graphs. He found the strange graph at right and brought it to the team:

    a. Describe the graph as completely as you can.

    b. Predict what the equation for this line looks like. Be ready to **justify** your team prediction.

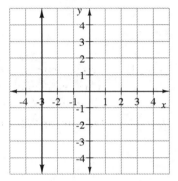

METHODS AND MEANINGS

MATH NOTES

Absolute Value

    Absolute value is the distance a number is from zero on the number line in either direction. We use the symbol $|x|$ to indicate the absolute value of any number x. For example:

$$|-3| = 3 \quad \text{and} \quad |3| = 3$$

11-19. Read the Math Notes box for this lesson. Then simplify each of the following expressions.

a. $|-15|+|-26|$

b. $-|-40|$

c. $|0.5|+|-1\frac{1}{2}|$

11-20. Find the area of the shape at right. Show your steps.

10 m   21.25 m   7.6 m

11-21. Marcus subscribes to several different magazines. On his bookshelf now he has 32 magazines about cars, 14 news magazines, 17 magazines about the outdoors, and 7 magazines about sports. If Marcus randomly pulls a magazine off of the shelf, what is the probability that he will not choose one about the outdoors?

11-22. Answer the comparison questions below.

a. How many times larger is $3\cdot3\cdot3$ than $3+3+3$?

b. How many times larger is $\frac{1}{3}+\frac{1}{3}+\frac{1}{3}$ than $\frac{1}{3}\cdot\frac{1}{3}\cdot\frac{1}{3}$?

Age of car (years)	Avg. miles per gallon
7	28
2	36
5	29
1	42
4	32
10	16
2	39
3	35
8	18

11-23. Graph the data in the table at right on graph paper. Is there a correlation?

11-24. Simplify each expression.

a. $\frac{3}{8}+(-\frac{4}{6})-\frac{1}{3}$

b. $-\frac{5}{7}+\frac{4}{9}-(-\frac{2}{3})$

c. $\frac{2}{5}\cdot\frac{3}{8}-\frac{3}{4}$

d. $-\frac{6}{11}+(-\frac{2}{3})-\frac{5}{6}$

e. $-\frac{2}{3}\cdot2\frac{1}{4}\cdot\frac{3}{4}$

f. $\frac{5}{7}+(-\frac{1}{3})-(-\frac{1}{2})$

11.2.1 How likely is it?

Revisiting Probability

Have you ever had someone do a card trick with you by asking you to *"pick a card, any card"*? How do you determine the chances of getting a particular card? In Chapter 1, you learned about theoretical and experimental probabilities. In this lesson, you will continue to investigate probability by looking at a standard deck of playing cards.

As you work with your team, ask the following questions:

How many outcomes are there?

How likely is the outcome?

How do I represent it?

11-25. PICK A CARD, ANY CARD

A standard deck of playing cards has four suits in two colors: diamonds and hearts are red; clubs and spades are black. Each suit has 13 cards: an ace, the numbers two through ten, a jack, a queen, and a king. What is the probability of picking the following cards from the deck?

a. What is P(black)?   b. What is P(ace)?   c. What is P(club)?

d. If you drew a card from the deck and then replaced it, and repeated this 100 times, about how many times would you expect to draw a face card (king, queen, or jack)?

e. What would happen to the probability of getting an ace on a second draw if you draw an ace on the first draw and do not return it to the deck? **Justify** your answer.

11-26.   Get a deck of playing cards from your teacher. Make sure that you have removed the directions and the Jokers. Shuffle the cards at least six times before drawing the first card. You do not need to shuffle the deck between draws. With your team, take turns removing a card, recording the value of the card, and returning the card to the deck somewhere in the middle. Record the number of the card you drew, or whether it was a king, queen, or jack. You do not need to record the suit or color of the card. Do this 50 times.

   a.   Compare your results with the rest of the class. Which card(s) were selected the most?

   b.   How close were the experimental probabilities to the theoretical probabilities?

11-27.   Rob decided to play a card game with his friend, Travis. He told Travis that, if he picked a black card with a value of nine or greater, Travis would win. (Jack, Queen, and King are considered to be greater than nine.) If Rob picked a red card of less than nine, Rob would win. (Ace is considered to have the value of one.)

   a.   What is the probability that Travis will win?

   b.   What is the probability that Rob will win?

   c.   Is this a fair game?

11-28.   The state has created a new contest to raise funds for a big Fourth of July fireworks celebration. People buy tickets and scratch off a special section on the ticket to reveal if they have won a prize. One out of every five people who play get a free entry in a raffle. Two out of every fifteen people who play win a small cash prize.

   a.   If you buy a scratch off ticket, is it more likely that you will win a free raffle ticket, or a cash prize?

   b.   How can you use the probabilities you have already calculated to write an expression for the probability that you will win anything?

   c.   What is the probability that you will win nothing at all? Write an expression and find the result, and **justify** your thinking.

11-29.   **Additional Challenge:** Alicia's favorite candy is Fruiti Tutti Chews, which come in three flavors: Killer Kiwi, Crazy Coconut, and Ridiculous Raspberry. This year will be the 50th year that the candy has been made. To celebrate, the company that makes Fruiti Tutti Chews is running new advertisements and introducing a fourth flavor: Perfect Peach.

a.   One of the new ads states that if you reach into any bag of Fruiti Tutti Chews, you have a $\frac{2}{3}$ probability of pulling out a Killer Kiwi candy. Another ad says that $\frac{3}{5}$ of each bag is Ridiculous Raspberry. Are the ads telling the truth?

b.   Alicia learns that when she opens a new bag of candy, she has a $\frac{2}{5}$ chance of pulling out a piece of Ridiculous Raspberry and a $\frac{1}{3}$ chance of pulling out a piece of Killer Kiwi. Could she have a $\frac{4}{15}$ chance of pulling out a piece of Perfect Peach? Explain your **reasoning**.

c.   When they introduce the new flavor, the company plans to make Perfect Peach $\frac{3}{10}$ of the candy in each bag. If there is an equal amount of the remaining three flavors, what is the probability that the first piece you pull out of the bag will be Crazy Coconut? **Justify** your answer.

Review & Preview

11-30.   Find the probability of each event. Write your answer as a fraction and as a percent.

a.   Drawing a diamond from a standard deck of cards.

b.   Rolling a number less than five on a standard number cube.

c.   Drawing a blue marble from a bag of 18 marbles, three of which are blue.

11-31.   Imagine a standard deck of cards with all of the aces and twos removed. Find each probability below.

a.   P(heart)

b.   P(black)

c.   P(face card)

d.   How is the P(face card) different with this deck from the probability if the deck was not missing any cards? Which probability is greater? Why?

11-32.   Graph each of the pairs of points listed below and draw a line segment between them. Use the graph to help you find the length of each line segment.

a. $(-3, 0)$ and $(0, -3)$ b. $(2, 3)$ and $(-1, 2)$ c. $(3, 2)$ and $(3, -3)$

11-33.   Johanna is planting tomatoes in the school garden this year. Tomato plants come in packs of six. She needs 80 plants in the garden and already has 28. How many packs of plants will she need?

11-34.   Two mechanics can assemble 10 bicycles in 8 hours. At the same rate, how many mechanics would be needed to assemble 25 bicycles in 10 hours?

11-35.   Simplify each expression.

a. $|-5 + -1|$ b. $|-2 \cdot 4|$ c. $3|-8|$

d. $-3 \cdot |8|$ e. $5 - |-5 + 10|$ f. $|6 - 10|$

11.2.2   Which is more likely?
· ·
Comparing Probabilities

Have you ever played a game where everyone should have an equal chance of winning, but one person seems to have all the luck? Did it make you wonder if the game was fair? Sometimes random events just happen to work out in one player's favor, such as flipping a coin that happens to come up heads four times in a row. But it is also possible that games can be set up to give an advantage to one player over another. If it is not equally possible for different players to win, a game is considered unfair. The game Rob and Travis played in problem 11-27 is an example of an unfair game.

In this lesson you will find probabilities to determine whether different outcomes are equally likely. Ask these questions in your study team as you work:

How likely is it?

Is another outcome equally likely?

Which player has a greater chance?

11-36.   RANDOM NUMBER GENERATOR

A random number generator produces numbers without using a pattern or rule. An example of this is a standard number cube, which will randomly generate a number from 1 to 6 when you roll it because each of the numbers is equally likely to show when the cube lands. Other tools can generate numbers with a wider range of values. Imagine a random number generator that produces numbers from 1 to 20. In each game below, if the stated outcome happens, Player X wins. If it does not, then Player Y wins.

Game 1:   A prime number = Player X wins

Game 2:   An even number = Player X wins

Game 3:   A number not divisible by three = Player X wins

a.   In each case, what is the probability that Player X wins? That Player Y wins? Decide whether each game above is fair.

b.   In which of the three games is Player X most likely to win? Why?

c.   In Game 1, the prime number game, if you play 40 times, how many times would you expect Player X to win? What if you played 50 times?

d.   Obtain a random number generator from your teacher and set it up to generate integers from 1 to 20. Play the prime number game (Game 1) 10 times with a partner. Start by deciding who will be Player X and who will be Player Y. Record who wins each time you play.

e.   How did the experimental and theoretical probabilities of Player X winning from part (a) and part (d) compare?

11-37.   A BETTER CHANCE OF WINNING

Each of the problems below describes two different games you can play with a random number generator. In each case, you will win if the random number generator gives you the indicated kind of number. Find the probability that you win each game below. Decide and **justify** whether Game I or Game II in each part gives you a better chance of winning.

	Game I	**Game II**
a.	Picking a prime number from the integers between 1 and 20	Picking a prime number from the integers between 21 and 40
b.	Picking a multiple of 5 from the integers between 1 and 20	Picking a multiple of 5 from the integers between 1 and 40
c.	Picking a multiple of 7 from the integers between 1 and 40	Picking a multiple of 6 from the integers between 1 and 25

11-38. Using a random number generator for the numbers from 1 through 20, what is the probability of getting each of these outcomes?

    a. A multiple of three *or* a multiple of 7, P(multiple of 3 or multiple of 7)

    b. P(even or odd)

    c. P(prime or 1)

    d. How did you find the probabilities of these events? Be ready to share your ideas with the class.

11-39. LEARNING LOG

So far you have calculated probabilities of different events and have compared them to decide if events are equally likely to happen. You have also found the probability of one or another event taking place (such as drawing a king or a queen from a deck of cards).

In your Learning Log, create an example and explain how you would calculate the probability when two different outcomes are asked for (such as the example of drawing a king or queen from a deck of cards). Then, record any questions you have about probability. Your questions might relate to things that you have already worked on or may be about situations you have not yet studied. Title this entry "Multiple Outcomes and Questions," and label it with today's date.

11-40. Marissa is drawing erasers from a bag containing 6 pink erasers, 2 yellow erasers, 5 green erasers, and 3 purple erasers.

    a. What is the probability that she will draw a pink eraser?

    b. If one yellow, two green, and one purple eraser are added to the bag, what is the new probability that she will draw a pink eraser?

    c. In which situation is it more likely that she will draw a pink eraser?

11-41.   For each of the experimental results described, write the indicated probability.

   a.   A coin is flipped 80 times. It lands tails 47 times. What is P(heads)?

   b.   A bag contains purple and orange marbles. Sam randomly takes out one marble then returns it to the bag. He does this 18 times, and 12 of those times an orange marble is pulled out. What is P(green)?

   c.   Sarah pulls a card from a standard deck and then replaces it. She does this 30 times, and 40% of the time it is hearts. What is P(~hearts)? Recall that ~ means "not hearts."

11-42.   Simplify each of the following expressions.

   a. $4x^3y \cdot 3xy^2$

   b. $6a^5b^2 \cdot 3ab^2$

   c. $m^2n \cdot 9mn$

   d. $\dfrac{3^5 \cdot 8 \cdot 5^3}{3^2 \cdot 2^3 \cdot 5^3 \cdot 3^3}$

   e. $\dfrac{m^4 \cdot n}{n^3}$

   f. $\dfrac{9a^4b^2}{15b}$

11-43.   Solve the following equations.

   a. $12 = \frac{6}{7}x$

   b. $3x + (-4) = 2x + 9$

   c. $3x - 8 = 4x + (-2)$

   d. $2x - 6 = 1 - 3x$

   e. $\frac{38}{6} = \frac{x}{18}$

   f. $\frac{9}{x} = \frac{85}{10}$

11-44.   Which table or tables below show a proportional relationship? **Justify** your answers.

   a.

x	5	7	9	−8	0	11	15
y	9	13	17	−17	−19	21	29

   b.

x	7	14	91	9	−12	−36	81
y	$2\frac{1}{3}$	$4\frac{2}{3}$	$30\frac{1}{3}$	3	−4	−12	27

   c.

x	−3	−10	0	10	5	4	$\frac{1}{2}$	$-\frac{3}{2}$
y	−27	−1000	0	1000	125	48	$\frac{1}{8}$	$-\frac{27}{4}$

11-45.   Find the volume of the prism at right.
All angles are right angles.

9 mm

3 mm

3 mm

3 mm

7 mm

7 mm

5 mm

15 mm

11.2.3   What if there is more than one event?

Modeling Probabilities of Compound Events

In Chapter 1 and earlier in this chapter, you have investigated ways to find out how likely it is that single events will happen, such as drawing one card from a deck of playing cards, pulling one marble from a bag, or spinning a color on a wheel. How would the probabilities you find change if you draw two cards from a deck of cards or roll two number cubes? In this lesson you will work with different models for organizing outcomes of multiple events.

11-46.   WALKING THE DOG

Marcus and his brother always argue about who will walk the dog. Their father wants to find a random way of deciding who will do the job. He invented a game to help them decide. Each boy will have a bag with three colored blocks in it: one yellow, one green, and one white. Each night before dinner, each boy draws a block out of his bag. If the colors match, Marcus walks the dog. If the two colors do not match, his brother walks the dog. Marcus' father wants to be sure that the game is fair. Help him decide.

a.   Make a **systematic list** (organized list) or table of all of the possible combinations of draws that Marcus and his brother could make. How many possibilities are there?

b.   What is the probability that the boys will draw matching blocks? Is the game fair? **Justify** your answer.

Making Connections: Course 2

11-47.   THE DOUBLE SPIN

In Chapter 1, you found probabilities for the Giant
Spin carnival game in which players spin a giant
wheel that is equally divided into 24 sections labeled
–2, –1, 0, 1, or 3. In that problem, players could spin
only one time. At the Double Spin, players spin the
smaller wheel shown at right two times. The sum of
their spins determines whether they win.

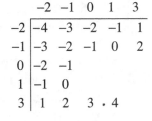

Work with your team to determine probabilities of
different outcomes by answering the questions below.

a.   Make a list of the possible sums you could get.

b.   Which sum do you think will be the most probable?

c.   Travis set up the chart at right, called an
     outcome chart, to find out which sum would
     occur the most often. He listed the possibilities
     for Spin 1 across the top and for Spin 2 down
     the left side.

	–2	–1	0	1	3
–2	–4	–3	–2	–1	1
–1	–3	–2	–1	0	2
0	–2	–1			
1	–1	0			
3	1	2	3 . 4		

     Copy the chart on your paper. Determine how
     Travis found the numbers inside the chart, and
     fill in the missing numbers.

d.   If Travis could choose the winning sum for the Double Spin game, what
     sum would you advise him to choose? What is the probability of getting
     that sum with two spins?

11-48. Scott's job at Crazy Creations Ice Cream Shop is to design new ice cream flavors. The company has just received some new ingredients, and Scott wants to be sure to try all of the possible combinations. He needs to choose one item from each category to create the new flavor.

Base flavor	Chunky mix-in	Fruit swirl
Vanilla	Hazelnuts	Apricot
Chocolate	Sprinkles	Plum
	Toffee bits	Berry
		Grape

a. Without talking with your teammates, list three different combinations Scott could try. Then, share your combinations with your study team. How many different combinations did you find? Do you think you found all of the possibilities?

b. Creating a list of all of the possibilities would take time and require a lot of writing the same words over and over. Because there are more than two options, an outcome chart is also challenging. An alternative is creating a **tree diagram** to show the different combinations. A tree diagram, like the one started at right and on the Lesson 11.2.3 Resource Page, shows the different possibilities branching off each other. In this case, the two lines on the left show the base flavors. Each different mix-in choice branches off of the base flavor, and each fruit swirl branches off each mix-in choice. The first letter of each choice is used to label this diagram.

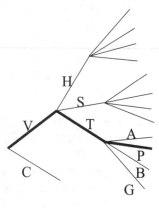

The bold line in the diagram shows the combination vanilla, toffee, plum swirl. Complete the tree diagram to find all of the possible combinations.

c. How many different flavor combinations are possible? Where do you look on the diagram to count the number of complete combinations?

d. Use your tree diagram to help you find the probability that Scott's final combination will include plum swirl.

e. What is the probability that his final combination will include hazelnuts?

11-49.   In a power outage, Rona has to reach into her closet in the dark to get dressed. She has three different pairs of pants hanging there: one black, one brown, and one plaid. She also has two different shirts: one white and one polka dot.

a.   Draw a tree diagram to organize the different outfit combinations Rona might choose.

b.   What is the probability that she will wear a polka dot shirt with plaid pants?

c.   What is the probability that she will not wear the black pants?

11-50.   Find the indicated probability in each situation below. Represent all of the possible outcomes using a systematic list, an outcome chart, or a tree diagram.

a.   You flip a coin three times in a row, and get heads exactly twice.

b.   You spin the two spinners at right and exactly one spinner lands on 4.

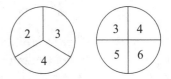

c.   At the car rental agency you will either be given a truck or sedan. Each model comes in four colors: green, black, white, or tan. If there is one vehicle of each color for each model available, what is the probability you will get a green truck?

METHODS AND MEANINGS

Probability Models for Multiple Events

To determine all possible outcomes for multiple events, there are several different models you can use to help organize the information.

Consider spinning each spinner at right once.

If you are able to find the outcomes in an order, a **systematic list** can be helpful. For example, assume that you first spin B on spinner 1. Then, list all of the possible outcomes on spinner 2. Next, assume that your first spin is W on spinner 1 and complete the list.

Systematic List

BR	WR
BG	WG
BY	WY

A **probability outcome chart** can also organize information if there are only two events. The possibilities for each event are listed on the sides of the chart as shown, and the combinations of outcomes are listed inside the chart. In the example at right, the possible outcomes for spinner 1 are listed on the left side and the possible outcomes for spinner 2 are listed across the top. The possible outcomes of the two events are shown inside the rectangle. In this chart, the top and side are divided evenly because the outcomes are equally likely. Inside the table you can see the possible combinations of outcomes.

Outcome Chart

	R	G	Y
B	BR	BG	BY
W	WR	WG	WY

A **probability outcome tree** is another method for organizing information. The different outcomes are organized as branches of a tree. The first section has two branches because there are two possible outcomes of spinner 1, namely B and W. At the end of the first branches are three branches to represent the possible outcomes of the second spinner. These possible outcomes of the two events are shown as the six branch ends.

Outcome Tree

11-51. Nicole has a random number generator that will produce the numbers from 1 through 50 when she pushes a button. If she pushes the button, what is:

a. P(multiple of 10)?

b. P(~100)?

c. P(~multiple of 4)?

d. P(one-digit number)?

11-52. Graph the points $(-2, 4)$, $(2, 1)$, and $(-2, -2)$ and connect the points to create a triangle. What is the perimeter of the triangle?

11-53. For the rule $y = 6 + (-3)x$:

a. What is the y-intercept?

b. What is the slope?

11-54. Scooter rides his skateboard every day after school. He often stops to do tricks. On Monday, he rode for 2 hours and went 3 miles. By the end of the week, he had gone a total of 11 miles and it took him a total of 9 hours. Did he ride the same time and distance every day after school? **Justify** your answer.

11-55. Find the volume of the cone.

11-56. Simplify each numerical expression.

a. $|5 - 6 + 1|$

b. $-2|-16|$

c. $|6 - 2| + |-8 - 1|$

11.2.4 What if the events are not equally likely?

Compound Events

In Lesson 11.2.3, you used systematic lists, outcome charts, and tree diagrams to organize the outcomes of different probability situations. Today you will use an outcome chart to help organize events when one outcome is more likely than another.

11-57. Nina is buying a new pet fish. At the pet store, the fish tank has an equal number of two kinds of fish – tetras and guppies. Each kind of fish comes in four different colors: yellow, orange, blue, and silver. There is an equal number of each color of fish in the tank.

 a. If Nina scoops out a fish at random, what is the probability that she will scoop out a silver tetra? Show how you decided.

 b. Nina set up the chart below to organize the different possible outcomes. She represented the kind of fish on one side of her chart and the color possibilities on the other. What do the fractions inside her chart represent?

	Yellow	Orange	Blue	Silver
Tetra	YT = $\frac{1}{8}$	OT = $\frac{1}{8}$	BT = $\frac{1}{8}$	ST = $\frac{1}{8}$
Guppy	YG = $\frac{1}{8}$	OG = $\frac{1}{8}$	BG = $\frac{1}{8}$	SG = $\frac{1}{8}$

 c. As Nina looked at her work, she noticed that her chart looked a lot like a rectangle with the area divided up into parts. *"Could that help me calculate the probabilities?"* she wondered. She used the length and width of the silver tetra section to set up this equation: $\frac{1}{4} \cdot \frac{1}{2} = \frac{1}{8}$.

 How does this equation relate to the length, width, and area of this section of the rectangle? Does this match the probability you found in part (a)?

 d. What is the area of the complete large rectangle?

Making Connections: Course 2

11-58.   TESTING THE AREA MODEL

Nina decided to see if finding area would help find other probabilities. She put three cubes in a bag – two blue cubes and one yellow cube. She pulled one cube out, put it back in the bag, and then drew another.

a.   Use a list or a tree diagram to organize the possible color combinations she could draw. How many are there? What is P(blue and blue)?

b.   This time Nina made the chart at right. Based on the chart, what is the probability of drawing two blue blocks? Is this the same probability you found in part (a)?

	B	B	Y
B	BB	BB	BY
B	BB	BB	BY
Y	YB	YB	YY

c.   Looking at her work, Luis said, "I think I can simplify this diagram." His rectangle is shown at right. What is the area of the section representing blue and blue? Does this match the probability that Nina found?

	B ($\frac{2}{3}$)	Y ($\frac{1}{3}$)
B ($\frac{2}{3}$)	BB	BY
Y ($\frac{1}{3}$)	YB	YY

11-59.   The pet store sells a lot of pet food. On a slow day at the pet store, three people buy cat food, two people by dog food, and one person buys food for a pet snake. If half of the customers pay with cash and half pay with credit card, what is the probability that a customer buying pet food will buy dog food with cash? Set up an outcome table to help you find the probability.

11-60.   SPINNING ODDS AND EVENS — PART 1

Your team is going to play against your teacher in a game with two hidden spinners. Spinner A has the numbers 2, 3, and 4 on it. Spinner B has the numbers 6, 7, and 8 on it. The rules are:

1.   Spin each spinner.

2.   Add the results.

3.   If the sum is even, one team gets a point. If the sum is odd, the other team gets a point.

4.   The first team to earn 10 points wins.

Should you choose the odd or even numbers in order to win? Discuss the choices with your team and decide which side to take. Be prepared to **justify** your choice with mathematics.

11-61. Play the game at least three times with your teacher. Your teacher will spin the spinners and announce the results. Record the results of each spin and their sum. Is the result odd or even most often? Does this match with your prediction?

11-62. **SPINNING ODDS AND EVENS — PART 2**

Now that you have played the game several times, obtain a Lesson 11.2.4 Resource Page from your teacher and take a close look at the hidden spinners.

a. Are the spinners different from what you expected? How? Be as specific as you can. Do you still think you made the correct choice of odd or even numbers?

b. What is the probability of spinning each outcome on Spinner A? On Spinner B?

11-63. Raul had imagined that the spinners were divided into equal parts before he saw them. He created the chart at right to organize the outcomes. *"I thought there would be a $\frac{1}{3}$ chance of spinning a 3 on Spinner A. But now that I see the spinners, I know that is not true. I need to make a new rectangle in order to find the probability."*

	6	7	8
2	8	9	10
3	9	10	11
4	10	11	12

a. Create a new rectangle. Label each side with the outcomes and their probabilities.

b. Write a multiplication problem to show the probability of spinning a three and a seven. Calculate P(3 and 7).

c. What is the probability of spinning an odd sum? What is the probability of spinning an even sum?

d. Did you make the right choice of an odd or even number in problem 11-62? Explain your **reasoning**.

Making Connections: Course 2

11-64. Elliot loves music, especially listening to his music player on shuffle. He has songs stored in four categories: country, blues, rock, and classical. Two-fifths of his songs are country songs, one sixth of his songs are classical, one third are blues, and the rest are rock.

    a.   What is the likelihood that the first two songs will be a country song and then a classical?

    b.   What is the likelihood that a blues song *or* a country song will come up first?

MATH NOTES

METHODS AND MEANINGS

Compound Probability

Sometimes when you are finding a probability, you are interested in either of two outcomes taking place, but not both. For example, you may be interested in drawing a king or a queen from a deck of cards. At other times, you might be interested in one event followed by another event. For example, you might want to roll a one on a number cube and then roll a six. The probabilities of combinations of simple events are called **compound probabilities**. For an explanation of finding probability of simple events, see the Math Notes box on probability in Lesson 1.2.1.

To find the probability of one event *or* another event that has nothing in common with the first, you can find the probability of each event separately and then add their probabilities. Using the example above of drawing a king or a queen from a deck of cards:

$$P(\text{king}) = \tfrac{4}{52} \quad \text{and} \quad P(\text{queen}) = \tfrac{4}{52} \quad \text{so} \quad P(\text{king or queen}) = \tfrac{4}{52} + \tfrac{4}{52} = \tfrac{8}{52} = \tfrac{2}{13}$$

Two events are **independent** when the occurrence of one does not change the probability of the other one occurring. To find the probability of two independent events both occurring, you can find the probability of each event separately and then multiply their probabilities. Using the example of rolling a one followed by a six on a number cube:

$$P(1) = \tfrac{1}{6} \quad \text{and} \quad P(6) = \tfrac{1}{6} \quad \text{so} \quad P(1 \text{ then } 6) = \tfrac{1}{6} \cdot \tfrac{1}{6} = \tfrac{1}{36}$$

Note that you would carry out the same computation if you wanted to know the probability of rolling a one on a green cube and a six on a red cube if you rolled both of them at the same time.

11-65. Alan is making a bouquet to take home to his grandmother. He needs to choose one kind of greenery and one kind of flower for his bouquet. He has a choice of ferns or leaves for his greenery. His flower choices are daisies, carnations, and sunflowers.

    a. Draw a tree diagram to show the different bouquets he could make. How many are there?

    b. What is the probability he will use ferns?

    c. What is the probability he will not use sunflowers?

11-66. Imagine spinning the spinner at right.

    a. What is the probability you will spin a P or a Q on your first spin?

    b. Find all of the possible outcomes of spinning the spinner twice. What is the probability you will spin a P on your first spin and then a Q on your second spin? Explain how you decided.

11-67. Make a table for the rule $y = 2x^3$ that includes x-values from -3 to 3. Graph the rule on graph paper.

11-68. Solve for x.

    a. $2(x+18) = 10$ b. $\frac{4}{3}x - 9 = -3$

    c. $24 = 2(2x+4)$ d. $2(x-4) = x - 7$

11-69. Dawn drove 420 miles in 6 hours on a rural interstate highway. If she maintains the same speed, how far can she go in 7.5 hours?

11-70. Lucas is having yogurt and an apple for a snack. There are five containers of yogurt in the refrigerator: three are raspberry, one is vanilla, and one is peach. There are also two green apples and three red apples.

a. If he reaches into the refrigerator to get a yogurt without looking, what is the probability Lucas will choose a raspberry yogurt?

b. What is the probability he will choose a red apple if it is the first item he selects?

c. What is the probability Lucas will eat a raspberry yogurt and a red apple?

11-71. Find the probability of each event, based on the given information.

a. If P(getting clubs) = $\frac{1}{4}$, what is P(~getting clubs)?

b. If P(A) = 0.4, what is P(~A)?

c. If P(win) = $x\%$, what is P(~win)?

11-72. Graph the points $(0, 2)$, $(6, 2)$, $(7, 4)$, and $(1, 4)$ and connect the points in order to create a parallelogram. What is the perimeter of the parallelogram?

11-73. Determine which nets below will form a prism. If a net will not form a prism, explain why not.

a.　　　　b.　　　　c.　　　　d.

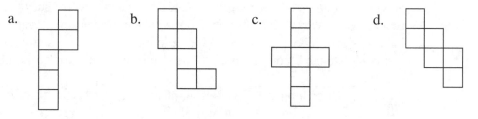

11-74.   Tim wants to invest some money that his grandmother gave him. He has $2000 and can put it in an account with simple interest or an account with compound interest.

a.   The simple interest account is for 5 years with an interest rate of 10%. Use the formula $I = P \cdot rt$ to find the interest he earned at the end of five years. How can you use the interest to calculate the total amount in the account at the end of 5 years? What is the total?

b.   The compound interest account is also for 5 years (compounded yearly) at an interest rate of 8%. Find the total in the account (A) using the formula $A = P(1+r)^t$. What is the total?

c.   Which account is a better investment?

11.3.1 How many cubes fit inside of it?

Exploring Volume

Children often enjoy putting smaller toys into larger containers. A child might stack small blocks inside a wagon or put toys away in a toy box. But how do you know how much will fit inside a container? As you explore the concept of volume today, think about how many cubes can fit inside each shape.

11-75.   BUILDING CUBES

How many one inch cubes will fit inside a larger cube with faces that measure two inches by two inches? What about a cube that measures six inches by six inches by six inches? Discuss your predictions with your teammates and copy and complete the second column of the table below for four different cube sizes.

Edge length of cube	Prediction of number of one-inch cubes that fit inside	Actual number of one-inch cubes that fit inside
1 inch		
6 inches		
9 inches		
12 inches		

Making Connections: Course 2

11-76. Today each member of your team will construct a one-inch cube and then together you will build one larger cube that your teacher will assign you. The one-inch cube will be your unit of measure.

    a. Make a sketch of a net for your one-inch cube. What should the dimensions of each edge be? How will the dimensions change for the larger cube? Explain how you will put each cube together. Check with your teacher and then get a sheet of one-inch grid poster paper to create your cubes.

    b. Cut the paper and carefully make the one-inch cube. Then work together to design and construct the larger cube. As you construct the larger cube, leave one side open like a lid.

    c. When you have finished, use your smaller cubes to check your predictions and complete the third column of the table from problem 11-75. You may want to work with other teams who have different sized cubes to check your predictions.

11-77. The one-inch cube and the larger cube your team built are similar solids. That is, they have the same shape and the same angle measures. Their edge lengths are related by a common scale factor.

    a. What is the scale factor ($\frac{\text{large}}{\text{small}}$) between your small cube and the larger cube?

    b. Are the volumes of the two cubes related by the same scale factor? If not, what is the scale factor between the volumes?

    c. Find the area of one face of each cube. Are those areas related by the same scale factor as the edges? By the same scale factor as the volume?

11-78. Find a team that has built a cube that has an edge twice as long or half as long as the edge of your team's cube. For example, if your cube has an edge of 3 inches, find a team with a cube that has an edge of 6 inches.

    a. By what scale factor is the edge of the small cube multiplied to make the edge of the large cube?

    b. Predict how many of the smaller cubes would fit inside the larger cube. Then, use the cubes to check your prediction.

11-79.   There are several ways to describe parts of a cube. You have learned about volume, surface area, and dimensions, but now you will have a chance to look more closely at some of the special features of this three-dimensional shape. Record your work for this problem on the Lesson 11.3.1 Resource Page. You should carefully record your answers in words or drawings so you can understand the concepts if you do not have an actual cube in front of you.

   a.   Sketch two intersecting lines and mark the intersection. Name the geometric figure that marks the intersection of two lines.

   b.   Darken two different intersecting edges on the cube. Name the geometric figure that marks the intersection of two edges.

   c.   Find and darken a pair of parallel edges on the cube and shade the face that contains them.

   d.   Darken two parallel edges on the cube that are not part of the same face and sketch in the flat surface that contains them. This flat region is part of a **plane**, a flat surface that extends infinitely in all directions.

   e.   Darken a pair of edges on the cube that can be extended to create **skew lines** (lines in three-dimensional space that do not lie in the same flat surface, do not intersect, and are not parallel).

   f.   Shade a pair of intersecting faces on the cube and darken the edge that marks the intersection. Extend each edge with a dotted line and add arrows to show that the line is infinite. Name the geometric figure that is made by the intersection of the faces.

   g.   Shade three intersecting faces on the cube. Name the geometric figure that marks the intersection.

   h.   Darken a pair of opposite corners and draw the diagonal that connects them.

11-80.   Name the geometric figures formed by the intersection of:

   a.   Two distinct lines

   b.   Two distinct planes (flat surfaces)

   c.   Three distinct planes (flat surfaces)

11-81. Imagine a cube that has edges that are each one foot long.

   a. How long is each edge in inches?

   b. What is the area of one face, measured in square feet? What is the area measured in square inches?

   c. What is the volume of one cube, measured in cubic feet? What is the volume measured in cubic inches?

   d. Do these results surprise you? Why or why not? Describe any patterns you notice in these numbers.

═══════════ Review & Preview ═══════════

11-82. The two triangles at right are similar.

   a. Find the area of each triangle.

   b. What is the scale factor for the side lengths of the two triangles?

   c. What is the ratio of the areas ($\frac{\text{Area B}}{\text{Area A}}$)? How is this ratio related to the ratio you found in part (b)?

11-83. Skye's Ice Cream Shoppe is Mario's favorite place to get ice cream. Unfortunately, because he was late arriving there, his friends had already ordered. He did not know what they ordered for him. They told him that it was either a waffle cone or a sundae and that the ice cream flavor was either apricot, chocolate, or blackberry.

   a. What is the probability that Mario will get something with apricot ice cream?

   b. What is the probability that he will get a sundae?

   c. What is the probability that he will get either something with chocolate or a waffle cone with blackberry?

   d. What is the probability that he will get orange sherbet?

11-84. Simplify each expression.

   a. $x^2 x^3 x^2$ b. $(xy^3z)(xy)$ c. $5 \cdot t^2 \cdot 5^3 \cdot t$

11-85.   The area of the base in the prism at right is 96 square inches.

a.   Find the volume of the prism.

b.   Find the volume of a pyramid with the same base and height.

25 in.

c.   If another prism has the same volume as this prism, but its base area is 80 square inches, what is its height?

11-86.   Sixty-five percent of the 8th grade class is selling magazines for the class fundraiser. If 112 students are selling magazines, how many students are in the 8th grade class?

11-87.   Think about the different three-dimensional vocabulary you learned in this lesson.

a.   Name two sets of geometric figures that can intersect to form a point.

b.   Is the face of a cube an example of a point, a plane (flat surface), or skew lines? Explain why it cannot be either of the other two.

11-88.   **Multiple Choice:** Which of the cylinders matches the net? Explain how you know. Note that the length above each cylinder is the radius of the base.

11-89.   Simplify each of the following expressions.

a. $(5x^3)^2$

b. $\dfrac{14a^3b^2}{21a^4b^3}$

c. $2m^3n^2 \cdot 3mn^4$

11-90.   Janet sells erasers at a price of 8 erasers for 60 cents. She started this table to show the price for different numbers of erasers. Complete her table.

Erasers	8	4	1	12	10	16	100
$	0.60						

11-91.   The attendance at the county fair was lowest on Thursday, the opening day. On Friday 5500 more people attended than attended Thursday. Saturday doubled Thursday's attendance, and Sunday had 3000 more people than Saturday. The total attendance was 36,700. Write and solve an equation to find how many people attended the fair each day.

11-92.   Make a table for the rule $y = -2x^2$ that includes x-values from -3 to 3. Graph the rule on graph paper.

11.3.2 How does the volume change?
· ·

Scale Factor and Volume

In Chapter 9 you investigated the relationship between the areas of two shapes that are similar and their scale factor. If a box is enlarged so that each edge is three times longer than the original, how will the surface area change? What will happen to the volume? In this lesson you will answer these questions using different three-dimensional shapes. With your team you will practice **visualizing** three-dimensional shapes, finding patterns, and describing patterns.

11-93.   The city of Lakewood is building a new playground in the city park. The contractor will use sand to provide a soft landing area under the swings. On the architect's scale model, the sand is 1 cm deep by 15 cm long by 20 cm wide. On the actual playground, the length, width, and depth of the sand area will each be 100 times larger.

When the model was finished, the architect figured out how many cubic centimeters of sand she used for the model, and then ordered 100 times that volume. Work with your team to decide whether she ordered the right amount of sand *without making any calculations*.

11-94.   GROWING, GROWING, GROWING, ...

To investigate how the volume of a solid
changes as the edge length changes, obtain a
Lesson 11.3.2A Resource Page and a set of
cubes from your teacher.

a.   For this problem, the edge length of a single cube will be called one unit.
     Use your small cubes to build a larger cube with a scale factor of 2.

b.   Calculate the length of one edge, the area of one face, and the volume of the
     cube you built, then record your work in the table on the Lesson 11.3.2
     Resource Page.

c.   Repeat this process for cubes with scale factors of 3 and 4, and record your
     work on the resource page.

d.   With your team, discuss any patterns you can find in the data for different
     scale factors so far. Then complete the resource page for cubes with scale
     factors of 5, 6, 7, 8, 9, and $\frac{1}{2}$.

e.   Suppose that a cube had a scale factor of x units. What would the edge
     length, area of one face, and the volume be? Add these expressions to your
     table.

11-95.   Now that you know the area of one face for all of the cubes in problem 11-94,
          find the total surface area for each of the cubes, including a cube with a scale
          factor of x.

11-96.   Next, work with your team to use graphs to investigate the question: How is the
          volume changing? On the axes on the Lesson 11.3.2B Resource Page, make
          three graphs: one comparing scale factor and edge length, the second comparing
          scale factor and surface area, and the third comparing scale factor and volume.
          With your team, describe how each quantity (edge length, surface area, and
          volume) changes as the scale factor changes.

11-97.   Look again at the sand order the architect placed in problem 11-93. Calculate
          the volume of the sand in her scale model and in the actual playground. Did she
          order the correct amount of sand? How does your result make sense based on
          what you learned in problems 11-94 and 11-95?

11-98. Use the rectangular prism shown at right to complete parts (a) through (d) below.

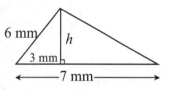

a. Calculate the surface area of the prism. Show all your subproblems.

b. Explain why the exponent for area units is 2 (that is, cm²).

c. Calculate the volume of the prism.

d. Explain why the exponent for volume units is a 3 (that is, cm³).

11-99. Calculate the height and area of this triangle.

11-100. A bag contains 3 red, 5 yellow, and 7 purple marbles. Find the probability of drawing a purple marble followed by a red marble. The purple marble is put back in the bag between draws.

11-101. Estimate each square root below to the nearest tenth. Then check your estimate on your calculator. Be sure to write down your estimate before you check!

a. $\sqrt{45}$ b. $\sqrt{260}$ c. $\sqrt{650}$ d. $\sqrt{57}$

11-102. Consider the expression $(56 \cdot 25) \cdot 4$.

a. How can regrouping the numbers in this expression make it easier to simplify? Rewrite the expression and simplify it.

b. What property did you use to rewrite the expression?

11.3.3 What if it is not a cube?

More Scale Factor and Volume

Today you will continue to explore how the volume of a three-dimensional shape changes as the sides are multiplied by a scale factor.

11-103. Bethany's study team just bought her an amazing Cube-o-saurus for her birthday. The package says, "Soak in water overnight and the Cube-o-saurus will get an amazing eight times larger." The cube-shaped dinosaur starts out about one centimeter on a side. Bethany and her study team members are looking forward to seeing the 8-centimeter long creature. Bethany went home and soaked the Cube-o-saurus in water. When she brought it to school the next day, her team was disappointed to see that the Cube-o-saurus was the same shape and only 2 centimeters long, 2 centimeters tall, and 2 centimeters wide. Was the Cube-o-saurus falsely advertised? Is the new shape eight times larger?

11-104. HOW DOES THE VOLUME CHANGE?

In Lesson 11.3.2, you worked with different sized cubes and saw that when cubes are enlarged by a scale factor, the surface area and volume grow, but in different ways than the edge lengths.

Use the data from the Lesson 11.3.2A Resource Page to complete the table on the Lesson 11.3.3 Resource Page or copy the table below on your paper and complete it.

Scale Factor	Edge Length	Face Area	Volume
1	1	1	1
2	2	4	8
3			
...			
9			
x			

Problem continues on next page. →

11-104.   *Problem continued from previous page.*

    a.   Use the pattern in the table to explain how the area changes compared to the length of the edge in similar cubes. How is this change related to the scale factor?

    b.   Use the pattern in the table to explain how the volume changes compared to the length of an edge in similar cubes. How is this change related to the scale factor?

    c.   If the scale factor for a $1 \times 1 \times 1$ cube is 12, what is the face area of its enlargement? The volume?

11-105.   Does the pattern you found for length and volume with cubes apply to all similar solids? Answer the questions below with your team to decide.

    a.   Use the original figures on the Lesson 11.3.3 Resource Page (at right) and the scale factors to find the dimensions of the enlarged shapes.

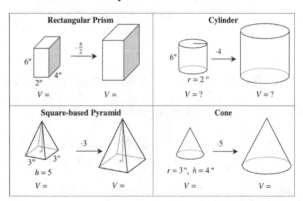

    b.   Find the volumes of each original and enlarged shape.

    c.   Use your results from part (b) to complete the table on the Lesson 11.3.3 Resource Page (shown below).

Figure	Scale Factor	(scale factor)^3	$\frac{\text{enlarged volume}}{\text{original volume}}$	Volume ratio reduced
Rectangular Prism				
Cylinder				
Square-based prism				
Cone				

    d.   Compare each scale factor, its cube, and the reduced ratio of the two volumes. What pattern do you see?

    e.   If two prisms are similar with a scale factor of 3 and the volume of the smaller prism is 21 cm^3, what is the volume of the enlarged prism?

11-106. The graph at right shows how the
height, base area, and volume of a
cone change for different scale
factors. Which graph represents
the base area of the cone? Which
graph represents the height?
Which graph represents the
volume? Explain how you
determined your choices.

11-107. Back at the store, David sees a Prismasaur that is advertised to grow 64 times
bigger. If this advertisement refers to the growth of the volume and the
Prismasaur is shaped like a rectangular prism that starts out 2 cm wide by 4 cm
long by 2 cm tall, will the Prismasaur be 8 cm long after it is soaked overnight?
How many times longer will each side be?

11-108. Consider the square-based pyramid at right.

a. What is the volume of the pyramid?

b. Each triangular face has an area of 3.16 cm².
What is the total surface area of the pyramid?

c. If each dimension of the pyramid is increased
by a scale factor of 5, what will the new
volume be? Make your prediction based on
the patterns you found so far.

d. Calculate the volume of the new pyramid. Was your prediction correct?

11-109. LEARNING LOG

If the linear dimensions (edges) of a three-dimensional
shape grow by a scale factor of 10, how will the volume
grow? Show and explain your answer in your Learning
Log. Title your entry "Volume in Similar Shapes," and
label it with today's date.

Making Connections: Course 2

METHODS AND MEANINGS

Ratios of Similarity — 3D

When a three-dimensional solid is enlarged proportionally, each dimension is multiplied by the same scale factor.

The ratio of the edges is the scale factor, $\left(\frac{a}{b}\right)$.

The **surface area ratio** is the square of the scale factor.

$$\left(\frac{\text{surface area of new}}{\text{surface area of original}}\right) = (\text{scale factor})^2 = \left(\frac{a}{b}\right)^2$$

The **volume ratio** is the cube of the scale factor.

$$\left(\frac{\text{volume of new}}{\text{volume of original}}\right) = (\text{scale factor})^3 = \left(\frac{a}{b}\right)^3$$

Figure 1

2 m, 2 m, 4 m

SA = 40 m^2
Vol = 16 m^3

Figure 2

6 m, 6 m, 12 m

SA = 360 m^2
Vol = 432

For example, comparing the rectangular prisms at right, for $\frac{\text{figure 2}}{\text{figure 1}}$:

The scale factor is $\frac{3}{1}$.

The surface area ratio is $\frac{360}{40} = \frac{9}{1} = \left(\frac{3}{1}\right)^2$.

The volume ratio is $\frac{432}{16} = \frac{27}{1} = \left(\frac{3}{1}\right)^3$.

11-110. Rick's favorite drink, Aloha Pineapple Juice, is packaged in a can like the one shown at right. It contains 350 ml of juice. Even after drinking it, he always feels thirsty. He wants the company to package the juice in a larger can.

a. If the company enlarges the dimensions of the can by a ratio of $\frac{4}{1}$, how much juice would the can hold? Show your work or explain how you got your answer.

b. Does it seem likely that the company will make a can that size? Explain.

11-111. The label of the Aloha Pineapple Juice can is seven inches high and has an area of 140 square inches. What is the diameter of the can?

11-112. On a piece of grid paper, plot the following points and connect them: $A(-3, -4)$, $B(2, 4)$, $C(5, -4)$.

a. What is the area of triangle ABC?

b. What is the perimeter of triangle ABC?

11-113. Simplify each expression.

a. $-\frac{11}{15} + \frac{3}{4}$

b. $5\frac{2}{9} + (-2\frac{1}{10})$

c. $-\frac{7}{8} + \frac{2}{3} - (-\frac{1}{4})$

11-114. Sherice can fill lemonade cups at a rate of four cups per minute.

a. How many cups can she fill in 6 minutes?

b. How many cups can she fill in 10 minutes?

11.4.1 How can I find the measurement?

Indirect Measurement

When most people think of measurement, they think of using a ruler or tape measure to find a length. However, during this course you found the measures of objects using other types of information, a process called **indirect measurement**. Today's activity will provide you opportunities to connect several ways you know how to find measures. As you work with your team, ask the following questions:

How can we **visualize** it?

What information do we need?

Which **strategy** should we use?

11-115. The beautiful young princess of Polygonia is very sad. A mean ogre has locked her into a tower of a castle. She could escape through the window, but it is 50 feet above the ground (a long distance to jump). A moat full of alligators surrounds the tower. Naturally, her prince charming wants to rescue her.

The prince has some rope. His plan is to use an arrow to shoot one end of the rope up to her window. The princess can then slide down the rope to the other side of the moat, and off they will ride into the sunset.

Help the prince save the princess by answering the questions below.

castle
7.5 in.

a. The prince knows that the closer he is to the tower, the less rope he will need. However, he is not sure how wide the moat is around the castle.

In a book about the castle, the prince found a photograph of the tower and moat. Using his ruler, he found that the window in the photo is 7.5 inches above the moat, while the farthest edge of the moat is 1.5 inches from the base of the tower. How close to the tower can the prince get? Draw diagrams and show your work.

1.5 in.
moat

Problem continues on next page. →

11-115.   *Problem continued from previous page.*

    b.   Before he shoots the arrow, the prince wants to make sure he has enough rope. If he needs an extra 2 feet of rope for tying it to the window frame and holding it on the ground, how long does his rope need to be? Explain.

    c.   The princess thinks she might fall off the rope if the slope is steeper than $\frac{5}{4}$. The prince plans to attach the rope to the ground at the edge of the moat and the princess will attach the rope to the window frame 50 feet above the ground.

        i.   According to the prince's plan, what would be the slope of the rope? Would it be too steep? **Justify** your answer.

        ii. Should the princess worry about the prince's plan? How steep would the prince's rope be? Find the angle the rope would make with the ground. Use a protractor to measure the angle.

    d.   If one end of the rope is attached to the window frame and the prince holds his end of the rope 2 feet above the ground, where would the prince need to stand so that the slope of the rope is only $\frac{5}{4}$? If he has a rope that is 62 feet long, will his rope be long enough? **Justify** your conclusion. Draw a picture and label it with all your measurements.

    e.   What if the prince holds his end of the rope 5 feet above the ground? Can he stand in some location so that the rope is not steeper than $\frac{5}{4}$? (The rope is still 62 feet long.) **Justify** your conclusion.

11-116.   MAKING CONNECTIONS

When you solved this problem, you needed to use what you learned about several different math ideas.

    a.   Discuss how you solved the problem with your team.

        • Use colors to mark parts of your solution that used particular math ideas. (For example, did you compare portions? Did you solve equations?)

        • Label each math idea with words in the margin of your paper.

    b.   Contribute your ideas to a class discussion. Did any other teams identify math ideas that you used but did not notice? If so, add them to your notes. Then write each math idea on an index card.

    c.   How are these different math ideas connected in this problem? Work with your team and follow your teacher's instructions to make a concept map. Work with your team to find ways to show or explain each of the connections you find.

11-117.   THINKING ABOUT THINKING

This course focuses on five different Ways of Thinking: generalizing, reasoning and justifying, reversing thinking, choosing a strategy and visualizing. Some of the Ways of Thinking you used in this lesson were **reasoning and justifying** and **choosing a strategy**.

a.   With others, read and discuss the descriptions of **reasoning and justifying** and **choosing a strategy** below.

   Reasoning and justifying: When you **reason** and **justify** as you solve problems, you think about what makes sense and why. Often, reasoning and justifying helps you to answer the question, "Why?" You think this way when you say or ask, *"If this is true, then..."* and *"We know that..., because..."* and *"How can we be sure?"*

   Choosing a strategy: To **choose a strategy** means to think about what you know about a problem and match that information with methods and processes for solving problems. You think this way when you ask/answer questions like, "What strategy might work for...?" or , "How can I use this information to answer...?"

b.   What questions did you ask yourself and your team that helped you to understand your thinking and the thinking of others, that is, to **reason** through problem 11-116? How did you decide what information was necessary to **justify** your conclusions? Be ready to explain your ideas.

c.   How did your team **choose a strategy** as you figured out how to solve the different parts of problem 11-116? Did you choose different strategies for different parts? Be ready to share your ideas with the class.

11.4.2 How does it grow?

Representing and Predicting Patterns

You have often worked with teams to describe relationships between quantities. For example, you have used tables, graphs, and rules to show how pigs have grown, how runners have traveled, and how money has increased over time. In this lesson, you will revisit a game you may have played early in the course and apply your learning to analyze it. While you work, keep the following questions in mind:

Which representation should we use?

Is this like any other problem we have seen?

11-118.   TOOTHPICKS AND TILES RETURN!

Laurel and Sandra are playing a new version of the Toothpick and Tiles game from Chapter 1. In this game, each player takes turns building shapes that form a pattern.

They have taken three turns so far, shown below. A player will get an extra point if the number of tiles ever equals the number of toothpicks. Remember that the toothpicks create the border (perimeter) of the shape.

| Turn 1 | Turn 2 | Turn 3 |
| by Laurel | by Sandra | by Laurel |

a.   Represent the number of toothpicks for each turn in a table and with a rule. Let x represent the turn number.

b.   Represent the number of tiles for each turn in a table and with a rule. Let x represent the turn number.

c.   Will anyone get the extra point? If so, on which turn and who will get the extra point? Use two different representations to **justify** your answer.

d.   Laurel is worried that they might run out of toothpicks and tiles. They only have 30 of each. How many tiles will they need to build the shape on the 10th turn? How many toothpicks?

Problem continues on next page. →

Making Connections: Course 2

11-118.   *Problem continued from previous page.*

     e.   Laurel won this game. That means she gets to choose the next pattern. She wants to create a pattern that will have its perimeter grow by 3 units each turn. Is this possible? Test this idea out and explain your thinking.

     f.   Laurel wants your help to create a pattern so that the perimeter would be represented with the graph at right. Draw Turn #1, Turn #2, and Turn #3 of a pattern that would match this graph. Explain how your design is changing with each turn.

11-119.   THINKING ABOUT THINKING

This course focuses on five different Ways of Thinking: generalizing, reasoning and justifying, reversing, choosing a strategy and visualizing. Two of the Ways of Thinking you may have used in this lesson are **generalizing** and **reversing your thinking**.

     a.   With others, read and discuss the descriptions of **generalizing** and **reversing your thinking** below.

        Generalizing: When you **generalize**, you make a statement about a characteristic that a group of things shares, based on a collection of evidence. Often, a generalization is the answer to the question, "What is in common?" When you think or say, *"I think this is always true…"*, you are generalizing.

        Reversing thinking: To **reverse your thinking** can be described as "thinking backward." You think this way when you want to understand a concept in a new direction. Often, it requires you to try to undo a process. When you think or say, *"What if I try to go backwards?"*, you are reversing your thinking.

     b.   How did your algebra skills help you to **generalize** the pattern created in this game? How is generalizing important in problems such as this one?

     c.   How did **reversing your thinking** help you solve problem 11-118? Be ready to explain your ideas.

     d.   Work with your team to brainstorm other problems in this course in which you **generalized** and used **reversing your thinking**. Be ready to share your ideas with the class.

11.4.3 How much should it cost?

Volume and Scaling

Have you ever made choices about which size of an item (such as a pizza or bottle of juice) to buy? If so, you may have considered which size was priced to give you the most for your money. In this lesson, you will work with your team as you analyze pricing of popcorn at a popular movie theater.

11-120.   The Maverick Movie Theater sells a small tub of popcorn for $1.

a. To keep their prices proportional to the amount of popcorn offered, what should they charge for the large tub shown at right? Show how you found your answer.

b. The medium size tub is a cylinder with diameter 9 inches and height 12 inches. It currently costs $6 and is not selling well. The owner wants you to decide if this price is fair. How much should it cost? Write a note to the owner that explains whether the medium-sized tub is priced correctly.

c. Customers have complained that the large tub is too wide to carry into the theater without spilling. The owner wants to change the diameter to be 10 inches instead. To keep the same volume, the owner thinks that the new tub will need to be 14 inches tall. She **reasons** that if the width gets two inches shorter, the height should grow by two inches.

Do you agree? If so, show how you know. If not, determine the new height of the tub.

d. The owner decided to create a new size that is 50% wider and 50% taller than the small tub. The owner plans to charge 50% more. Do you agree? If not, what should the owner charge and what percent increase is this price? **Justify** your answer.

e. The owner wants to offer a box of popcorn that would cost $6. She wants you to design the box. Assume that the price should be proportional with the amount of popcorn in the small tub of popcorn. While the box can have any length, width, and height, be sure to make it a reasonable design for someone to hold and for the employees to fill with popcorn.

Draw a diagram of your box with all measurements labeled.

Making Connections: Course 2

11-121.   MAKING CONNECTIONS

When you solved this problem, you needed to use what you learned about several different math ideas.

a.   Discuss how you solved the problem with your team.

- Use colors to mark parts of your solution that used particular math ideas. (For example, did you compare portions? Did you solve equations?)

- Label each math idea with words in the margin of your paper.

b.   Contribute your ideas to a class discussion. Did any other teams identify math ideas that you used but did not notice? If so, add them to your notes. Then write each math idea on an index card.

c.   How are these different math ideas connected in this problem? Work with your team and follow your teacher's instructions to make a concept map. Work with your team to find ways to show or explain each of the connections you find.

11-122.   THINKING ABOUT THINKING

This course focuses on five different Ways of Thinking: generalizing, reasoning and justifying, reversing, choosing a strategy and visualizing. Two of the Ways of Thinking you used in this lesson are **choosing a strategy** and **visualizing**.

a.   Read the descriptions of **choosing a strategy** and **visualizing** below.

Choosing a strategy: To **choose a strategy** means to think about what you know about a problem and match that information with methods and processes for solving problems. You think this way when you ask/answer questions like, "What strategy might work for…?" or , "How can I use this information to answer…?"

Visualizing: To **visualize** means to think about what something looks like or could look like in order to better understand the problem or situation. You think this way when you ask or answer questions like, *"What does it look like when…?"* or *"How can I draw…?"*

b.   How did your team **choose a strategy** as you figured out how to solve the different parts of problem 11-120? Did you choose different strategies for different parts? Was there ever more than one strategy you could have used? Explain.

c.   A lot of the **visualizing** you did in this lesson related to geometry and shapes. Find a different problem you did in this course that was *not* about a geometric shape, but for which **visualizing** the mathematical ideas helped you make sense of the problem or understand the problem more deeply. Describe what you **visualized** and explain how this helped you work through the problem.

11.4.4 How is it changing?

Analyzing Data to Identify a Trend

Have you ever tried to figure out whether you could earn enough money to be able to buy something that you want? In this lesson, you will consider the relationship between the time you work and your pay rate as you work with your team to analyze data and make predictions.

11-123. Devon hopes to get a job in the summer at an amusement park. He is hoping to earn enough money during the summer to buy a laptop for $875. He is not sure what pay rate he will be offered so he asked his friends who work at the same amusement park for information from their last paycheck. The information he gathered is in the table at right.

	Time (hours)	Pay (dollars)
Frieda	21	$200.00
Ben	25	$305.00
Emory	36	$252.00
Si Yun	50	$480.00
Jillian	55	$600.00
Malik	64	$512.00
Dazjon	72	$600.00
Grace	80	$700.00

a.   On graph paper, set up a graph, carefully decide how to scale the axes, and graph Devon's data.

b.   Find the hourly rate for each of Devon's friends.

c.   What is the highest rate per hour one of Devon's friends is earning? What is the lowest rate per hour? Explain how you found your answer.

d.   Draw a trend line that represents this data. Use your trend line to help Devon predict how much he will earn. Why does it make sense that the trend line should pass through the origin?

e.   Devon hopes to work 4 hours each day. If he works Friday through Sunday for 10 weeks, how many hours would he work?

f.   Based on your trend line, how much money can Devon expect to be paid per hour? Show how you found your answer.

g.   Devon knows that he will need to pay 7.5% tax for his laptop. Will he make enough money? Explain how you know.

Making Connections: Course 2

11-124. MAKING CONNECTIONS

When you solved this problem, you needed to use what you learned about several different math ideas.

a. Discuss how you solved the problem with your team.

- Use colors to mark parts of your solution that used particular math ideas. (For example, did you calculate volume? Did you use transformations?)

- Label each math idea with words in the margin of your paper.

b. Contribute your ideas to a class discussion. Did any other teams identify math ideas that you used but did not notice? If so, add them to your notes. Then write each math idea on an index card.

c. How are these different math ideas connected in this problem? Work with your team and follow your teacher's instructions to make a concept map. Work with your team to find ways to show or explain each of the connections you think of.

Chapter 11 Closure What have I learned?

Reflection and Synthesis

The activities below offer you a chance to reflect about what you have learned during this chapter. As you work, look for concepts that you feel very comfortable with, ideas that you would like to learn more about, and topics you need more help with. Look for connections between ideas as well as connections with material you learned previously.

①   WHAT HAVE I LEARNED?

Working the problems in this section will help you to evaluate which types of problems you feel comfortable with and which ones you need more help with.

Solve each problem as completely as you can. The table at the end of this closure section has answers to these problems. It also tells you where you can find additional help and practice on problems like them.

CL 11-125. Look at the graph at right. What type of equation does it represent? Explain how you know.

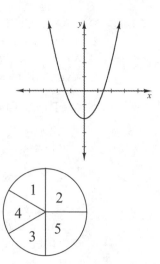

CL 11-126. Erika is playing a game where the number of spaces she moves is determined by the spinner at right. Each half of the spinner — left and right — is divided into equal regions as shown.

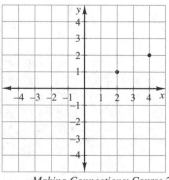

a. What is the probability that Erika will spin an even number on her next spin?

b. If Erika spins a four she will land on a space that says "Get an extra turn." If she then spins a five, she gets 50 bonus points and she will win the game. What is the probability that she can spin a four and then a five?

CL 11-127. Find the volume of a pyramid with a square base with sides of eight inches and a height of 12 inches.

CL 11-128. Ella's cat has climbed up on the roof of her house and cannot get down! The roof of the house is 24 feet above the ground. The fire department has set up a 28-foot ladder to climb to rescue the cat. The base of the ladder is resting on the ground, and the top of the ladder extends 2 feet beyond the edge of the roof. How far away from the base of the house is the base of the ladder? You may want to draw a diagram to help you solve the problem.

CL 11-129. Simplify the following exponential expressions.

a. $4^3 \cdot 4^7$

b. $(5x^4)^3$

c. $\dfrac{3^7}{3^4}$

d. $(4x^5)(3x^8)$

CL 11-130. **Visualize** a line through the two points on the graph at right.

a. What is the slope of the line?

b. What is the rule for the line?

Making Connections: Course 2

CL 11-131.   Manuela found a great deal on pens at 3 for $0.99. It was such a good deal that she decided to buy 2 dozen. How much did she pay for all of the pens?

CL 11-132.   Casey was building a rectangular pen for his pigs. He has 62 feet of fencing. The length of his pen is 9 feet longer than the width. Write and solve an equation to find the dimensions of the pen.

CL 11-133.   For each of the problems in this section of closure, do the following:

Draw a bar or number line like the one below that represents 0 to 10.

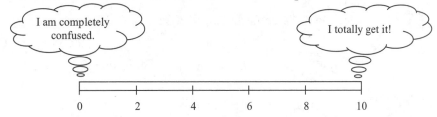

Color or shade in a portion of the bar that represents your current level of understanding and comfort with completing that problem on your own.

If any of your bars are less than a 5, choose *one* of those problems and do one of the following tasks:

• Write two questions that you would like to ask about that problem.

• Brainstorm two things that you DO know about that type of problem.

If all of your bars are a 5 or above, choose one of those problems and do one of these tasks:

• Write two questions you might ask or hints you might give to a student who was stuck on the problem.

• Make a new problem that is similar and more challenging than that problem and solve it.

You have several tools and references available to help support your learning – your teacher, your study team, your math book, and your Toolkit to name only a few. At the end of each chapter you will have an opportunity to review your Toolkit for completeness as well as to revise or update it to better reflect your current understanding of big ideas.

The main elements of your Toolkit should be your Learning Log, Math Notes, and the vocabulary used in this chapter. Math words that are new to this chapter appear in bold in the text. Refer to the lists provided below and follow your teacher's instructions to revise your Toolkit, which will help make it useful for you as you complete this chapter and as you work in future chapters.

Learning Log Entries

- Lesson 11.2.2 – Multiple Outcomes and Questions
- Lesson 11.3.3 – Volume in Similar Shapes

Math Notes

- Lesson 11.1.2 – Absolute Value
- Lesson 11.2.3 – Probability Models for Multiple Events
- Lesson 11.2.4 – Compound Probability
- Lesson 11.3.3 – Ratios of Similarity — 3D

Mathematical Vocabulary

The following is a list of vocabulary found in this chapter. Some of the words have been seen in a previous chapter. The words in bold are the words new to this chapter. It is a good idea to make sure that you are familiar with these words and know what they mean. For the words you do not know, refer to the glossary or index. You might also want to add these words to your Toolkit for a way to reference them in the future.

absolute value	**compound probability**	experimental probability
independent event	linear	**outcome chart**
parabola	**plane**	point
ratio	scale factor	**skew line**
symmetry	**systematic list**	theoretical probability
tree diagram	volume	

Process Words

These words describe problem solving strategies and processes that you have been involved in as you worked in this chapter. Make sure you know what each of these words means. If you are not sure, you can talk with your teacher or other students or look through your book for problems in which you were asked to do these things.

analyze	construct	describe
estimate	explain	express
justify	organize	reason
record	represent	reverse
scale		

Answers and Support for Closure Activity #1
What Have I Learned?

Problem	Solution	Need Help?	More Practice
CL 11-125.	It represents an equation of the form $y = x^2$.	Lesson 11.1.1	Problems 11-1 through 11-3, 11-92
CL 11-126.	a. $\frac{1}{4} + \frac{1}{6} = \frac{3}{12} + \frac{2}{12} = \frac{5}{12}$ b. $\frac{1}{6} \cdot \frac{1}{4} = \frac{1}{24}$	Lessons 11.2.3 and 11.2.4 Math Notes boxes in Lessons 11.2.3 and 11.2.4	Problems 11-46 through 11-51, 11-57 through 11-66, 11-70, 11-71, 11-83, and 11-100
CL 11-127.	Volume = 256 in^3	Lesson 10.2.6 Learning Log (problem 10-145)	Problems 10-144, 11-9, 11-85 (b), and 11-108

Problem	Solution	Need Help?	More Practice
CL 11-128.	The base of the ladder will be approximately 10 feet from the base of the house.	Lessons 9.3.2, 9.3.3, and 9.3.4 Math Notes boxes in Lessons 9.3.2 and 9.3.3 Learning Logs (problems 9-105 and 9-122)	Problem CL 10-160
CL 11-129.	a. 4^{10} b. $125x^{12}$ c. 3^3 d. $12x^{13}$	Lessons 10.1.2, 10.1.4, and 10.1.5 Math Notes boxes in Lessons 10.1.2 and 10.1.6 Learning Log (problem 10-58)	Problems CL 10-153, 11-10, 11-42, and 11-84
CL 11-130.	a. The slope is $\frac{1}{2}$. b. $y = \frac{1}{2}x$	Lessons 6.1.6, 7.1.4, and 7.1.5 Math Notes box in Lesson 7.1.6 Learning Log (problem 7-47)	Problems CL 7-94 and CL 10-147
CL 11-131.	$7.92	Lessons 9.1.1, 9.1.2, and 9.1.3 Math Notes boxes in Lessons 9.1.2 and 9.1.3 Learning Log (problem 9-8)	Problems CL 9-133, 11-69, and 11-90
CL 11-132.	$2x + 2(x + 9) = 62$ OR $4x + 18 = 62$ The dimensions of the pen are 11 feet by 20 feet.	Lesson 6.2.4 Math Notes boxes in Lessons 6.2.4 and 6.2.6 Learning Log (problem 6-107)	Problems CL 6-147, 11-33, and 11-91

PI-21. SECRET CODE

Arianna wants to send a secret code through her computer. By using a two-digit number for every letter, she can build secret words with numbers. For example, using her code below, "SECRET" becomes "180402170419."

A	B	C	D	E	F	G	H	I	J	K	L	M
00	01	02	03	04	05	06	07	08	09	10	11	12

N	O	P	Q	R	S	T	U	V	W	X	Y	Z
13	14	15	16	17	18	19	20	21	22	23	24	25

a. To answer the question "who is your favorite mathematician," Arianna wrote 00170207081204030418. Decipher her message. Remember that every pair of numbers represents a letter.

b. To send secret messages through computers, the numeric codes must be changed so that they only contain the digits 0 and 1. These are called **binary codes**, and use the base-2 number system. The base-2 number system counts in sets of 2 instead of sets of 10. The first 12 counting numbers in base-2 are shown in the table below. Based on this counting system, how would you write "12" in base-2? What about 15? 16?

Base 10:	00	01	02	03	04	05	06	07	08	09	10	11
Base 2:	00	01	10	11	100	101	110	111	1000	1001	1010	1011

c. To make a computer code for the entire alphabet, plus a code for a space and a code for an exclamation point, you will need the base-2 equivalents for the numbers 0 through 27. The codes will have 5 digits so that every letter has the same number of digits. Copy and complete the table below.

A = 00	00000	H = 07		O = 14	01110	V = 21	
B = 01	00001	I = 08		P = 15		W= 22	10110
C = 02	00010	J = 09		Q = 16		X = 23	
D = 03	00011	K = 10		R= 17		Y = 24	
E = 04	00100	L = 11		S = 18	10010	Z = 25	
F = 05		M = 12		T = 19		= 26	
G = 06		N = 13	01101	U = 20		! = 27	11011

c. To send the message "NOSE," Arianna's computer would change 13141804 to 01101011101001000100. What would be the computer code for "MATH"?

d. Decipher Arianna's secret message below. Remember that every 5 digits is a letter.

0111110100110011100101011001001101000101101000110111011

PI-22.   STAIRCASES

Study the following staircases.

The first staircase is made of
one cube. Its volume is 1 cubic
unit and its surface area is 6
square units.

a.   Show that the second staircase has a volume of 6 cubic units and a surface
      area of 22 square units.

b.   Find the volume and surface area of the third staircase.

c.   Describe in words what the 50th staircase will look like. For example, how
      many steps will it have? How wide will it be?

d.   Use geometric patterns, tables, and sketches to find the volume and surface
      area of the 50th staircase. In your explanation, describe as many **patterns**
      as you can and explain how you arrived at your answers and why you think
      they are correct.

Glossary

5-D Process An organized method to solve problems. The 5 D's stand for Describe/Draw, Define, Do, Decide, and Declare. This is a problem-solving strategy for which solving begins by making a prediction about the answer or one element of it (a trial), and then confirming whether the result of the trial is correct. If not, information is gained about how close the trial is to the correct value, so that adjustments to the trial value may be made. Being organized is extremely important to the success of this method, as well as writing a usable table. The 5-D process leads to writing equations to represent word problems. (p. 179)

absolute value The absolute value of a number is the distance of the number from zero. Since the absolute value represents a distance, without regard to direction, absolute value is always non-negative. Thus, the absolute value of a negative number is its opposite, while the absolute value of a non-negative number is just the number itself. The absolute value of x is usually written "$|x|$." For example, $|-5| = 5$ and $|22| = 22$. (p. 637)

acute angle An angle with a measure greater than 0° and less than 90°. An example is shown at right. (p. 304)

acute triangle A triangle with all three angle measures less than 90°.

addition (+) An operation that tells how many objects there are when two sets are combined. The result is the number of objects in the two sets together which is called a sum. In arithmetic, the word "object" usually means "number." (p. 90)

Additive Inverse Property The Additive Inverse Property states that for every number a there is a number $-a$ such that $a + (-a) = 0$. For example, the number 5 has an additive inverse of -5; $5 + (-5) = 0$. The additive inverse of a number is often called its opposite. For example, 5 and -5 are opposites. (p. 290)

adjacent angles For two angles to be adjacent, the angles must satisfy these three conditions: (1) the two angles must have a common side; (2) the two angles must have a common vertex; and (3) the two angles may have no interior points in common. Meeting these three conditions means that the common side must be between the two angles. No overlap between the angles is permitted. In the example at right, $\angle ABC$ and $\angle CBD$ are adjacent angles.

algebra A branch of mathematics that uses variables to generalize the rules of numbers and numerical operations.

algebra tiles An algebra tile is a manipulative whose area represents a constant or variable quantity. The algebra tiles used in this course consist of large squares with dimensions x-by-x and y-by-y; rectangles with dimensions x-by-1, y-by-1, and x-by-y; and small squares with dimensions 1-by-1. These tiles are named by their areas: x^2, y^2, x, y, xy, and 1, respectively. The smallest squares are called "unit tiles." In this text, shaded tiles will represent positive quantities while unshaded tiles will represent negative quantities. (p. 156)

algebraic expression See *expression*.

algorithm A fixed rule for carrying out a mathematical procedure. For example, to find the average of a set of values, find the sum of the values and divide by the number of values.

altitude of a triangle The length of a segment that connects a vertex of the triangle to a line containing the opposite base (side) and is perpendicular to that line. (See *height*.)

angle Generally, an angle is formed by two rays that are joined at a common endpoint. Angles in geometric figures are usually formed by two segments that have a common endpoint (such as the angle shaded in the figure at right). (Also see *acute angle*, *obtuse angle*, and *right angle*.) (p. 304)

arc

angle bisector A ray that divides an angle into two congruent parts.

arc A part of a circle or curve between two points on the circle.

area For this course, area is the number of square units needed to fill up a region on a flat surface. In later courses, the idea will be extended to cones, spheres, and more complex surfaces. (Also see *surface area*.) (p. 10, 603)

Area = 15 square units

area of a circle $A = \pi r^2$, where r is the length of the radius of the circle. (See "circle.") (p. 319)

area of a triangle To find the area of a triangle, multiply the length of the base b by the height h and divide by two: $A = \frac{1}{2}bh$. (Also see *altitude of a triangle*.) (p. 127)

Associative Property of Addition   The Associative Property of Addition states that if a sum contains terms that are grouped, then the sum may be grouped differently with no effect on the total, that is, $a+(b+c)=(a+b)+c$. For example, $3+(4+5)=(3+4)+5$. (p. 78)

Associative Property of Multiplication   The Associative Property of Multiplication states that if a product contains terms that are grouped, then the product may be grouped differently with no effect on the result, that is, $a(bc)=(ab)c$. For example, $2\cdot(3\cdot4)=(2\cdot3)\cdot4$. (p. 581)

average   The sum of given values divided by the number of values used in computing the sum. For example, the average of 1, 4, and 10 is $(1+4+10)/3$. (See *mean*.) (p. 13)

axis (plural: axes)   In a coordinate plane, two number lines that meet at right angles at the origin (0, 0). The *x*-axis runs horizontally and the *y*-axis runs vertically. (p. 85, 94)

bar graph   A bar graph is a set of rectangular bars that have height proportional to the number of data elements in each category. Each bar stands for all of the elements in a single distinguishable category (such as "red"). Usually all of the bars are the same width and separated from each other. (Also see *histogram*.) (p. 219)

base of a geometric figure   (a) The base of a triangle: any side of a triangle to which a height is drawn. There are three possible bases in each triangle. (b) The base of a trapezoid: either of the two parallel sides. (c) The base of a parallelogram (including rectangle, rhombus, and square): any side to which a height is drawn. There are four possible bases. (d) The base of a solid: also see *cone*, *cylinder*, *prism*, and *pyramid*. (p. 115, 595)

base of an exponent   When working with an exponential expression in the form a^b, *a* is called the base. For example, 2 is the base in 2^5. (5 is the exponent, and 32 is the value.) (Also see *exponent*.) (p. 572)

bimodal   A set of numbers that has two modes.

boundary point   The endpoint or endpoints of a ray or segment on a number line where an inequality is true, marked with a solid dot. For strict inequalities (that is, inequalities involving < or >), the point is not part of the solution, and is marked with an open dot. Boundary points may be found by solving the equality associated with the given inequality. For example, the solution to the equation $2x+5=11$ is $x=3$, so the inequality $2x+5\geq11$ has a boundary point at 3. A boundary point is also sometimes called a "dividing point." (p. 294)

box-and-whisker plot   A graphic way of showing a summary of data using the median, quartiles, and extremes of the data. (p. 230)

center (center point)   Within a flat surface, the point that is the same distance from all points of a circle. (Also see *circle*.)

central angle   An angle with its vertex at the center of a circle. (Also see *circle*.) (p. 339)

certainty   When an event will definitely happen. The probability of a certain event is 1. (p. 33)

chord   A line segment with its endpoints on a circle. A chord that passes through the center of a circle is called a "diameter." (Also see *circle*.) (p. 309)

circle   The set of all points on a flat surface that are the same distance from a fixed point. If the fixed point (center) is O, then the symbol $\odot O$ represents a circle with center O. If r is the length of the radius of a circle and d is the length of its diameter, then the circumference of the circle is $C = 2\pi r$ or $C = \pi d$. (p. 309)

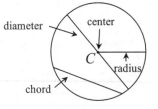

circumference   The perimeter of (distance around) a circle. (Also see *circle*.) (p. 309, 319)

coefficient (numerical)   A number multiplying a variable or product of variables. For example, –7 is the coefficient of $-7xy^2$. (p. 159)

combining like terms   Combining two or more like terms simplifies an expression by summing constants and summing those variable terms in which the same variables are raised to the same power. For example, combining like terms in the expression $3x + 7 + 5x - 3 + 2x^2 + 3y^2$ gives $8x + 4 + 2x^2 + 3y^2$. When working with algebra tiles, combining like terms involves putting together tiles with the same dimensions. (p. 161)

common   Shared.

common factor   A common factor is a factor that is the same for two or more terms. For example, x^2 is a common factor for $3x^2$ and $-5x^2y$.

common multiple   A number that is a multiple of the two or more numbers. For example, 24 and 48 are common multiples of 3 and 8.

Commutative Property of Addition   The Commutative Property of Addition states that if two terms are added, then the order may be reversed with no effect on the total. That is, $a + b = b + a$. For example, $7 + 12 = 12 + 7$. (p. 78)

Making Connections

Commutative Property of Multiplication   The Commutative Property of Multiplication states that if two expressions are multiplied, then the order may be reversed with no effect on the result. That is, $ab = ba$. For example, $5 \cdot 8 = 8 \cdot 5$. (p. 581)

complementary angles   Two angles whose measures add up to 90°. Angles T and V are complementary because $m\angle T + m\angle V = 90°$. Complementary angles may also be adjacent, like $\angle ABC$ and $\angle CBD$ in the diagram at far right. (p. 313)

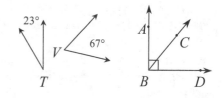

complementary probabilities   Two probabilities are complementary if the sum of the probabilities is one.

complex fraction   A fraction with a fraction in the numerator and/or denominator.

composite figure   A shape made of several simpler figures.

composite number   A number with more than two factors.

compound event   A compound event in probability is an outcome that depends on two or more other events. For example, finding the probability that both a red ball and also a blue block are drawn from a bag in two draws. (p. 650, 655)

compound interest   Interest that is paid on both the principal and the previous interest earned which grows over time. Compound interest may be calculated using the formula $B = p(1+r)^t$, in which B is the balance, p is the principal, r is the annual rate, and t is the time in years that the account earns interest. (p. 576)

cone   A three-dimensional figure that consists of a circular face, called the "base," a point called the "apex," that is not in the flat surface (plane) of the base, and the slant surface that connects the apex to each point on the circular edge of the base. (p. 614)

congruent   Two shapes are congruent if they have exactly the same shape and size. Congruent shapes are similar and have a scale factor of 1. The symbol for congruence is $\cong$. (p. 235, 250)

conjecture   An educated guess that often results from noticing a pattern. Conjectures are also often written in conditional ("If..., then...") form. Once a conjecture is proven, then the conjecture becomes a theorem. (p. 103)

consecutive numbers   Integers that are in order without skipping any integers. For example, 8, 9, and 10 are consecutive numbers. (p. 185)

constant A symbol representing a value that does not change. For example, in the equation $y = 2x + 5$, the number 5 is a constant. (p. 161, 273)

construction with a compass and straightedge The process of using a straightedge and compass to solve a problem and/or create a geometric diagram. (p. 299)

coordinate The number corresponding to a point on the number line or an ordered pair (x, y) that corresponds to a point in a two-dimensional coordinate system. In an ordered pair, the x-coordinate appears first and the y-coordinate appears second. For example, the point $(3, 5)$ has an x-coordinate of 3. (See *ordered pair*.) (p. 79)

coordinate grid (system) A system of graphing ordered pairs of numbers on a coordinate plane. An ordered pair represents a point, with the first number giving the horizontal position relative to the x-axis and the second number giving the vertical position relative to the y-axis. (Also see *ordered pair*.) (p. 92)

correlation A measure of the relationship between two sets of data. (p. 355)

corresponding parts Points, sides, edges, or angles in two or more figures that are images of each other with respect to a transformation. If two figures are congruent, then the corresponding parts of the figures are congruent to each other. (See *ratio of similarity* and *congruent*.) (p. 242)

cube A polyhedron of six faces, each of which is a square.

cubic unit A cube, each of whose edges measure 1 unit in length. Volume is measured in cubic units. (p. 603)

cylinder A three-dimensional figure that consists of two parallel congruent circular regions (called *bases*) and a vertical surface containing segments connecting each point on the circular boundary of one base to the corresponding point on the circular boundary of the other. (p. 617)

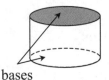

bases

decimal point The dot separating the whole number from the decimal portion, that is, the ones and tenths places in a decimal number. (p. 46)

decompose If a geometric figure is broken up into separate parts, then the figure is decomposed. Similarly, if a number is written as a sum or difference (such as $28 = 30 - 2$), then the number is decomposed. (Also see *recompose*.) (p. 123)

denominator The lower part of a fraction, which expresses into how many equal parts the whole is divided. (p. 37)

dependent events   Two events are dependent if the outcome of one event affects the probability of the other event. For example, if one card is drawn out of a deck of cards, then the probability that the first card is red is $\frac{26}{52} = \frac{1}{2}$ because 26 of the 52 cards are red. However, the probability of the second card now depends on the result of the first selection. If the first card was red, then there are now 25 red cards remaining in a deck of 51 cards, and the probability that the second card is red is $\frac{25}{51}$. The second event (selecting the second card) is dependent on the first event (selecting the first card).

diagonal   In a polygon, a diagonal is a line segment that connects two vertices of the polygon but is not a side of the polygon.

diagonal

diameter   A line segment drawn through the center of a circle with both endpoints on the circle. The length of a diameter is usually denoted d. Note that the length of the diameter of a circle is twice the length of its radius. (Also see *circle*.) (p. 309)

difference   The result of subtraction. (p. 90)

digit   One of the ten numerals: 0, 1, 2, 3, 4, 5, 6, 7, 8, or 9.

dilation   A transformation which produces a figure similar to the original by proportionally shrinking or stretching the figure. In a dilation, a shape is stretched (or compressed) proportionally from a point, called the point of dilation. (p. 102)

dimensions   The dimensions of a figure that is a flat region or space tell how far that the figure extends in each direction. For example, the dimensions of a rectangle might be 16 cm wide by 7 cm high. (p. 603)

Distributive Property   For any a, b, and c, $a(b+c) = ab + ac$. For example, $10(7+2) = 10 \cdot 7 + 10 \cdot 2$. (p. 279)

dividend   A quantity to be divided. (See *divisor*.)

divisible   A number is divisible by another if the remainder of the division is zero.

division ($\div$)   The inverse operation to multiplication, or the operation that creates equal groups.

divisor   The quantity by which another quantity is to be divided. dividend/divisor = quotient + remainder (if there is any).

edge   In three dimensions, a line segment formed by the intersection of two faces of a polyhedron. (p. 595)

edge

endpoint   Either of the two points that mark the ends of a line segment. (Also see *line segment*.) (p. 304)

enlargement ratio The ratio of similarity comparing a figure to a similar larger figure is often called the enlargement ratio. This ratio shows by what factor the first figure is enlarged to get the second figure. (p. 250, 477)

equal ($=$) Two quantities are equal when they have the same value. For example, when $x = 4$, the expression $x + 8$ is equal to the expression $3x$ because the values of the expressions are the same. (p. 285)

equal ratios Two equivalent fractions, also called a proportion. For example, $\frac{40 \text{ miles}}{2 \text{ gallons}} = \frac{100 \text{ miles}}{50 \text{ gallons}}$. (p. 205)

equation A mathematical sentence in which two expressions appear on either side of an "equals" sign ($=$), stating that the two expressions are equivalent. For example, the equation $7x + 4.2 = -8$ states that the expression $7x + 4.2$ has the value -8. In this course, an equation is often used to represent a rule relating two quantities. For example, a rule for finding the area y of a tile pattern with figure number x might be written $y = 4x - 3$. (p. 371)

equilateral A polygon is equilateral if all of its sides have equal length. The word "equilateral" comes from "equi" (meaning "equal") and "lateral" (meaning "side"). Equilateral triangles not only have sides of equal length, but also angles of equal measure. However, a polygon with more than three sides may be equilateral without having congruent angles. For example, see the rhombus at right. (p. 308)

equivalent Two expressions are equivalent if they have the same value. For example, $2 + 3$ is equivalent to $1 + 4$. Two equations are equivalent if they have all the same solutions. For example, $y = 3x$ is equivalent to $2y = 6x$. Equivalent equations also have the same graph. (p. 278)

equivalent fractions Two fractions are equivalent if they have the same numerical value. For example, 3/6 and 5/10 are equivalent fractions. (p. 38, 46, 243)

evaluate (an expression) To find the numerical value of. To evaluate an expression, substitute the value(s) given for the variable(s) and perform the operations according to the order of operations. For example, evaluating $2x + y - 10$ when $x = 4$ and $y = 3$ gives the value 1. (Also see *expression*.) (p. 273)

even number A whole number that is divisible by two with no remainder. (p. 185)

event One or more results of an experiment. (p. 33)

experimental probability The probability based on data collected in experiments. The experimental probability of an event is defined to be $\frac{\text{number of successful outcomes in the experiment}}{\text{total number of outcomes in the experiment}}$. (p. 33)

exponent   In an expression of the form a^b, b is called the exponent. For example, in the expression 2^5, 5 is called the exponent (2 is the base, and 32 is the value). The exponent indicates how many times to use the base as a multiplier. For example, in 2^5, 2 is used 5 times: $2^5 = 2 \cdot 2 \cdot 2 \cdot 2 \cdot 2 = 32$. For exponents of zero, the rule is: for any number $x \neq 0$, $x^0 = 1$. (p. 572, 591)

expression   An expression is a combination of individual terms separated by plus or minus signs. Numerical expressions combine numbers and operation symbols; algebraic (variable) expressions include variables. For example, $4 + (5 - 3)$ is a numerical expression. In an algebraic expression, if each of the following terms, $6xy^2$, 24, and $\frac{y-3}{4+x}$, are combined, the result may be $6xy^2 + 24 - \frac{y-3}{4+x}$. An expression does not have an "equals" sign. (p. 273)

expression mat   An organizing tool used to visually represent an expression with algebra tiles. An expression mat has two regions, a positive region at the top and a negative region at the bottom. The tiles on the expression mat at right represent a value of –3. (p. 277)

Value: –3

face   One of the flat surfaces of a polyhedron, including the base(s). (p. 595)

factor   (1) In arithmetic: when two or more integers are multiplied, each of the integers is a factor of the product. For example, 4 is a factor of 24, because $4 \cdot 6 = 24$.
(2) In algebra: when two or more algebraic expressions are multiplied together, each of the expressions is a factor of the product. For example, x^2 is a factor of $-17x^2y^3$, because $(x^2)(-17y^3) = -17x^2y^3$. (3) To factor an expression is to write the expression as a product. For example, the factored form of $x^2 - 3x - 18$ is $(x - 6)(x + 3)$. (p. 44)

family of fractions   All fractions that are equivalent to each other form a family of fractions. (See *equivalent fractions*.) (p. 38, 243)

formula   An equation that shows a mathematical relationship. (p. 129)

fraction   A number expressed in the form $\frac{a}{b}$ for which a and b are integers and b is not equal to 0. A fraction is also called a rational number. (p. 22, 103)

frequency   The number of times that something occurs within an interval or data set. (p. 219)

generic rectangle   A type of diagram used to visualize multiplying expressions without algebra tiles. Each expression to be multiplied forms a side length of the rectangle, and the product is the sum of the areas of the sections of the rectangle. For example, the generic rectangle at right may be used to multiply $(2x + 5)$ by $(x + 3)$.

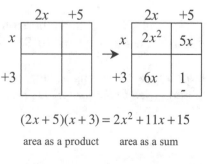

$$(2x + 5)(x + 3) = 2x^2 + 11x + 15$$

area as a product   area as a sum

graph   A graph represents numerical information in a visual form. The numbers may come from a table, situation (pattern), or rule (equation or inequality). Most of the graphs in this course show points, lines, and/or curves on a two-dimensional coordinate system like the one at right or on a single axis called a number line (see diagram below right). (p. 94, 359)

greatest common factor (GCF)   (1) For integers, the greatest positive integer that is a common factor of two or more integers. For example, the greatest common factor of 28 and 42 is 14. (2) For two or more algebraic monomials, the product of the greatest common integer factor of the coefficients of the monomials and the variable(s) in each algebraic term with the smallest degree of that variable in every term. For example, the greatest common factor of $12x^3y^2$ and $8xy^4$ is $4xy^2$. (3) For a polynomial, the greatest common monomial factor of its terms. For example, the greatest common factor of $16x^4 + 8x^3 + 12x$ is $4x$.

height   (a) Triangle: the length of a segment that connects a vertex of the triangle to a line containing the opposite base (side) and is perpendicular to that line. (b) Trapezoid: the length of any segment that connects a point on one base of the trapezoid to the line containing the opposite base and is perpendicular to that line. (c) Parallelogram (includes rectangle, rhombus, and square): the length of any segment that connects a point on one base of the parallelogram to the line containing the opposite base and is perpendicular to that line. (d) Pyramid and cone: the length of the segment that connects the apex to a point in the plane containing the base of a figure and is perpendicular to that plane. (e) Prism or cylinder: the length of a segment that connects one base of the figure to the plane containing the other base and is perpendicular to that plane. (See *altitude*.) (p. 115)

hexagon   A polygon with six sides. (p. 595)

histogram   A way of displaying data that is much like a bar graph in that the height of the bars is proportional to the number of elements. The difference is that each bar of a histogram represents the number of data elements in a range of values, such as the number of people who weigh from 100 pounds up to, but not including, 120 pounds. Each range of values should have the same width. (See *bar graph*.) (p. 219)

horizontal   Parallel to the horizon. The *x*-axis of a coordinate grid is the horizontal axis. (p. 93, 94)

hypotenuse   The longest side of a right triangle (the side that is opposite of the right angle). (See *Pythagorean Theorem* for a diagram.) (p. 541)

Identity Property of Addition   The Identity Property of Addition states that adding zero to any expression leaves the expression unchanged.   That is, $a + 0 = a$.   For example, $7 + 0 = 7$, and $-2y + 0 = -2y$. (p. 290)

Identity Property of Multiplication   The Identity Property of Multiplication states that multiplying any expression by 1 leaves the expression unchanged.   That is, $a(1) = a$.   For example, $437x \cdot 1 = 437x$. (p. 39)

impossibility   An event with a probability of zero. (p. 33)

independent events   If the outcome of a probabilistic event does not affect the probability of another event, then the events are independent.   For example, assume that a normal six-sided die is being rolled twice to determine the probability of rolling a 1 twice.   The result of the first roll does not affect the probability of rolling a 1 on the second roll.   Since the probability of rolling a 1 on the first roll is $\frac{1}{6}$ and the probability of rolling a 1 on the second roll is also $\frac{1}{6}$, then the probability of rolling two 1s in a row is $\frac{1}{6} \cdot \frac{1}{6} = \frac{1}{36}$. (p. 655)

inequality   An inequality consists of two expressions on either side of an inequality symbol.   For example, the inequality $7x + 4.2 < -8$ states that the expression $7x + 4.2$ has a value less than –8. (p. 285, 294)

inequality symbols   The symbol $\leq$ read from left to right means "less than or equal to," the symbol $\geq$ read from left to right means "greater than or equal to," and the symbols $<$ and $>$ mean "less than" and "greater than," respectively.   For example, "$7 < 13$" means that 7 is less than 13. (p. 285)

integers   The set of numbers $\{..., -3, -2, -1, 0, 1, 2, 3, ...\}$. (p. 86, 90)

intersect   To meet or cross.   The x-axis intersects the y-axis at the origin.   (See *axis*.) (p. 441)

interval   A set of numbers between two given numbers. (p. 51)

inverse operation   An operation that undoes another operation.   For example, multiplication is the inverse operation for division. (p. 266)

irrational numbers   The set of numbers that cannot be expressed in the form $\frac{a}{b}$, where a and b are integers and $b \neq 0$.   For example, π and $\sqrt{2}$ are irrational numbers. (p. 545)

isosceles triangle   A triangle with two sides of equal length.

iterate   The process of repeating a measurement many times, such as the use of a one-foot ruler to measure a long room by placing the ruler end-to-end many times.

kite   A quadrilateral with two distinct pairs of consecutive congruent sides.

least common multiple (LCM)   (1) The smallest common multiple of a set of two or more integers. For example, the least common multiple of 4, 6, and 8 is 24. (2) For two or more algebraic monomials, the product of the least common integer multiples of the coefficients of the monomials and the variable(s) in each algebraic term with the greatest degree of that variable in every term. For example, the least common multiple of $12x^3y^2$ and $8xy^4$ is $24x^3y^4$.

leg of a right triangle   Either of the two shorter sides of a right triangle that form the right angle. (See *Pythagorean Theorem* for a diagram.) (p. 539, 541)

less than   (1) One expression is less than another if its value is not as large. This relationship is indicated with the less than symbol "$<$." For example, $1+1$ is less than $4+5$, so the comparison is written as $1+1<4+5$. (2) Sometimes the comparison is made that one amount is a certain quantity less than another amount. For example, a student movie ticket might cost two dollars *less than* an adult ticket. (p. 285)

like terms   Two or more terms that contain the same variable(s), with corresponding variables raised to the same power. For example, $5x^2$ and $2x^2$ are like terms. (See *combining like terms*.) (p. 161)

line   A line is an undefined term in geometry. A line is one-dimensional and continues without end in two directions. A line is made up of points and has no thickness. A line may be named with a letter (such as *l*), but also may be labeled using two points on the line, such as $\overleftrightarrow{AB}$ shown the right.

line segment   The portion of a line between two points. A line segment is named using its endpoints. For example, the line segment at right may be named either $\overline{AB}$ or $\overline{BA}$.

linear equation   An equation in two variables whose graph is a line. For example, $y=2.1x-8$ is a *linear equation*. The standard form for a linear equation is $ax+by=c$, where a, b, and c are constants and a and b are not both zero. Most linear equations may be written in $y=mx+b$ form, which is more useful for determining the slope and y-intercept of the line. (p. 359)

linear expression   An expression in the form of $ax+b$ for which a and b are numbers.

lower quartile   The median of the lower half of an ordered set of data is the lower quartile. (p. 226)

lowest common denominator (LCD)   The smallest common multiple of the denominators of two or more fractions. For example, the LCD of $\frac{5}{12}$ and $\frac{3}{8}$ is 24. (p. 44)

mean   The mean, or average, of several numbers is one way of defining the "middle" of the numbers. To find the average of a group of numbers, add the numbers together then divide by the number of numbers in the set. For example, the average of the numbers 1, 5, and 6 is $(1+5+6) \div 3 = 4$. (See *average*.) (p. 13)

measure of central tendency   Mean, median, and mode are all measures of central tendency, reflecting special statistical information about a set of data. (p. 13, 18)

median   The middle number of an ordered set of data. If there is no distinct middle, then the average of the two middle numbers is the median. (p. 18)

midpoint   A point that divides a segment into two segments of equal length. For example, D is the midpoint of $\overline{BC}$ in $\triangle ABC$ at right. (p. 307)

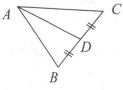

mixed number (fraction)   A number that consists of an integer and a fraction. For example, $3\frac{3}{8}$. (p. 103)

mode   The number or numbers that occur the most often within a set of data. There may be more than one mode for a set of data. (p. 18)

multiple   The product of a whole number and any other (nonzero) whole number. For example, 15 is a multiple of 5.

multiplication ($\cdot$)   An operation that reflects repeated addition. For example, $3 \cdot 4 = 4 + 4 + 4$. (p. 44, 108)

Multiplicative Identity   The Multiplicative Identity Property states that multiplying any expression by 1 leaves the expression unchanged. That is, $a(1) = a$. For example, $437x \cdot 1 = 437x$. (p. 39)

natural numbers   The counting numbers beginning with 1. For example, 1, 2, 3….

negative correlation   A relationship between two sets of variables in which one generally increases while the other decreases. (p. 355)

negative number   A negative number is a number less than zero. Negative numbers are graphed on the negative side of a number line, which is to the left of the origin. (p. 83)

negative slope   Lines are said to have negative slope if they slant downward from left to right. That is, as the x-values increases, the y-value decreases. (p. 433)

non-linear   A set of points that do not lie on a straight line when connected. (p. 631)

number line   A diagram representing all real numbers as points on a line. All real numbers are assigned to points. The numbers are called the coordinates of the points and the point for which the number 0 is assigned is called the origin. (Also see *boundary point*.) (p. 11)

numeral   A symbol that names a number. For example, each item of the following list is a numeral: 22.6, –19, 0.

numerator   The number above the bar in a fraction that tells the numbers of parts in relationship to the number of parts in the whole. (p. 37)

obtuse angle   Any angle that measures between (but not including) 90° and 180°. (p. 304)

obtuse triangle   A triangle with one obtuse angle. (p. 112)

octagon   A polygon with eight sides. (p. 595)

odd number   An integer that cannot be evenly divided by two. (p. 185)

operation   A mathematical process such as addition, subtraction, multiplication, division, raising to a power, or taking a root. (p. 130)

order of operations   The specific order in which certain operations are to be carried out to evaluate or simplify expressions: parentheses (or other grouping symbols), exponents (powers or roots), multiplication and division (from left to right), and addition and subtraction (from left to right). (p. 133)

ordered pair   Two numbers written in order as follows: (x, y). The primary use of ordered pairs in this course is to represent points in an xy-coordinate system. The first coordinate (x) represents the distance from the x-axis. The second coordinate (y) represents the distance from the y-axis. For example, the ordered pair $(3, 5)$ represents the point shown in bold at right. (p. 94)

origin   The point on a coordinate plane where the x-axis and y-axis intersect is called the origin. This point has coordinates $(0, 0)$. The point assigned to zero on a number line is also called the origin. (See *axis*.) (p. 94)

outcome   Possible result in an experiment or consequence of an action. (p. 33, 650)

outlier   A number in a set of data that is much larger or much smaller than the other numbers in the set. (p. 13)

Making Connections

parallel Two or more straight lines on a flat surface that do not intersect (no matter how far they are extended) are parallel. If two lines have the same slope and do not coincide, then they are parallel. For example, the graphs of $y = 2x + 3$ and $y = 2x - 2$ are parallel (see diagram at right). When two equations have parallel graphs, the equations have no solutions in common. (p. 119)

parallelogram A quadrilateral with two pairs of parallel sides. (p. 119, 342)

pentagon A polygon with five sides. (p. 595)

percent (%) A ratio that compares a number to 100. Percents are often written using the "%" symbol. For example, 0.75 is equal to $\frac{75}{100}$ or 75%. (p. 22, 57)

perfect square The product of an integer multiplied by itself gives a perfect square. For example, 1, 4, and 9 are perfect squares because $1 = 1 \cdot 1$, $4 = 2 \cdot 2$, and $9 = 3 \cdot 3$. (p. 543)

Perimeter =
$5 + 8 + 4 + 6 = 23$ units

perimeter The distance around a figure on a flat surface. (p. 10)

perpendicular Two rays, line segments, or lines that meet (intersect) to form a right angle (90°) are called perpendicular. A line and a flat surface may also be perpendicular if the line does not lie on the flat surface but intersects the surface and forms a right angle with every line on the flat surface passing through the point of intersection. A small square at the point of intersection of two lines or segments indicates that the lines form a right angle and are therefore perpendicular. (p. 119, 301)

perpendicular bisector A line, ray, or segment that divides a segment into two congruent segments and is perpendicular to the segment. (p. 307)

pi (π) The ratio of the circumference (C) of the circle to its diameter (d). For every circle, $\pi = \frac{\text{circumference}}{\text{diameter}} = \frac{C}{d}$. Numbers such as 3.14, 3.1416, or $\frac{22}{7}$ are approximations of π. (p. 313, 319)

place value The number assigned to each place that a digit occupies. (p. 46)

plane. A plane is a two-dimensional flat surface that extends without end. It is made up of points and has no thickness. (p. 660)

point An exact location in space. In two dimensions, an ordered pair specifies a point on a coordinate plane. (See *ordered pair*.) (p. 94)

polygon A two-dimensional closed figure of three or more line segments (sides) connected end to end. Each segment is a side and only intersects the endpoints of its two adjacent sides. Each point of intersection is a vertex. At right are two examples of polygons. (p. 595)

polyhedron A three-dimensional figure with no holes for which all faces are polygons. (p. 595)

population A collection of objects or group of people about whom information is gathered.

portion A part of something; a part of a whole. (p. 22, 57)

portions web The web diagram at right illustrates that fractions, decimals, and percents are different ways to represent a portion of a number. Portions may also be represented in words, such as "four-fifths" or "seven-fourths," or as diagrams. (p. 57)

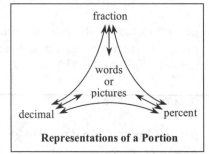

Representations of a Portion

positive correlation A relationship between two sets of variables in which one generally increases while the other also increases. (p. 355)

positive numbers Numbers that are greater than zero.

positive slope Lines are said to have positive slope if they slant upwards from left to right. That is, as the x-value increases, the y-value also increases. (p. 433)

power A number or variable raised to an exponent in the form x^n. (See *exponent*.) (p. 572)

prime factorization The expression of a number as the product of prime factors. (p. 45)

prime number A positive integer with exactly two factors. The only factors of a prime number are 1 and itself. For example, the numbers 2, 3, 17, and 31 are all prime. (p. 45)

prism A three-dimensional figure that consists of two parallel congruent polygons (called *bases*) and a vertical surface containing segments connecting each point on each side of one base to the corresponding point on the other base. The lateral surface of a prism consists of parallelograms. (p. 595)

probability A number that represents how likely an event is to happen. When a event has a finite number of equally-likely outcomes, the probability that one of those outcomes, called *A*, will occur is expressed as a ratio and written as: $P(A) = \frac{\text{number of successful outcomes}}{\text{total number of possible outcomes}}$. For example, when flipping a coin, the probability of getting tails, *P*(tails), is 1/2 because there is only one tail (successful outcome) out of the two possible equally likely outcomes (a head and a tail). Probability may be written as a ratio, decimal, or percent. A probability of 0 (or 0%) indicates that the occurrence of that outcome is impossible, while a probability of 1 (or 100%) indicates that the event must occur. Events that "might happen" will have values somewhere between 0 and 1 (or between 0% and 100%). (p. 27, 33, 650, 655)

product The result of multiplying. For example, the product of 4 and 5 is 20. The product of $3a$ and $8b^2$ is $24ab^2$.

proportion An equation stating that two ratios (fractions) are equal. For example, the equation at right is a proportion. A proportion is a useful type of equation to set up when solving problems involving proportional relationships. (p. 517)

$$\frac{68 \text{ votes for Mr. Mears}}{100 \text{ people surveyed}} = \frac{34 \text{ votes for Mr. Mears}}{50 \text{ people surveyed}}$$

proportional relationship Two values are in a proportional relationship if a proportion may be set up that relates the values. (p. 512)

protractor A geometric tool used for physically measuring the number of degrees in an angle. (p. 302)

pyramid A polyhedron with a polygonal base formed by connecting each point of the base to a single given point (the apex) that is above or below the flat surface containing the base. Each triangular slant face of the pyramid is formed by the segments from the apex to the endpoints of a side of the base and the side itself. A tetrahedron is a special pyramid because any face may act as its base. (p. 614)

Pythagorean Theorem The statement relating the lengths of the legs of a right triangle to the length of the hypotenuse: $(\text{leg \#1})^2 + (\text{leg \#2})^2 = \text{hypotenuse}^2$. The Pythagorean Theorem is powerful because if the lengths of any two sides of a right triangle are known, then this relationship may be used to find the length of the third side. (p. 541)

quadrants The coordinate plane is divided by its axes into four quadrants. The quadrants are numbered as shown in the first diagram at right. When graphing data that has no negative values, sometimes a graph that shows only the first quadrant is used. (p. 93)

4-quadrant graph:

II   I

x-axis

III   IV

y-axis

1ˢᵗ-quadrant graph:

y-axis

x-axis

quadrilateral A polygon with four sides. The shape at right is a quadrilateral. (p. 342, 595)

quartile Along with the median, the quartiles divide a set of data into four groups of the same size. (p. 226)

quotient The result of a division problem.

radius (plural: radii) Of a circle: The line segment drawn from the center of a circle to a point on the circle. Of a regular polygon: A line segment that connects the center of a regular polygon with a vertex. The length of a radius is usually denoted r. (p. 309)

random sample A sample in which each item in the population or sample space has an equal chance of being selected.

range The range of a set of data is the difference between the highest and lowest values. (p. 211)

rate A ratio comparing two quantities, often a comparison of time. For example, miles per hour. (p. 420, 433, 459)

ratio A ratio compares two quantities by division. A ratio may be written using a colon, but is more often written as a fraction. For example, the comparison may be made of the ratio of female students in a particular school to the total number of students in the school. This ratio could be written as 1521:2906 or as the fraction shown at right. (p. 205, 250)

$$\frac{1521 \text{ female students}}{2906 \text{ total students}}$$

ratio of similarity The ratio of any pair of corresponding sides of two similar figures. This means that once it is determined that two figures are similar, all of the pairs of corresponding sides of the figures have the same ratio. For example, for the similar triangles $\triangle ABC$ and $\triangle DEF$ at right, the ratio of similarity is $\frac{5}{11}$. The ratio of similarity may also be called the linear scale factor. (p. 250)

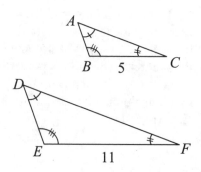

rational number   Numbers that may be expressed in the form $\frac{a}{b}$, where a and b are integers and $b \neq 0$. For example, 0.75 is a rational number because 0.75 may be expressed in the form $\frac{3}{4}$. (p. 545)

ray   A ray is part of a line that starts at one point and extends without end in one direction. In the example at right, ray $\overrightarrow{AB}$ is part of line $\overleftrightarrow{AB}$ that starts at A and contains all of the points of $\overleftrightarrow{AB}$ that are on the same side of A as point B, including A. Point A is the endpoint of $\overrightarrow{AB}$. (p. 304)

real numbers   Irrational numbers together with rational numbers form the set of the real numbers. For example, the following are all real numbers: $2.78, -13267, 0, \frac{3}{7}, \pi, \sqrt{2}$. All real numbers are represented on the number line.

reciprocals   The reciprocal of a nonzero number is its multiplicative inverse, that is, the reciprocal of x is $\frac{1}{x}$. For a number in the form $\frac{a}{b}$, where a and b are non-zero, the reciprocal is $\frac{b}{a}$. The product of a number and its reciprocal is 1. For example, the reciprocal of 12 is $\frac{1}{12}$, because $12 \cdot \frac{1}{12} = 1$.

recompose   If a geometric figure is broken up into pieces and the pieces are put back together, possibly in a new way, then the figure is recomposed. Similarly, if two or more numbers have been written as sums or differences in an expression and these numbers are put back together into sums or differences, then the expression is recomposed. (Also see *decompose*.) (p. 123)

rectangle   A quadrilateral with four right angles. (p. 10, 342)

reduce   To put a fraction into simplest form. (p. 243)

reflection   A transformation across a line that produces a mirror image of the original (pre-image) shape. The reflection is called the "image" of the original figure. The line is called a "line of reflection." Note that a reflection is also sometimes referred to as a "flip." See the example at right above. (p. 99)

original   image

Line of reflection

regular polygon   A polygon is regular if the polygon is a convex polygon with congruent angles and congruent sides. For example, the shape at right is a regular hexagon. (p. 94)

REGULAR HEXAGON

repeating decimal   A repeating decimal is a decimal that repeats the same sequence of digits forever from some point onward. For example, 4.56073073073... is a decimal for which the three digits 073 continue to repeat forever. Repeating decimals are always the decimal expansions of rational numbers. (p. 21)

representative sample   A subset (group) of a given population with the same characteristics as the whole population.

rhombus   A quadrilateral with four congruent sides. (Also see *equilateral.*) (p. 342)

right angle   An angle that measures 90°. A small square is used to note a right angle, as shown in the example at right. (p. 304)

right triangle   A triangle that has one right angle. The side of a right triangle opposite the right angle is called the "hypotenuse," and the two sides adjacent to the right angle are called "legs." (See *Pythagorean Theorem* for a diagram.) (p. 451)

rigid transformations   Movements of figures that preserve the shape and size of the figures. (p. 99)

root fraction   The member of a family of fractions with the smallest integer values, the most simplified form. For the fraction family $\frac{2}{3}, \frac{4}{6}, \frac{6}{9}$, etc., $\frac{2}{3}$ is the root fraction. (p. 243)

rotation   A transformation that rotates (or turns) all of the points in the original (pre-image) figure the same number of degrees around a fixed center point (such as the origin on a graph). The result is called the "image" of the original figure. The point that the shape is rotated about is called the "center of rotation." To define a rotation, the measure of turn (in degrees) must be stated, the direction in which the shape is turned (such as clockwise or counter-clockwise), and the center of rotation. See the example at right. Note that a rotation is also sometimes referred to as a "turn." (p. 99)

scale (scaling)   The ratio between a length of the representation (such as a map, model, or diagram) and the corresponding length of the actual object. For example, the map of a city may use one inch to represent one mile. (p. 250, 468)

scale factor   A ratio that compares the sizes of the parts of one figure or object to the sizes of the corresponding parts of a similar figure or object. (p. 250, 468)

scalene triangle   A triangle with no congruent sides. (p. 177)

scatterplot   Two related sets of data may have the corresponding values of the sets listed as ordered pairs. If these ordered pairs are graphed in the coordinate plane, then the result is a scatterplot. (Also see *negative correlation* and *positive correlation.*) (p. 346, 355)

scientific notation   A number is expressed in scientific notation when the number is in the form $a \times 10^n$, where $1 \le a < 10$ and n is an integer. For example, the number 31,000 may be expressed in scientific notation as 3.1×10^4. (p. 587)

sector   A region formed by two radii of a central angle and the arc between the endpoints of the radii on the circle. The shaded portion of the drawing at right is a sector. (p. 347, 460)

sector

semi-circle   In a circle, a semicircle is an arc with endpoints that are endpoints of any diameter of the circle. A semi-circle is a half circle and has a measure of 180°.

set   A collection of items.

similar figures   Similar figures have the same shape but are not necessarily the same size. For example the two triangles at right are similar. In similar figures, the measures of corresponding angles are equal and the lengths of corresponding sides are proportional. (p. 235)

simple interest   Interest that is paid only on the principal (the amount originally invested). Simple interest (I) is found by multiplying the principal (P), the rate (r), and the amount of time (t): $I = Prt$. (p. 491)

simplest form of a fraction   A fraction for which the numerator and the denominator have no common factor greater than one. (p. 243)

simplify   To simplify an expression is to write a less complicated expression with the same value. A simplified expression has no parentheses and no like terms. For example, the expression $3 - (2x + 7) - 4x$ may be simplified to $-4 - 6x$. When working with algebra tiles, a simplified expression uses the fewest possible tiles to represent the original expression. (p. 273)

skew lines   Lines that do not lie in the same flat surface. (p. 660)

slope   A ratio that describes how steep (or flat) a line is. Slope may be positive, negative, or even zero, but a straight line has only one slope. Slope is the ratio $\frac{\text{vertical change}}{\text{horizontal change}}$ or $\frac{\text{change in } y\text{-value}}{\text{change in } x\text{-value}}$, sometimes written $\frac{\Delta y}{\Delta x}$. When the equation of a line is written in $y = mx + b$ form, m is the slope of the line. A line has positive slope if the line slopes upward from left to right on a graph, negative slope if the line slopes downward from left to right, zero slope if the line is horizontal, and undefined slope if the line is vertical. Parallel lines have equal slopes, and the slopes of perpendicular lines are opposite reciprocals of each other (e.g., $\frac{3}{5}$ and $-\frac{5}{3}$). (p. 433)

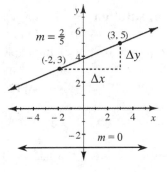

solution   The number or numbers that when substituted into an equation or inequality make the equation or inequality true. For example, $x = 4$ is a solution to the equation $3x - 2 = 10$ because $3x - 2$ equals 10 when $x = 4$. A solution to a two-variable equation is sometimes written as an ordered pair (x, y). For example, $x = 3$ and $y = -2$ is a solution to the equation $y = x - 5$. This solution may be written as $(3, -2)$. (p. 379, 391, 441)

square   A quadrilateral with four right angles and four congruent sides. (p. 342)

square

square measure   The units used to describe the measure of an area in the form of 1×1 unit squares. (p. 10)

square number   The numbers in the pattern 1, 4, 9, 16, 25, …. That is, the squares of the counting numbers 1, 2, 3, 4, 5, … are known as square numbers. (p. 543)

square root ($\sqrt{}$)   A number a is the square root of b if $a^2 = b$ and $a \geq 0$. The square root of 9 ($\sqrt{9}$) is 3. A negative number has no real square root, a non-negative number has just one square root. (p. 543)

stem-and-leaf plot   A frequency distribution that arranges data so that all digits except the last digit in each piece of data are in the stem, the last digit of each piece of data are the leaves, and both stems and leaves are arranged in order from least to greatest. The example at right displays the data: 49, 52, 54, 58, 61, 61, 67, 68, 72, 73, 73, 73, 78, 82, 83, 108, 112, and 117. (p. 213)

"leaf"

4	9
5	2 4 8
6	1 1 7 8
7	2 3 3 3 8
8	2 3
9	
10	8
11	2 7

"stem"

straight angle   An angle that measures 180°. This occurs when the rays of the angle point in opposite directions, forming a line. (p. 304)

180°

subproblems   A problem solving strategy that breaks a problem into smaller parts that must be solved in order to solve the original, more complex problem.

substitution   Replacing one symbol with a number, a variable, or another algebraic expression of the same value. Substitution does not change the value of the overall expression. For example, suppose that the expression $13x - 6$ must be evaluated for $x = 4$. Since x has the value 4, 4 may be substituted into the expression wherever x appears, giving the equivalent expression $13(4) - 6$. (p. 130, 273)

subtraction (–)   An operation that gives the difference between two numbers. (p. 90)

sum   The result of adding two or more numbers. For example, the sum of 4 and 5 is 9. (p. 90)

supplementary angles Two angles *A* and *B* for which $A + B = 180°$. Each angle is called the supplement of the other. In the example at right, angles *A* and *B* are supplementary.
Supplementary angles are often adjacent. For example, since $\angle LMN$ is a straight angle, then $\angle LMP$ and $\angle PMN$ are supplementary angles because $m\angle LMP + m\angle PMN = 180°$. (p. 313)

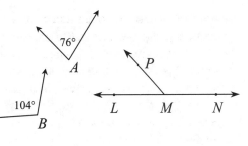

surface area The sum of all the area(s) of the surface(s) of a three-dimensional solid. For example, the surface area of a prism is the sum of the areas of its top and bottom bases, and its vertical surfaces (lateral faces). (p. 592, 599, 617)

term A term is a single number, variable, or the product of numbers and variables, such as –45, 1.2*x*, and $3xy^2$. (p. 133, 273)

terminating decimal A terminating decimal is a decimal that has only a finite number of non-zero digits, such as 4.067. Terminating decimals are a particular kind of repeating decimal for which the repeating portion is zeros, so the example could be written 4.0670000000… but it is not necessary to write the zeros at the end. (p. 53)

tetrahedron A polyhedron with four faces.

theoretical probability A calculated probability based on the possible outcomes when each outcome has the same chance of occurring: (number of successful outcomes)/(total number of possible outcomes). (p. 33)

tick mark A symbol that shows that a number line has been divided into intervals of equal length. (See *number line*.)

translation A transformation that preserves the size, shape, and orientation of a figure while sliding (moving) it to a new location. The result is called the "image" of the original figure (pre-image). See the example at right. Note that a translation is sometimes referred to as a "slide." (p. 99)

trapezoid A quadrilateral with at least one pair of parallel sides. (p. 125)

triangle A polygon with three sides. (p. 595)

unit of measure   A standard quantity (such as a centimeter, second, square foot, or gallon) that is used to measure and describe an object. A single object may be measured using different units of measure. For example, a pencil may be 80 mm long, meaning that the pencil is 80 times as long as a unit of 1 mm. However, the same pencil is 8 cm long, so that the pencil is the same length as 8 cm laid end-to-end. This is because 1 cm is the same length as 10 mm. (p. 10, 84, 464)

unit price   The cost of one item or one measure of an item. For example, cost for one pound or one gallon.

unit rate   A rate with a denominator of one when simplified. (p. 420)

units digit   The numeral in the ones place.

upper quartile   The median of the upper half of an ordered set of data. (p. 226)

variable   A symbol used to represent one or more numbers. In this course, letters of the English alphabet are used as variables. For example, in the expression $3x - (8.6xy + z)$, the variables are x, y, and z. (p. 156, 384)

Venn diagram   A type of diagram used to classify objects that is usually composed of two or more overlapping circles representing different conditions. An item is placed or represented in the Venn diagram in the appropriate position based on the conditions that the item meets. In the example of the Venn diagram at right, if an object meets one of two conditions, then the object is placed in region A or C but outside region B. If an object meets both conditions, then the object is placed in the intersection (B) of both circles. If an object does not meet either condition, then the object is placed outside of both circles (region D).

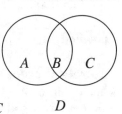

vertex (plural: vertices)   (a) For polygon, a vertex is the point at which two line segments meet to form a "corner." (See *regular polygon*.) (b) For an angle, the common endpoint of the defining rays. (See *vertical angles*.) (c) For a three-dimensional polyhedron, a vertex is a point where the edges of the solid meet. (See *edge*.) (p. 93, 595)

vertical   At right angles to the horizon. In a coordinate grid, the y-axis runs vertically. (p. 93, 94)

vertical angles   The two opposite (that is, non-adjacent) angles formed by two intersecting lines. "Vertical" is a relationship between pairs of angles, so one angle cannot be called vertical. Angles that form a vertical pair are always congruent.

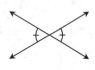

volume A measurement of the size of the three-dimensional region enclosed within an object. Volume is expressed as the number of $1 \times 1 \times 1$ unit cubes (or parts of cubes) that fit inside a solid. (p. 593, 603)

x-axis The horizontal number line on a coordinate grid. (See *axis*.) (p. 94)

x-coordinate In an ordered pair, (x, y), that represents a point in the coordinate plane, x is the value of the x-coordinate of the point. That is, the distance from the x-axis that is needed to plot the point. (p. 94)

x-intercept The point(s) where a graph intersects the x-axis. A graph may have several x-intercepts, no x-intercepts, or just one. An x-intercept may be written as an ordered pair $(x, 0)$ or as a single number. For example, in the graph below for "y-intercept," the x-intercept may be written as $(-2, 0)$ or simply -2. (See *y-intercept*.) (p. 358, 359)

y-axis The vertical number line on a coordinate grid. (See *axis*.) (p. 94)

y-coordinate In an ordered pair, (x, y), that represents a point in the coordinate plane, y is the value of the y-coordinate of the point. That is, the distance from the y-axis that is needed to plot the point. (p. 94)

y-intercept The point(s) where a graph intersects the y-axis. A function has at most one y-intercept while a relation may have several. The y-intercept of a graph is important because the y-intercept often represents the starting value of a quantity in a real-world situation. A y-intercept may be written as an ordered pair $(0, y)$ or as a single number. For example, it may be said that that the y-intercept of the graph at right is $(0, 2)$, or it may also be said that the y-intercept is 2. When a linear equation is written in $y = mx + b$ form, b is the y-intercept of the graph. For example, the equation of the graph at right is $y = x + 2$ and its y-intercept is 2. (p. 358, 359)

Index
Student Version

Many of the pages referenced here contain a definition or an example of the topic listed, often within the body of a Math Notes box. Others contain problems that develop or demonstrate the topic. It may be necessary to read the text on several pages to fully understand the topic. Also, some problems listed here are good examples of the topic and may not offer any explanation. The page numbers below reflect the pages in the Student Version. References to Math Notes boxes are bolded.

5-D Process, 175, 177, **179**, 181, 185, 187, 381
  word problems, 383

A
Absolute value, 635, 636, **637**
Acute triangle
  side length patterns, **550**
Addition
  associative property, 78
  commutative property, 77, **78**
  of fractions, 44, 50
  of integers, 75, 80, **90**
Additive identity, 39, **290**
Additive inverse, **90, 290**
Algebra tiles, **156**
  area, 148, **161**, 165, 167
  naming, **156**
  perimeter, 153, **161**, 165, 167
  removing zeros, 283
Algebraic expression, 147, **156, 273**
Angle, **304**
  acute, **304**
  circular, **304**
  complementary, 306, **313**
  measure, 302
  straight, **304**
  supplementary, 306, **313**
Area, 9, **10, 603**
  circle, 315, 318, **319**
  composition, 113
  conservation of, **123**
  decomposition, 113
  of irregular shapes, 113, 114
  parallelogram, 117, 118, 123
  proportional, 524
  ratio of similar figures, **527**, 531
  rearranging shapes, 114

  trapezoid, 125, 126, 132, **151**
  triangle, 121, 123, **127**
Arithmetic average, **13**
Associative Property of Addition, 78
Associative Property of Multiplication, **581**
Average, **13**
Axes, 85

B
Balanced set, **371**
  removing, 283
Bar graph, 14, **219**
Base, 571, **572**
  of a rectangle, **115**
  prism, 593, **595**
Becoming an Artist, 105
Biking the Triathalon, 422
Bin, 216, 217, **219**
  size, 212
Birthday Sweets, 601
Bisect, 307
Boundary point, 296, 297
  finding, 298
Box-and-whisker plot, 217, 225, 228, 229, **230**
  analyzing, 223
  maximum, **230**
  median, **230**
  minimum, **230**
  quartiles, **230**
Building Cubes, 658

C
Celsius
  conversion to fahrenhiet, 132
Central angle, 339
Certainty, 29, **33**
Changing Bases, 631

Direct variation, **512**
Distance, 457, **459**
  between parallel lines, **119**
  perpendicular, **119**
Distributive Property, 272, **279**, 373
Division by zero, 278
Double Spin, The, 647

E
Edge
  polyhedron, **595**
Endpoint
  angle, **304**
Energy of mass, 132
Enlarge, **250, 477**
Equation
  checking solutions, **379**
  infinite solutions, **391**
  no solution, **391**
  proportional, 509, 511, 516
  solution, **391**
  solving, 368, **371**, 377, 379
  solving with fractions, 481
  system of, 435, 438, **441**, 443, 444
  word problem, 381
  writing and solving, 383, 385
Equation Mat, 369, 370, **371**
Equiangular, 308
Equilateral, 308
Equivalent
  expressions, 158, 278
  fractions, 38, **46**
  measurements, **464**
  ratio, **205**
Evaluate, **273**
  a numerical expression, **133**
  expression, 163, **165**
Event, **33**
  compound, 41, 646, 652
  independent, **655**
  multiple, **650**
  probability, **27**
Experimental probability, 30, **33**
Exponent, 571, **572**, 578, 584
  negative, 588
  rules, 583, **591**
  Simplifying expressions, 586
Exponential
  form, **572**, 578
  growth, 574

Expression
  algebraic, 147, **156, 273**
  coefficient, 159
  comparing, 282, 283
  constant, 159, **161**
  equivalent, 158, 278
  evaluate, 163, **165**
  numerical, **133**
  simplify, 279, 290
  variable, 149, 269
Expression Comparison Mat, 282, 283
  comparing, 287, 288, 292, 293
  inequality, 294
  removing zeros, 287
Expression Mat, 277
Extension Activity, 366

F
Face
  lateral, **595**, 609, 610
  polyhedron, **595**
  prism, 593
Facilitator, 4
Factor
  prime, 45
Fahrenheit
  conversion to celsius, 132
Fencing the Basketball Court, 174
First quadrant graph, 85
Flip
  reflection, 92
  rigid transformation, 89
Four quadrant graph, 79
Fractal, 143
Fraction
  addition, 44, 50
  as a decimal, 54, **57**
  as a percent, 31, 36, **57**
  equivalent, 38, **46**
  family, 243
  greater than one, **103**
  multiplication, 108
  root, 243
Frequency, **219**
Funky Trapezoid Rules, 129

G
Generalizing (Way of Thinking), 2, 3, 326
Giant One, 37, **46, 205**
  solving proportions, 514, **517**

THIS BOOK IS THE
PROPERTY OF:

Book No._____

ISSUED TO	Year Used	CONDITION	
		ISSUED	RETURNED

PUPILS to whom this texbook is issued must not write on any part of it in any way, unless otherwise instructed by the teacher.